MY FATHER KILLED
PRESIDENT
JOHN F. KENNEDY

A Memoir

REVISED EDITION

Bruce H. Bell

BOOKSIDE Press

BookSide Press
877-741-8091
www.booksidepress.com
orders@booksidepress.com

CONTENTS

Mr. Bell is an adult survivor of significant trauma, resulting from personally witnessing the planning of the Kennedy assassination and its aftermath.

For Celeste, Ciel, Sarah, Kattie,
and Jeanie, with all my love.

Val Anisimow, Research Consultant.

Quote from General Curtis LeMay during the Cuban Missile Crisis in the Oval Office in the presence of all Joint Chiefs

General LeMay: *"Mr. President, it looks like you're in a hell of a fix here."*
President Kennedy: *"What did you say?"*
General LeMay: *"I said it looks like you're in a hell of a fix here."*

Eisenhower's Parting Speech on the 'Military Industrial Complex'

Our military organization, today, bears little relation to that known by any of my predecessors in peacetime or indeed by the fighting men of World War II or Korea.

Until the latest of our world conflicts, the United States had no armaments industry. American makers of plowshares could, with time and as required, make swords as well. But, now, we can no longer risk emergency improvisation of national defense; we have been compelled to create a permanent armaments industry of vast proportions. Added to this, three and a half million men and women are directly engaged in the defense establishment. We, annually, spend on military security more than the net income of all United States corporations.

This conjunction of an immense military establishment and large-arms industry is new in the American experience. The total influence—economic, political, even spiritual—is felt in every city, every statehouse, and every office of the Federal Government. We recognize the imperative need for this development. Yet we must not fail to comprehend its grave implications. Our toil, resources, and livelihood are all involved; so is the very structure of our society.

In the councils of government, we must guard against the acquisition of unwarranted influence, whether sought or unsought, by the military- industrial complex. The potential for the disastrous rise of misplaced power exists and will persist.

We must never let the weight of this combination endanger our liberties or democratic processes. We should take nothing for granted. Only an alert and knowledgeable citizenry can compel the proper meshing of the huge industrial and military machinery of defense with our peaceful methods and goals, so that security and liberty may prosper together.

Air Force General Barry M. Goldwater Quote from 1964 Speech

On July 16, 1964, Barry Goldwater, as he accepted the Republican Presidential Nomination in San Francisco, said,

"Extremism in the defense of liberty is no vice," and "Moderation in the pursuit of justice is no virtue."

On this same day in, 1999, John F. Kennedy Jr. and his wife, Carolyn, and her sister, Lauren Bessette, died when their single engine plane, piloted by Kennedy, plunged into the Atlantic Ocean, near Martha's Vineyard, Mass.

1

THE BOOK: FINALLY
THE TRUTH

Introduction by Robert Groden

My name is Robert Groden. I have been asked to write this forward because of my reputation as an expert about the John F. Kennedy assassination for 53 years and because of my long-time acquaintance with Mr. Bruce H. Bell and the unique and startling story of his firsthand knowledge of the actual events on November 22, 1963.

My background was initially as a film and photo technician for motion pictures, when I was involved in the optical enhancement of the now infamous Zapruder film of the assassination. That film had been kept from public view, until I brought to international attention in 1975. Since then, I have been involved with several prominent authors and was a consultant for Oliver Stone's epic movie 'JFK.'

I became acquainted with Mr. Bell in 1998, when he first approached me with fragments of his story. Only fragments, because he, obviously, was concerned about possible repercussions from the authorities and others who might be affected by his revelations. Since that first meeting nearly 20 years ago, we have had numerous meetings and together visited the sites in, both, Dallas and Fort Worth that he recalled from his and his father's involvement in the assassination and its planning.

I must admit that I was somewhat skeptical because of his initial reluctance to reveal all the specifics of his story, but as time has progressed, I have become increasingly convinced that his narrative rings true. And that his ability to name the names and motives of those involved is a significant development in our understanding of the assassination and concern for the inner workings of our government and its agencies.

And now that I and you, the reader, can finally read the whole story, I am impressed and gratified for his persistence in getting the story out.

In my more than half century of studying the issues of the assassination, I have heard many stories and have never been as impressed as I am with Bruce's. I do believe that this is a true and factual story concerning the assassination of President Kennedy, finally.

In the fourteen publications that I have released since 1975, I have always dealt with the physical evidence in the case and never tried to deal with a story of the inner workings of the conspiracy. This is the first time that I've dealt with that part of the biggest crime of the twentieth century. Others have, unfortunately, rushed to judgment and scorned other stories about the assassination, and thrown away what might have been important historical evidence. I suggest that the reader keep an open mind and understand what Bruce has gone through to bring you his story.

Robert Groden
Dallas, Texas
August 2017

My Story; A Little Historical Perspective

My story is the story of the assassination in November 1963 and how and by whom it was planned and executed. I knew that this is one of many 'conspiracy' accounts and that many others' theoretical accounts get close to the true story, but they do not give the whole story. I also know that many layers of disinformation have been employed to protect both those involved and the public. My story implicates both individuals and governmental agencies because that is simply what took place; a conversion of individuals and agencies that wanted Kennedy dead and his policies dead with him.

This book is an historical memoir involving my life, 1962 through 1964. My life with my father Orris Bell and his participation in the planning and execution of the President Kennedy assassination. The CIA has gone to great lengths to stop this story from getting to the public, including attempting to destroy my credibility.

General Charles Born was a lackey of General Curtis LeMay and the other Joint Chiefs of the U.S. military structure. They in turn were lackeys of Allen Dulles, former chief of the CIA. When the decision to assassinate the President was made, my father would become the primary coordinator and, eventually the primary assassin. And his business, U.S. Sonics Inc., already a CIA 'front,' would become the organizational site.

The assassination was not something that these men did just out of hatred for him or the Kennedys in general. They killed him for the security of the nation. This is realistically how they saw it, something that was completely necessary. And the situation so dire that it was an emergency, something that couldn't depend on democratic, less drastic means.

The literal structure of our government was changed in 1963 and has never recovered. A coup took place that was not just a public assassination of a president, but one hidden from the public by the very people depended on to prevent such catastrophes. A coup beginning a slide towards fascism that we see more clearly today.

I witnessed this planning, came to know most of the participants, and suffered greatly as a result.

I had never written a book before when I started in 2006. Since then, I have completely rewritten it three times. I wrote it with regret and sadness because although the story I'll present is not a pretty memory, I felt it needed to be told for historical, ethical, and political reasons.

As I progressed in my writing and contemplated scenes from my memory over and over again, new material would come back to me. Of course, it's been fifty years since this all took place, but when you're eleven and twelve years old and such a world-changing, very dramatic event takes place with you in the front seat, these impressions stay with you for the rest of your life. No matter how hard the government tries to force you to forget them, they keep coming back in full brilliance with all the terror and horror fully intact.

My effort now is to tell the truth and not just through the eyes of an eleven/twelve-year-old boy, but also with the knowledge gained since from my father and his people concerning the events and their politics in general. Of course, I have also become more knowledgeable about other associated events and history. So, I am writing this from the vantage point of a mature and well-experienced man.

As I matured, I became a more liberal man than my father and his people. They came to recognize this and of course, disagreed with my position. But they had no choice. I had become very independent and they couldn't change me, although they tried.

Many of the men who killed the Kennedys and others lived to regret their heavy-handed actions in their old age. They lived long enough to become wise and realize that the severe damage they had done to the nation should have been avoided, accomplished through means, other than murder.

How I Knew What I Know

As you start to read my story, I know you will invariably ask yourself how I know what I know and why they, Orris and the other planners, would accept and choose me, a child, in this role of decoy and confidant to my father in the Kennedy assassination planning.

My father and others realized I wasn't a 'normal' child by the time I was five. That I was very intelligent and curious about things that most other kids could care less about. More sophisticated and perceptive, with interests instilled by my father. Knowledgeable about the stock market, American history and world affairs, especially the Cold War. And how it all came together.

Because of this, I believe my father, like many fathers, had a degree of pride in this offspring. Began to see me as destined to assume his place. So, began taking me with him to be involved in his business and social life. To the point that he would even take me on out-of-town business trips. This wasn't particularly unusual; It has always been common for people in power to single out those who have the most potential to succeed them. But I believe the degree that my father did this was unusual.

Actually, I rather enjoyed the experience. I didn't mind being the only child present, but viewed it as normal. And being accepted by the men in these settings was not only ego-inflating, but allowed me to pose questions which they seemed to enjoy answering. Questions about the aerospace industry, mainly physical and engineering applications.

For example, at the age of five and six, I would go to U.S. Chemical Milling, Inc. in California, where my father was vice president of sales. By the age of seven, I was going to Convair in Fort Worth, where he would take me out on the main assembly line to witness the manufacturing of B-58s. A few years later, I went to General Dynamics in Fort Worth many times and met with scientists working on a top-secret project involving a new spaceship that would fly by electromagnetic force, something the public still knows nothing about. At the age of nine, I went to the Strategic Air Command (SAC) headquarters in Omaha, Nebraska for an entire week with Orris and his aerospace industry associates. And there were many other similar experiences.

I quickly learned to sit back, listen and observe, to determine which person was welcoming. Then smile reassuringly. If the situation had to do with the assassination, I would usually act as if I wasn't paying attention, silently whistling to myself and staring at some unseen object, when in reality I was riveted to every word. My father appreciated all this, and sometimes would wink at me to show I wasn't fooling him.

In 1961, when Orris and his partners started U.S. Sonics in Dallas, I already knew all of the primary men involved. When it began operating, I would go there on Saturdays and Sundays during the school year, and more often in the Summer. So, I was already quite familiar with this environment prior to the Kennedy assassination planning. Most of the men involved were familiar with me as well and, except for a few notable exceptions, were quite open with their discussions in front of me, both, political and otherwise.

Also, I usually overheard at least portions of Orris' phone calls. I knew who he was talking with because he would have a secretary or my mother place the call. And he never ever asked me to leave. This way he could converse with me with the understanding that I had heard and understood at least one side of the conversation.

When my father would leave town, I would always know where to, because If I didn't accompany him and my mother to the airport, I would ask her after; it was important that she always knew. And of course, he would always answer any of my questions.

During the course of the planning of the assassination, I met many people who would become publicly known as involved in it: Jack Ruby, George Senator, Roscoe White, J. D. Tippit, Joseph Civello, Johnny Roselli, Ruth and Michael Paine, Lee and Marina Oswald, Clint Murchison, Clint Murchison Jr., Walter DeMohrenschildt, and Sam Giancana. I also heard my father talking on the phone to Clay Shaw, Carlos Marcello, and Santo Trafficante about the assassination many times.

Others who have not been known to the public, I met with or saw with my father, discussing the assassination. They included Air Force General Charles Born, Edwin Nesbitt, Jeffrey Miller, Charles Lundquist, Charles Lyon, Clarence Bentley, Norris Lawrence, and Tom Lawrence. I know that all these people were involved in the assassination, at some level, and how they were involved.

I'm certain my father didn't tell me everything about what was going on, but enough so that I could piece together a great deal of what he didn't. He must have realized it would be ridiculous to try to ignore my questions because he knew I was already aware and understood most of the plans. And his denial of information could have caused me to try to seek answers someplace else. It was essential then to 'keep me in the loop' and on their side, so I would only discuss the assassination with them. They did trust me and trusted me emphatically; they had to, they had no choice with me being with them so often and sitting right next to them in their clandestine meetings.

There was another reason my father wanted me to know as much about the assassination as he did. He had a justifiable concern that he might be killed during or after it, or arrested and executed. So, he wanted me to know as much as possible in case there were no one to answer my questions about what, how and why it took place. To my father, this was a type of legacy that I deserved.

Besides, I had already assumed the role of my father's confidant and sounding board and it seemed even more important now for him to have someone he could trust to talk to outside of the day-to-day players with whom he had to interact. I had always been this person, someone whom he could run things past and as a result be able to work through ideas without the pressure of direct peer interaction and questioning. Honest and naively trusting of him, I would be faithful to any cause of his.

I also believe that he felt I could protect him and the project; my being so close to him was an auspicious omen. He was a very superstitious man who believed in the occult and several times I had demonstrated unusual perceptibility. They began to rely on me, a status I took very seriously, reacting with them the way they expected. I believe they knew that if I felt that something was going terribly wrong, I would say so. In fact, my father would constantly ask me how I felt about certain decisions.

That my father and the group were using me was obvious to me then and is even more apparent and disturbing to me.

2

THE INSTIGATORS

General Curtis LeMay

I heard General Curtis LeMay's name spoken quite often at U.S. Sonics, even before Born's speech. I knew he was the Chief of the Air Force now, and as such, member of the Joint Chiefs of Staff, one of the most influential men in the military. Therefore, important not only to the success of U.S. Sonics, but also to the events that would unfold and end in the Kennedy assassination. But I never met him.

His many prior accomplishments were accompanied by an extreme approach to warfare and a complete disregard for the sanctity of human life, earning him the nickname, 'Iron Ass.'

The U.S. Joint Chiefs of Staff had met secretly before the atomic bombing of Japan to approve a new policy of 'striking the first blow.' LeMay commanded the B-2s that then firebombed Japan in 1944-45, killing hundreds of thousands and decimating cities. He totally supported the later atomic bombing of Hiroshima and Nagasaki; it was apparent he could see no difference between conventional firebombs and nuclear weapons.

He was present on the battleship Missouri on September 2, 1945, at Japan's surrender. A quote illustrates his thinking, "Killing Japanese didn't bother me very much at the time. I wasn't worried particularly about how many people we killed in getting the job done. I suppose if I had lost the war, I would have been tried as a war criminal. Fortunately, we were on the winning side."

In August of 1945, 'A Strategic Chart of Russian Cities' was developed, identifying cities that could be bombed with nuclear weapons if necessary. That autumn, LeMay and two other prominent World War II generals successfully flew three intercontinental B-29 bombers from Tokyo to Washington to prove they were capable of attacking from a foreign base. Then, the Joint Chiefs of Staff Joint Intelligence Committee began drafting a plan for a first strike on the Soviet Union.

In October 1945, LeMay was appointed to a new position; Deputy Chief of Air Staff for Research and Development (RAND), a think-tank created to assess military and political strategies. It made the first proposal for 'satellites,' ensuring their development would be in conjunction with that of the Air Force for intercontinental ballistic missiles. This enabled him to further research the feasibility of developing an Air Force ability to attack Russia with nuclear weapons.

And it was the break which allowed him to become who he would become! He was assigned the task of building the Strategic Air Command, SAC, the Air Force aviation group that was to be in charge of nuclear bombing of Russia. At the same time, he made persistent attempts to acquire control of U.S. nuclear weapons, actually independent of Presidential authorization.

In November 1945, he spoke to his Ohio State University alumni, "There should be no limit to the development of nuclear weapons and the necessary delivery systems in the U.S. In order to defend the U.S. in the future, it has to be prepared for the next war, to fully develop nuclear weapons and be prepared to use them first."

In August 1946, he was appointed to his second atomic bombing command, 'Operation Crossroads' at Bikini Atoll in the Pacific; a pair of nuclear weapon tests. He was extremely impressed when he personally observed the nuclear explosions, the first he had ever seen. Following this, he wrote a detailed report concerning the need to develop the most effective methods to deliver the atomic bomb to its target.

In September 1946, LeMay supervised the Allen Dulles-inspired 'Project Paper Clip' to oversee the military side of the massive effort to get as much of the captured German technology and research and development to America, instead of Russia. Importantly for the later planning of the Kennedy assassination, this brought LeMay and Dulles into a working relationship. Also important in this regard, is that the need for lighter metals for missiles would bring him into contact with Charles Lundquist, owner of U.S. Chemical Milling Corp. and eventually my father's boss and a figure in the assassination.

In October 1947, LeMay was given command of the U.S. air forces in Europe (USAFE). This had been General Charles Born's previous command during the end of World War II, and probably LeMay took the command from him. He was given his third star at this time, becoming a Lieutenant General.

During the early days of the Soviet confrontation over Berlin in May of 1948, LeMay and the Joint Chiefs approved a military plan named 'Halfmoon', which envisioned fifty atomic bombs on twenty Russian cities to control the Soviet threat. On October 19, 1948, he was appointed actual commander of SAC, inheriting an incompetent force, but quickly proclaimed he would "build SAC into a force so professional, so strong, so powerful, we would not have to fight the Russians."

In November 1948, he developed a plan for SAC, a "First Strike Nuclear Attack on Russia," arguing that was in reality the best defense; the Russians would win if they were first. He fought for nuclear bomb targeting requirements, wanting to be able to bomb industrial urban areas that would result in at least 2.7 million civilian deaths and another four million casualties; instead bombing strategic military targets in non-urban areas would result in much fewer casualties. This plan, involving eighty percent of American nuclear bombs, meant destroying seventy Soviet cities within thirty days with 133 atomic bombs. It was approved by USAF Chief of Staff, Hoyt Vandenburg, as a viable emergency attack plan allotting SAC top budget priority. American air power strategists had a name for such an attack; 'Killing a Nation.'

In 1949, wanting everyone in SAC in the correct frame of mind, he prodded, "We are at war now," and actually started to put in place the force of bombers for his first strike policy. In the same year, in the face of much moral opposition, he also began to fight for development of the hydrogen bomb.

Within a year, he had built SAC to a force with 868 aircraft and 71,000 personnel. A simulated 'Sunday Punch' mission using all SAC nuclear-capable bombers over U.S. cities was highly successful. Buttressing LeMay's approach, A CIA secret report determined that at this time Russia had a very poor anti-aircraft deterrent to such a first strike, but would highly likely have at least two hundred nuclear bombs by the end of 1955, when the U.S. mainland would be vulnerable to nuclear attack.

At the beginning of the Korean invasion in 1950, LeMay stated at the Pentagon, "Look, let us (SAC) go up to North Korea and nuclear bomb five of the biggest cities…and that ought to end this." The Pentagon refused because, "That would kill a lot of innocent civilians."

As an alternative, he proposed that he could firebomb the Koreans into oblivion, which, of course would also result in the mass killing of civilians. This actually conformed to the real plan he had stated to the press, to save SAC's nuclear arsenal for a 'Sunday punch' on Russia; not to 'piss them away' on the Korean war.

When China entered the war in December, he proposed that he personally go to the Far East to direct a possible nuclear bombing of China, again being denied. Later, as the war continued, he blamed his superiors for their misjudgment. Actually, President Truman did come to authorize the use of nine nuclear bombs in China and Russia during the War, but political pressure caused the reversal of the order.

But the nine bombs never were returned to the Atomic Energy Commission, which had authority over them. Instead, they remained in SAC's and Curtis LeMay's hands to be cherished. Despite this, he later complained, "We did not own nuclear weapons…the Atomic Energy Commission (AEC) owned the weapons, and they were all stored at Sandia Air Force Base in Albuquerque, New Mexico." Neither did the President, so LeMay continued to fight for the bombs and even forged an illegal plan with the General at Sandia Labs to gain access to them if he needed them.

LeMay was appointed Air Force Vice Chief of Staff in 1957, and served as Chief from 1961 to '65, and so an influential member of the Joint Chiefs of Staff. He would later run as a Vice-Presidential candidate under George Wallace and his American Independent Party; heavily segregationist.

General Charles Born

Air Force General Charles Born had a highly distinguished career. He had been in charge of bombing Germany in 1944-1945 and his counterpart in Japan had been LeMay. They became close friends during that time and remained so until their deaths.

When I first met him in 1961, I was informed that he was semi-retired with a half-time commitment to SAC under General LeMay, two weeks a month. His status with SAC was as its North Atlantic Wing Commander. For the two weeks on duty, he would remain in the air in a converted 707. In the leading mobile command position if a nuclear war was to erupt and SAC's land-based control center was destroyed. The theory was that the Russians wouldn't know where this 707 was because they lacked the necessary sophisticated radar and infrared satellite equipment. This placed him in direct communication with the White House via the 'red phone' and on the cutting edge of any problems with the U.S.S.R. Technically, he could be called to active duty at any time, which had put him directly in the hot seat during the Cuban Missile Crisis of October

Over the years, his career had placed him as Base Commander at all the Texas Air Force bases at one time or another. At one time, he was also President and Commander of the Texas Air Force, a private Air Force in Texas with immense influence.

This lengthy association with Texas had led him to be one of the most influential military persons in the state and its 'Military Industrial Complex, something he reveled in and took major advantage of. And his half-time status left him able to work in the private sector, where he was very good at supplying private corporations with profitable government defense contracts, for a fee of course.

For instance, at one point he worked at Texas Instruments in Dallas; first as a Vice President, but later as the head of engineering because of the obvious conflict of interest; regardless, he was supplying them.

In the mid to late 1950s, when LeMay had forged a relationship with U.S. Chem Mill, he assigned Born to work with that firm, thereby also bringing him into a relationship with Charles Lundquist. And with Orris, employed there at the time.

From the time I first met him, before he became a major partner with my father in US Sonics, and long before the final decision to kill President Kennedy was made, I would listen to many conversations between the two of them in which they stated that they would eventually have to do just that.

Born was Orris' primary Washington contact. They would continue close for the rest of his life, and they would do many other deviant, dirty deals together for the CIA. He was a very active man, to say the least,

As I write this and attempt to validate my story, I realize that Born's official Air Force biographies show him retiring from the Air Force in 1954 and make no reference to his fifty percent duty status with SAC in the 1960s, a different chronology. I can only propose that this is the result of the cover-up surrounding the assassinations.

Allen Dulles

Those attending General Born's speech surely believed Allen Dulles was the primary figure behind the assassination plot, enlisting the assistance of the CIA and Generals LeMay and Born. Dulles and LeMay were close friends.

Dulles came from a family, long influential. His father was a prominent Presbyterian minister and theologian. His maternal grandfather was the first Secretary of State to participate in the overthrow of a foreign government, the Hawaiian monarchy. And it was his maternal uncle, who as Woodrow Wilson's Secretary of State, actually appointed Dulles as an intelligence operative in Bern, Switzerland during World War I, to monitor other European governments and supply him with weekly reports.

Following the 'War to end all wars', Dulles returned to his partnership in the legal firm, Sullivan and Cromwell, one of the first American firms that consulted with international governments and businesses to arrange projects benefitting U.S. businesses. It was under the firm's auspices that both Allen and John Foster consulted with Hitler in helping create and improve the industrial capacity for what would become Germany's war machine. The Dulles brothers, like the Nazi government, identified the Soviet Union Communist government as contrary to capitalism. Not to democracy.

Although Dulles could be charming, Carl Jung, his acquaintance in Bern, psychoanalyzed him as a manipulative sociopath. In fact, a teenage incident is recounted that when his younger sister fell into the water, Dulles merely sat and watched as she struggled, apparently too fascinated to do anything to help. And the rigidity of his family's religiosity cannot be ignored.

Dulles' journey to power benefitted in 1944 when he served as a Berlin officer in the O.S.S., Office of Strategic Services, America's World War II intelligence agency. He developed one-to-one contacts with Nazi military and researchers and developed an admiration for their research techniques, for 'good Germans' and those who could be useful to him.

However, his intelligence work came under serious criticism. In fact, in January 1944, Washington required him to provide more accurate information and to verify his submitted information with more care. And much of his hands-on work was contrary to instructions he was receiving from director William Donovan.

At the time, he was meeting with Hans Bernd Gisevius, a participant in a conspiracy to overthrow Adolf Hitler. Dulles suggested that the most effective method to assassinate Hitler would be through the use of snipers to target the Fuhrer, as he moved about in his open-air vehicle, a plan eerily prescient of what would occur in Dallas in November 1963. While Gisevius concurred, he advised Dulles that an alternative plan had been adopted, to plant a bomb in a briefcase to be placed next to where Hitler sat during military meetings. This July 20 plot obviously failed.

Dulles then assisted Gisevius in escaping to America as German authorities swept up over seven thousand military and civilian officials as having participated in the plot. Of those arrested, almost five thousand were executed.

He proved to be proficient at negotiating with the German regime to end the war and played a similar role with the Japanese. Following the war, Dulles was instrumental in organizing the Paperclip project, through which many war criminals were given shelter in America; their talents then being put to good use.

In January 1951, he was appointed Deputy Director for Plans – read "Covert Ops " -- in August.1953, Deputy Director of the CIA, and in 1953, director by Eisenhower, the new President.

Lieutenant General James Doolittle's analysis of him and the CIA, ordered by President Eisenhower, warned that his relationship with his older brother, Secretary of State John Foster Dulles, might create policies without proper consultation with administration officials. And according to some sources, the Dulles brothers felt that government was too important to be left in the hands of the people or their elected representatives; it should be in the hands of 'intelligent' people like themselves.

In 1961, Dulles attempted to manipulate the new, inexperienced President Kennedy into triggering an all-out invasion of Cuba. However, Dulles underestimated JFK's reluctance to engage U.S. military forces and the 'Bay of Pigs' operation failed. Following this, realizing Dulles' attempted manipulation, Kennedy demanded his resignation and appointed John McCone as the new CIA head. Probably not someone he should have trusted either.

However, despite his lost position, Dulles maintained significant contacts within The Agency and continued to conduct various operations and functions. The CIA was essentially 'a government within the government' and Dulles considered it to be his kingdom. He was the longest tenured Director in its history and his influence within the government and the elite Eastern establishment was considerable.

And he would continue his tremendous enmity to Kennedy. According to author David Talbot, in the summer of 1963 a Russian Orthodox priest at a dinner party critical of Kennedy, reassured the other guests not to worry, "The Old Man will take care of it." "Old Man" was Dulles' nickname.

There was no hiding the President's leanings toward peace and disarmament; sentiments that were popular with citizens, not so much with the politicians and elite. In fact, when Washington columnist Andrew Tully asked Dulles in 1962 what The Agency would do if a foreign operative threatened the security of the nation, he casually replied "We'd kill him." Of course, he then backtracked, stating he "could not possibly conceive" such an event, but then adding "now." But it was just this attitude that figured into Kennedy's known advocacy of dismantling the CIA itself.

He was a guest at Lyndon Johnson's ranch in mid-August 1963. And in a late October book-promoting tour, he addressed the Dallas Council on World Affairs and met with a number of political elites, including the Dallas Mayor, brother of former CIA deputy, Charles Cabell who had also been dismissed by Kennedy. It is notable that Dallas was the only exception in a tour otherwise focused on the east and west coasts.

On the morning of November 22, 1963, the day of the assassination, through the 24th, the day of Oswald's death, he would be at "The Farm" near Williamsburg, Virginia, an alternate secret CIA command center. But in an apparent attempt to distance himself from these events, he let it be known instead, that his calendar reflected his being at his Washington residence.

Conveniently, he would be appointed to the Warren Commission to investigate Kennedy's assassination, and reportedly tell columnist Murray Kempton he was confident that the Commission would find no evidence of a conspiracy.

Significant is that the Rockefeller and Dulles families were distant cousins, cementing their governmental and business inter-relationships and that the Rockefellers had created their own intelligence sources. And importantly, they served as private bankers for "off-the-books" CIA operations.

3

THE EVENTS AND SPEECH STARTING IT ALL

The Quandry

Orris, Born and Lundquist were radically conservative and embedded in what Eisenhower had termed, "The Military Industrial Complex" that worked very hard to keep John F. Kennedy out of the White House in the 1960 Presidential election. But they supported different nominees. Lundquist, Richard Nixon because of their friendship and his indebtedness for Nixon's help acquiring the atoll cleanup contract.

Orris and Born on the other hand, tried to get Senator Barry Goldwater to challenge Nixon, who they felt would basically follow the policies set by Eisenhower. Although obviously a revered military man, as President he had been too soft on Communism. Not doing whatever necessary during a few years' window when the U.S. had a clear advantage, to stop the USSR from becoming a superpower, enabled by its development of its own nuclear arsenal and delivery system. Echoing

LeMay, they felt the U.S. could have overcome Russia with a first strike, preventing the Cold War. They never forgave Eisenhower for that or the parting admonition about the "Military Industrial Complex."

They consequently felt Goldwater's ultra-conservative position and foreign polies were preferable to Nixon's. They knew the Arizona Senator personally, but despite enormous pressure, he declined to run, feeling Nixon was unbeatable. So, supporting Nixon was the only alternative to keep Senator John F. Kennedy from becoming President. And then, to contemplate what measures could be taken, if he were elected.

And it would develop that from the beginning, their dire concerns were justified. Most obvious, the Bay of Pigs. The poorly handled Cuban Missile Crisis. But so much more.

The Bay of Pigs

Both Generals Born and LeMay had previously been involved in the planning of many covert operations. And long before the Nixon/Kennedy election in 1960, and before there was U.S. Sonics, they had been involved in the early planning of such an operation to invade and repatriate Cuba. Kennedy had actually inherited the plan from the Eisenhower administration. He was now given a CIA guarantee that it would be successful and would in no way harm or embarrass him. He had therefore given the go-ahead, and it was now to be put into action in April 1961.

There were several factors in the interest to 'repatriate' Cuba before the Russians were even interested in it as a potential ally. But the CIA foresaw that possibility and did not want Havana to become a warm port for the Russian Navy and nuclear-armed submarines, right off our coast. And there was the obvious pressure from the Cuban refugees, the need to re-establish America's image after 'losing' Cuba, and very significantly, the desire of Mafia bosses Carlos Marcello and Santo Trafficante, eager to re-establish their gambling, narcotics, and prostitution empire; the CIA had been quite tolerant of the Mafia's prior dominance in Cuba, working closely with it for years in its own clandestine operations.

Because of Born's prior involvement in the planning to take out Castro, it was natural that U.S. Sonics would be used as the CIA front company to do it now. That the eventual invasion of Cuba would be successful was of tantamount importance to all the parties involved.

The CIA had planned that the invasion be led by Cuban nationals, followed by waves of U.S. Marines. They knew that strong air support at the initial landing point would be essential and likely as the invasion continued. But Kennedy refused the CIA's request to use Navy aircraft carriers' light bombers for the operation.

This had been a severe disappointment to the Joint Chiefs and the CIA's Dulles. And even though they knew this invasion would fail without the bombers, they lied to Kennedy that it could still be successful. Planning to tell him after the landing craft had been launched, that they would in fact need to use them, having detected unexpected heavy forces of resistance at the landing zone. Dulles felt he would then cave-in and allow them the bombers rather than suffer the embarrassment of losing the war against Communist-leaning Cuba. When the entire world was watching so closely.

So, when the bomb-less invasion begun to fail, Dulles and the military did as planned, informed Kennedy the bombers were needed. The President, not fully trusting the CIA, had suspected such a ploy, and flew into a rage.

Even if Castro had not known of the invasion and exactly where and when the landing would take place, the operation still had little possibility of being successful without the use of American Marines. But with that information leaked to him, it would be a slaughter of the Cuban exile forces on the beach without that heavy air support.

The Cuban Missile Crisis

One afternoon in mid-October 1962, Orris called home to tell my mother to pack clothes for the family, fill the car with gas, and then wait for another call. If he then told us to leave, we were to drive to a town in the West Texas Davis Mountains where he was to contact a man who owned a ranch. He would take care of us until my father contacted us again. That could be a long time if a nuclear war were to take place and Dallas attacked. Perhaps then we would never hear from him again.

Orris and his military and CIA associates were fearing a nuclear war. It had been determined that Russia had placed offensive nuclear missiles in Cuba, using the justification that the U.S. had offensive nuclear missiles in Turkey. Air Force General LeMay and his fellow Joint Chiefs of Staff had warned President Kennedy this was not the time to play 'Russian Roulette' with them. If the Russians had gone this far, they might call his bluff and the situation could very quickly get out of control.

These men presumed Russia would only attempt such an action if they perceived Kennedy himself weak and could be taken advantage of; he would never respond militarily. So, the Joint Chiefs made the decision that these missile installations should be bombed immediately; to prevent them from becoming functional, and to prove the Russians' assessment wrong.

LeMay, always yearning for nuclear war, and now seeing sufficient provocation to justify his long-standing preemptive plan, did everything he could to get Kennedy's consent to go further. Have the Strategic Air Command (S.A.C.) launch its nuclear "Suncdy Punch" on Russia itself, before it had a chance to initiate its nuclear strike against the U.S.

The Russians' prediction was correct. Kennedy did not act militarily, giving them time to play it out their way. They were even allowed to down an American forward surveillance plane over Cuba without retaliation.

Orris had spent the last week at U.S. Sonics, so he could remain in constant contact with his Washington connections and the military. He was tasked to take certain actions in Dallas if war broke out with the Russians and then leave on a helicopter for a secured base to the west of the Dallas/Fort Worth area. These detailed instructions had been arranged with General Born about a week earlier, when they realized that the Cuban/Russian situation could get out of control and end in war; a war that now looked like a real possibility.

Kennedy, as usual, did not listen to the Joint Chiefs, but went ahead with a plan to play it politically as his advisers wanted. Ever since the 'Bay of Pigs' failed invasion, he had been perceived as being afraid to confront the Russians appropriately. So, he had to prove now that he could be tough when needed and that he had the ability to control the situation.

His political advisers recommended he first stall, to establish a committee supposedly to advise him; the ABSCOM Committee that would come to be described as a committee of 'Hawks and Doves' being comprised of opposing groups. The Hawks, conservative and consistent with the views of the Joint Chiefs. The Doves, liberal and consistent with those of the Kennedy Administration. This phraseology,

'Hawks and Doves' was to stick forever in the American jargon, when referring to Conservatives and Liberals.

The 'Dove' advisers suggested that politically, he should allow these issues to develop further to add drama to the situation for best impact on the public. Then when the time was right, a presidential address could hype it up further. They said that the Russians would always fold later and remove their missiles, rather than risk going to war.

Of course, the Joint Chiefs realized what he was up to and felt this was much too serious to be playing political games. They certainly didn't want him to try to dialogue with the Russians. They had been trained for just such a situation and knew there was only one way to deal with the Russians, be tough, firm, and quick to go to war if necessary. To be otherwise would allow them the time needed to make the missiles ready for launch. The Russians hadn't taken the risk of bringing them to Cuba to just call our bluff. They were meant for a first strike against the U.S.

General Born, as Commander of the North Atlantic Wing of SAC, had taken his designated place in an early AWACS airplane, a 707 fitted with electronic communication equipment and sleeping quarters for a full crew. If the Russians decided to attack the U.S., such an attack would come from two directions. Across the Atlantic with their numerous nuclear bombers and across the Eastern Arctic with their ICBM's. Born's aircraft would be the first to 'see' the bombers and would notify the President, the Joint Chiefs of Staff, and SAC in Omaha, so they could retaliate. His airplane would then become an 'airborne platform' from which to conduct this war. He would refuel in the air and stay airborne until the situation was resolved. This could mean weeks in the air. And in fact, General Born and his crew did not come down for over three weeks. A massive pressure on his shoulders!

The Joint Chiefs of Staff had reached a conclusion that the situation had deteriorated to the point that nuclear war was inevitable or so close to it that they had to take military action immediately. They knew that their Russian counterpart was telling Nikita Khrushchev the same thing, that Russia had to initiate a first strike on the U.S., or Russia would get caught with her pants down and lose the inevitable war.

This was a time before the concepts of 'Assured Mutual Destruction' and 'nuclear winter' would be introduced. A time when it was believed that the nation launching a full nuclear attack first had the advantage and therefore could 'win' a nuclear war.

As things heated up and after going to Kennedy several times, urging him to take military action and his refusing, LeMay and the Joint Chiefs actually ordered him to launch a nuclear strike on Russia. But the Presidency kept refusing, prompting them to consider seizing control of the nation for its own protection. LeMay even attempted to provoke Russia to go to a higher level of DEFCON by launching an ICBM from California towards it and instructing his bombers to fly directly towards targets there, with one pilot told to penetrate its airspace. If Russia were to go to a level of DEFCON right below war itself, Kennedy would have no choice but to allow a U.S. nuclear strike.

Thankfully, none of LeMay's efforts would provoke Russia to go to a higher level of DEFCON. The Russians apparently knew what he was attempting to do and wouldn't fall for it.

Nevertheless, the Russians appeared to be taking the situation very seriously, showing no signs of backing off, and doing everything they could, as quickly as they could, to prepare the Cuban-based missiles for launch, both, nuclear and anti-aircraft. And after discovering the Americans knew about these missiles and were considering bombing them, they put their entire military on alert and stepped up their work of readying them.

One of the problems for both Kennedy's and Khrushchev's teams was the absence of a clear line of communication between them; there was no 'hot phone' or 'red phone', so both sides were basically operating in the dark. Fortunately, through a fluke, Robert Kennedy was able to make contact with Khrushchev through a Russian Consulate employee, with an urgent message, straight and simple. Khrushchev had to give a sign to the Joint Chiefs that he was not going to attack the U.S., or our Joint Chiefs would take control from Kennedy and attack Russia.

Khrushchev responded that same night, passing the word through the Consulate that he was in control in Russia and was not going to attack America. And that communication should be opened immediately to prevent the situation from worsening. The Joint Chiefs now had no choice but to stand down, albeit with reservation.

Following negotiations between the two countries resulted in the removal of the offending missiles, but Khrushchev also demanded that the U.S. remove its missiles from Turkey first. Despite LeMay and the Joint Chiefs pressuring him not to, Kennedy agreed to this demand, not reported publicly at the time. But he also blockaded Cuba, not allowing any military equipment into Cuba until all the missiles were removed.

However, even though Kennedy had proven his ability to contain the situation, it was no enough for his enemies. After all, he had not done as they had demanded, order a nuclear attack.

The Hawk: A Sign

School was canceled for several days during the Cuban Missile Crisis. But I decided to walk there one day with my brother Stephen and our Basset Hound. We wanted to see if any of our friends were playing in the schoolyard. When we got there, we couldn't find anyone, so we decided to return home the long way, down a dirt road.

About a quarter of a mile along, the dog started fighting with something twenty yards, or so, in front of us. She was going crazy. Normally, very friendly, this baying and barking was strange. When we ran up to see what had upset her, I could hardly believe my eyes. It was a huge Red-Tailed Hawk. At first, I couldn't understand why it didn't just fly away, but then I saw it had been shot, shattering its wing.

Talk about cool. What a find for a boy who spends hours on his back staring up at flying hawks, dreaming what it would be like to be able to fly like that! Anything that flew was amazing to me. Partly because my father's work in aviation had exposed me to everything flying, ever since I could remember.

We quickly looked around for something to contain it. I really didn't want it to get away We found an old wire egg basket lying by the road, and I tried to place it over the hawk with one hand, while pulling my dog off of it with the other. But as soon as I got the basket over it, it reached up with its talons to grab my thumb and fingers, burying its talon deep into my thumb. It had happened so quickly, I hardly saw it reach out for me. I pulled back, but the basket and the bird came with me; we were definitely attached, and the hawk wasn't going to let go.

Stephen had been watching all this, mouth and eyes wide open. I know he couldn't believe I was now doing battle with a bird, one with a five-foot wingspan. And I wasn't about to let this bird get away, no matter what. Little did I realize that it couldn't have flown away anyway, because of its injury.

Finally, I got hold of the talon in my thumb to pull it out. I was bleeding badly, and the dog was still going crazy, trying to get to the hawk. So, I told Stephen to take it home and get a box we could use for the hawk. I thought it would calm down if the dog was gone. When Stephen got back about twenty minutes later, we were able to secure the bird in the box, but only after another hard battle.

When we got home, I showed our hawk to our mother. She let us put it in the garage, where I was able to build a large cage for it. When we tried to feed it some steak, it wouldn't eat at first, but later after calming down, it consumed some of the meat. It was still frightened of us, but, after a few days it allowed me to feed it from my gloved hand without too much of a fight.

Our father was still staying in Dallas because the Cuban Missile problem was at its peak. Our mother didn't tell him about the hawk because she knew how focused and worried he was. He finally came home a few days later and told us what had really happened with Russia and how close we had come to war.

I can still remember the look on his face when I proudly took him out to the garage to see my captive hawk. He obviously knew about the situation of the 'Hawks and Doves' in Washington and I know, given his penchant for omens, that he related this hawk to that situation. He even related my hawk's story to Lundquist and others who saw this as affirmation of my special status; I hadn't found the hawk, rather it had come to me. And the broken wing of the hawk represented the damage done by Kennedy to the U.S. Military, which was not being allowed to fly to do their duty.

With time, I had gotten the hawk to accept me completely as a friend. It would actually come, perch on my glove and feed from my hand. Although I tried to tape its injured wing, there was no way to repair it and a couple of weeks later my father talked me into the necessity of shooting it to put it out of its agony. That was a very hard thing to do, but shoot it, we did.

Other Mistakes

Kennedy embarked on an ambitious, some would say, over-zealous program. Of course, he knew he couldn't accomplish it all in two terms; supposedly the Kennedys envisioned Robert and Ted succeeding him. Nevertheless, with hindsight, it appears obvious that he did, in fact, move too quickly, angering too many who had the power to thwart him.

The CIA and Dulles

Kennedy's denial 'at the last minute' to use American bombers in the Bay of Pigs fiasco created severe enemies of the remaining Cuban exiles in the U.S., the Intelligence Community, and the Mafia. But Kennedy compounded the problem by firing Allen Dulles, the famous CIA Director whom he personally blamed for the CIA deception and the resulting political damage. Firing Dulles was not a wise move. He had spent years as Director and had cultivated a group of extremely loyal men to him who would follow him whenever possible, even after he had been fired. He was the CIA, and the CIA was Dulles.

To make matters worse, Kennedy swore that he would destroy the CIA itself, "Send the CIA to the far corners of the earth." He meant it, planning to dismantle it in his second term by breaking it into several smaller organizations, so it would lose its immense secret budget and power. Dulles and Curtis LeMay were close friends and not about to let Kennedy destroy it for obvious reasons.

Military Matters

Further, it was learned that he planned to engage in a full detente with Russia in his second term, attempt to rid the world of nuclear weapons, and thereby eliminate any need for huge Department of Defense budgets.

Kennedy's long-range plan was for the U.S. to stop acting as though it had the necessary prerogative to influence and control all other relevant nations. He wanted to encourage other world organizations to deal with world problems; his 'Peace Corps' was just one, but a beginning, of such world organizations. The U.S. was to drawback into its own borders and deal with national social problems, medicine, education, equal rights, women's rights, infrastructure problems, and so forth.

He planned on drawing down the use of the military by 1963, a major affront to the Military Industrial Complex. He felt the U.S. was fueling the Cold War by ever increasing the military technical capabilities; prodding Russia to do likewise. Most significantly this meant the Vietnam War involvement, even though he had originally supported it when running for office. So, he refused the Joint Chiefs of Staff's push for additional troops and nuclear bombing there. And in October had a National Security Action Memorandum, NSAM 263, drawn up making it official policy to withdraw troops. Of course, he also refused LeMay's push to deliver a first strike against the Soviet Union.

Financial Issues

He planned on revamping the American monetary system by passing legislation for balanced budgets, going back on the gold standard, and eliminating the Federal Reserve Bank, alienating the all-powerful banking consortium.

Of immediate concern to the Texas oil barons and Rockefellers was his proposal to eliminate the oil depletion allowance and to begin taxing offshore tax havens at the same levels as domestic corporations. In fact, oil was at the heart of the establishment's enmity for the President.

The Mafia

And last, but not least, he aimed for the entire elimination of the Italian=American Mafia from American soil, using his brother, Attorney General Robert Kennedy. This despite some crediting his election to Mafioso.

Hoover and the FBI

Obviously, this not only antagonized that organization, but also J. Edgar Hoover, the entrenched and all-too-powerful FBI Director who had reached an informal understanding with it. There were many other disagreements between Hoover and the Attorney General, purportedly his superior, and who the Director regarded as something of a young, naïve, child who had no idea what he was doing; at the least a confused and disrespectful up-start.

After all, Hoover was feared by everyone, even past presidents; nobody dared offend this man and his extensive, potential blackmailing files. Knowing all this, Kennedy planned on replacing him in his second term, for a more controllable man.

Vice President Lyndon Johnson

Kennedy and Johnson were already political enemies through their hard-fought battle for the presidential nomination. But it turned even more personal as Johnson was humiliated by being sent on ridiculous and meaningless missions around the world, to get him out of Washington where he, Lady Bird and his Texas friends were considered "hicks", an embarrassment to the Kennedys and their Camelot lifestyle. This was only exacerbated by Robert making fun of him to his face, imitating his Texas accent and mocking him in public; this was something you could not do to the politically powerful Johnson, without expecting some sort of retaliation.

Social Policies

Kennedy sought to implement a philosophy of persona freedom through his "Alliance for Progress" initiatives in Latin America, incurring the wrath of the political elite, including the Texas oil barons and Rockefellers. And his policies concerning the Black race were especially unpopular in the South, unnecessarily disrupting the comfortable – for them – status quo.

All this and more, did President Kennedy do to anger the necessary powers that would eventually come together to agree to assassinate him. Looking back, it almost seems he was on a suicide mission. When viewed from the perspective of Washington at the time, it's almost a wonder he wasn't assassinated earlier.

The Decision is Made

LeMay and his fellow Joint Chiefs felt that because Kennedy had essentially capitulated to the Russians in the Cuban Missile crisis, the Russians would conclude they had been largely successful in this episode, and they might once again do something militarily to take advantage of him. So, even though the crisis had been averted, the situation was the straw that broke LeMay's 'back,' and the event that drove the last nail in Kennedy's coffin.

And so, he saw it his duty to inform them Kennedy could no longer be trusted as Commander in Chief, he was a coward, and the Russians now knew. Knew he would never agree to use nuclear weapons against them, under any circumstances. Kennedy was a 'National Security' problem, and they would now have to eliminate, assassinate him. The fellow Joint Chiefs agreed and wanted it done as soon as possible.

LeMay contacted his close friend and ally, Allen Dulles, to inform of the decision. Dulles was more than willing to facilitate the plan and contacted those CIA people who he knew were fully interested in such a move and the ball began to roll. A complete plan was agreed upon, a plan to use Lee Harvey Oswald, a CIA operative previously falsely defected to Russia. He would be the 'fall guy' in the assassination and they would paint him as a Communist sent by Russia.

If this plan went well, it would further their efforts to move the American public against Russia, as well as these war mongers' interests in increasing the Defense Department budget. U.S. Sonics, Inc., in Dallas, was chosen as the CIA front to run the assassination planning, with Orris E. Bell as the front man.

In the meantime, the Joint Chiefs got the message to the Russians they would never tolerate anything like this 'Cuban/Russian Missile

Situation' again. If there ever were a next time, it would be war. And that Kennedy no longer mattered to them. He would not be allowed to let such a situation get out of control again. They would intervene early on, just ignore him.

The Russians knew the Joint Chiefs meant what they were saying, and they had been lucky this time. Their military capability was not equal to that of the United States at this time, especially with NATO on its side.

They also knew that the game would now change. The Americans would be allowed to continue the very long, very expensive war in South-East Asia "against Communism." An experience which would strengthen the U.S.; despite any domestic upheaval, such a war benefits the military, in training for future conflicts. Of course, many people were also lining their pockets.

The Test Ban Treaty

Despite constant problems with the Russians, the 'Cuban Missile Crisis' being only one serious example, Kennedy had a different agenda and approach than the Military Industrial Complex and its beneficiaries. In keeping with this agenda, he would sign the 'Test Ban Treaty' with the U.S.S.R. in August 1963. The treaty was to end all above-ground testing of nuclear weapons.

Of course, General Born, General LeMay, the other Joint Chiefs, Orris Bell, Charles Lundquist, and all the people in their group totally disagreed. For them, he was putting the U.S. at a great disadvantage, because the Russians were ahead in the race involving hydrogen-fission weapons.

There was also 'collateral damage' for this group because the Treaty severely impacted Charles Lundquist's 'South Pacific Islands' contract. Although Lundquist's company would continue that work for another twenty years, the long-term value of this contract had been damaged.

But of course, the issue was really moot. The decision to kill Kennedy had already been made. General Born had given his speech in November 1962.

My Introduction To The Plot

After getting ready for school one morning in late November 1962, I went into the dining room for breakfast. I was eleven years old, in the sixth grade. My father, Orris, was sitting at the table reading the Fort Worth Star Telegram and drinking his after-breakfast coffee. Halfway through my breakfast, he quietly looked over to me saying, "Bruce, I don't want you to go to school today. I want you to go to Dallas with me."

I hesitated for a moment. "*What's going on?*" This was not the first time he had asked me to go with him and not to school, but it was usually an out-of-town trip for several days and a planned event, not a spur of the moment thing. And I had accompanied him many times over the past two years from home in Fort Worth to his aerospace business, U.S. Sonics in Dallas, as well as to restaurants and other businesses. But I could sense that this was somehow different, not a spur of the moment thing, but part of a well-thought-out plan.

He was looking at me over the top of his newspaper, patiently waiting for my response. I replied obediently, "Yes, sir." I asked him no questions, knowing that there had to be some important reason he didn't wish to disclose right now. Important, because school and school attendance was an issue for my parents; we couldn't get away with missing school without a very good reason. So, I waited patiently, trying not to show my curiosity, until after my brothers and sisters left for school. Then I quietly followed him out the front door.

The drive was a little over an hour via the Dallas Fort Worth Turnpike. I was now looking forward to it, expecting to learn what this was all about; but also because I hadn't seen him very much in the past month. He had stayed in Dallas during the entire Cuban Missile Crisis to man the phone, keeping in touch with people in the military and aerospace defense industry. And even after he had returned home, he had been gone most of the time, traveling to Washington and Los Angeles.

But that was not to be; on my part, I knew I had to curb my need to know more, and to be honest, my need to spend a little time just talking with this man who had been away so much. And as usual, he himself was quiet, but I could tell there was something important he was thinking about. He didn't seem in a bad mood, just quiet and serious.

It took us about twenty minutes on this beautiful, but chilly fall day. to reach the entrance to the Dallas/Fort Worth Turnpike, during which he essentially maintained his silence. This would become a pattern over the next year; until we were up to speed on the Turnpike, he wouldn't talk about what he really wanted to. But then he would open up and say what was really on his mind -- and for the rest of his life, he would have a lot on that mind. A role for me as sounding board and confidant would emerge and become more intense over the next year. He would say things to me that were very complex and sophisticated, things that few people could imagine a father would say to an eleven-year-old.

Once we reached the Turnpike, I looked over at my handsome father and finally spoke up, "Daddy, why did you ask me to come today?" I certainly wasn't prepared at all for what I was to hear. Yes, I had heard them talk about killing President Kennedy many times in the past two years, but it had become so common place that I no longer put any real thought into it. It had just been rhetorical, until today.

But now, he looked at me with a very serious expression and without the slightest hesitation, calmly answered, "Bruce, we've made a decision to kill President Kennedy. We don't have a choice any longer; it has to be done. General Born is returning from Washington today and is going to give a speech at U.S. Sonics concerning this." There was no great excitement or emphasis as he said this; it was just as if he said, "General Born is flying in, so we can all go fishing this afternoon."

He continued, "There will be about twenty men today. I want you there. Just be polite, pay attention, and listen to what we have to say. Keep your eyes wide and let me know what you see. Over the next year, I'm going to be taking you with me often and you are going to be hearing a lot about this. We are going to use you as a cover when we are talking about our plans. I don't want you to talk about this and what you will be hearing to, or with anyone. Do you understand what I'm saying to you and why?

"If anyone you don't know approaches you when you're not with me and asks you about Kennedy or anything about someone planning to kill Kennedy, I want you to tell them you don't know anything about Kennedy and you've never heard anyone talk about killing him. Then I want you to call me immediately and tell me. If you can't find me, tell your mother and for her to find me. I'll talk to her about this and she will always know where I am and what to do."

He was then quiet for a while, giving me time to absorb it. all. As I looked out the window passing one of my favorite lakes, I couldn't think of all the wonderful times I had had fishing there; my mind was still struggling and trying to comprehend what my father had just so calmly said. I wasn't shocked by this news; I was surprised, but not shocked. It made sense to me after what I had heard so many times over the past two years. And I knew that my father telling me all this now meant they were serious; they would do exactly what he had just said; kill Kennedy. This was different than the rhetoric I had heard around U.S. Sonics for the past two years. They meant it this time. He and his people did not say they were going to do something and not do it. The President was a dead man. And to do this, they had to have a very good reason; it had to be necessary in their minds.

He continued, "We all came much closer to dying in a full nuclear war with Russia than the public knows. We can't allow that to happen again, and it very well could. And now Kennedy didn't respond as he should have, the Russians know his weakness and could take advantage of it. Killing him will send the correct message to the Russians that we are not weak and will do whatever is necessary to secure the nation."

I couldn't foresee the full impact for me. That this was only the beginning. Over the next year, I would make this same trip to Dallas many, many more times and I would miss many, many more days of school. Yesterday was the last day of school that I would ever be happy. My childhood, my youth, was being ripped from me.

Before the Meeting

At U.S. Sonics there were a number of cars I didn't recognize. Inside, there were already eight men waiting to greet my father and to attend General Born's speech. The General was due in at eleven, flying in on his personal Air Force jet; a two-place trainer that he kept at the Naval Air Station in Irving, Texas, about forty minutes away.

Of the eight men, I knew four: Ed Nesbitt, Jeff Miller, Clint Murchison Jr. and Charles Lundquist. The first three were Texan heavyweights who acknowledged me, but more formally than normal. Lundquist, my father's former boss, had obviously flown in from Los Angeles. The fact that he only nodded to me when I walked in was also unusual; normally, he would have come over to at least shake hands., be friendly. I could tell that this morning was to be very different.

These four men followed my father into his office where I could see them standing around his desk like hawks around a wounded rabbit.; not that they were aggressive toward him, just hungry—hungry for information and opinions; stuff he had just shared with me. Although he had been in constant contact with his and Born's people in Washington all through the Cuban Missile Crisis, it seemed obvious that these men, like the general public, had no real idea how close the world had come to complete annihilation; never before had the public media machine been kept so fully in the dark.

I joined them int the office where Lundquist seemed to take control and express full agreement with what needed to take place. It appeared that it was out of the question for Congress to impeach and remove the President from office, even though he had acted with gross negligence. So, there was only one answer: assassination. After all, in 1962 the military reigns supreme, not the president. Presidents come and go, but Eisenhower's 'Military Industrial Complex' is a reality. *"My father is on the right side."*

When I left the office, I realized that besides the four men I didn't know, I didn't recognize the lady acting as the receptionist today, taking the place of the one working since the business opened two years earlier. This new young lady had smiled professionally, stood, and greeted my father, "Good morning, Sir." Her formality and poise, almost as if she were 'coming to attention' was something I had seen when Orris and I had visited Air Force Bases. Similarly, I had noticed some days before that the secretaries were different and when I had asked my father what had happened to the others, he told me they had to let them go. I later came to learn that General Born had replaced them with Air Force secretaries, who he knew he could trust with what they would inevitably hear over the next year about the President Kennedy assassination; they all had Top Secret clearances.

By eleven, another four new men had arrived. I would soon learn that these eight men worked for the CIA. They looked younger than I would have expected, younger than my father and his friends. No facial hair, not even mustaches. They were sharp and intelligent looking. And while my father and friends all wore suits; these men wore casual clothes, slacks, and expensive shirts, no tie.

But I could clearly tell by the way they approached and interacted with one another that they were not 'normal' and that most of them did not know each other well, if at all. While my father shook hands with all of them, they did not introduce themselves to one another by name and shake hands, as was the standard with businessmen. Instead, they talked with one another in a somewhat cautious way, not too friendly. I had the clear feeling that most of these men weren't from Dallas/Fort Worth, but had flown in explicitly for this meeting. They did seem excited though about what was now to take place. I couldn't help but feel the excitement in the air. Every man knew why he was here and had some prior knowledge of what Born was going to be saying.

I would see many of them at U.S. Sonics over the next year, and they would dress, act, and interact with my father, General Born, Nesbitt, Miller, and Lundquist in this same unusual manner. I would come to know some of them by face, personality, and false name fairly well and they would become very friendly and courteous toward me in the many meetings we would attend over the next year. Meetings at U.S. Sonics and elsewhere, like a suite in a hotel with an attached meeting room. In fact, as time passed, meetings there became fewer and fewer until by mid-summer even those at other locations were rarely at the same location. One of the men I would see on several occasions was J. Walton Moore, an agent, who has since had some notoriety in association with the assassination. Of course, I didn't know his name then, but I clearly recognize his photograph today.

But now, these men didn't even seem to notice me. And I wasn't introduced to them as I usually would have been, meaning that I was to play something of an anonymous role.

After about half an hour, the receptionist informed my father, "General Born called from his flight and says he is going to be a little over an hour late. There were some last-minute changes. Other than that, everything seems on schedule; everyone will be here long before he arrives." Nodding acknowledgement, my father turned to me, "Bruce, will you go find Norris Lawrence and the two of you gather some extra chairs for the conference room." Norris was the plant supervisor for U.S. Sonics; I found him busying himself near the intake desk, preoccupied and a little concerned about something. When we greeted each other, he didn't seem surprised that I was here on a school day.

I looked directly at him and asked, "Do you know what this meeting is to be about?" "Of course, I know," he replied. I had assumed he would, but wanted to hear it from him first, see his reaction. "Is it true what my father told me on the way over, about killing President Kennedy.? "Yes, Bruce. Unfortunately, it's true and I'm afraid none of our lives will ever be the same. Not that I disagree with it; 'cause it looks like it has to be done." He obviously knew that I was to play this strange role or he wouldn't have been so forward and candid with me.

Over the next twenty minutes, six more men who I didn't know arrived and then two more. There would, now be twenty in the meeting, including myself, but not Norris, who would be left to keep his eyes on the front gate, in case some unexpected breach occurred. It appeared to me that my father hadn't expected so many and was unprepared. He, Ed Nesbitt, Jeff Miller, and Charles Lundquist ended up alternately playing 'host' to the gathering.

Norris and I found chairs in several different offices, but not enough, so I found two tall stools and put them in the far corners of the room. Then most of the men took their places. But, then my father came in to announce General Born's delay. Everyone resumed moving back and forth from the conference room to the receptionist area and a few offices, forming little groups of two and three.

Killing President Kennedy was being discussed. But it was different. What was missing this morning was the usual loud rhetoric I was accustomed to. Instead, they spoke quietly and more seriously. And General Curtis LeMay's name kept coming up. LeMay,and "kill Kennedy" in the same sentence. It seemed that General LeMay must have been the primary instigator of this sudden push to kill President Kennedy. But they were also mentioning Allen Dulles. These were names I had heard often at U.S. Sonics before. Dulles had headed the CIA.

I kept moving back and forth between the conference room, the back area of the plant and my father's office, where he was on the phone most of the time. I was excited and taking it all in. I knew this was history in the making and didn't want to miss any of it. At one point, I was so excited, I had to go back to the very quiet 'White Room' to try and relax and reflect on what it all really meant. Not just what it meant to my life personally, but to the United States and the world, to Russia and the Cold War, to the American people.

General Born Arrives

My father finally came out of his office to announce that General Born had landed at the Naval Air Base and was on his way. Most of the men moved back into the conference room, while my father, Lundquist, and Nesbitt waited for Born in the receptionist area where they could see his car arrive. Now my growing excitement gave way to concern about Born's reaction to my presence. I knew him quite well by this time, that he was the one to be concerned about. He had a different attitude towards children. A war-hardened General and veteran of two World Wars, they just seemed to aggravate him. So, if anyone might object it would be him. He might very well have me removed., especially if he could tell how interested I was.

He wasn't ever rude to me, but he wasn't overly friendly either; he tolerated me. He knew why I was coming to U.S. Sonics so often with my father and he obviously didn't disagree, or he would have objected at some point. What I recall now most about our personal involvement was the way he would look at me when I would glance at him as I was walking by his open door. – he had his own office there.

The eye contact was very brief, but very distinct. Occasionally, I would stop and look directly at him, our eyes would meet, and it would become a war of wills. Neither of us would look away, but I would distinctly win this war of wills, my innocence would prevail and his nerve would weaken. He could command thousands of men without the slightest sign of weakness, but he could not deal with the resolve and innocence of me in his doorway. I would finally turn and walk away to leave him to probably wonder, "*What a strange child he is.*" I would actually do this to amuse myself, play with him in this way. In retrospect, perhaps it wasn't the wisest thing I've ever done.

Despite this, Born knew that I would come to know everything about the Kennedy assassination and I'm sure that bothered him; an eleven-year-old boy that could know so much and have the responsibility of trusted silence squarely planted on his shoulders. I was aware that there were many fellow Generals that he could not trust with this, let alone a pre-teen.

When he finally arrived, a little after twelve, I had been standing in the receptionist room with my father, Lundquist, and Nesbitt. I stepped back a little to the side so I wouldn't be in his direct line of sight when he came through the front door. I didn't want him to see me and then look for me later in the conference room. He surely would expect I would want to be present to hear what I knew would be his world-changing speech on killing the President.

Looking closely at the four men, I saw when their eyes first met, that they had made the serious decision to do something that had never been done before; perform a silent coup in America and assassinate the President of the United States. Kennedy was the President, but to these men he was just another man, a man who had gone too far and was a serious danger to everything they believed in, everything they had spent their entire life working for and toward. The President of the United States had become a serious national security issue to them. Just as my father had explained to me.

Born was wearing his uniform as required when flying his personal Air Force jet. After their greeting, the four men quickly went to Born's office where he changed into a civilian suit. He wasn't going to issue an order to kill the President of the United States in his Air Force General's uniform. I walked over to eavesdrop. I knew this was the first time they had all been together in person since the beginning of the Cuban Missile Crisis, well over a month earlier. Born had communicated directly by phone from his airborne 707 with my father, informing him of the Joint Chief's perspective. the dire situation at hand.

After seeing the General change his outfit, and desperately wanting to witness their earth-shaking meeting and his speech, I decided I had better take my place in the conference room. Knowing I had better try to fade into the wall, I had already placed one of the stools in the back right-hand corner for myself hoping that they would let me attend, they wouldn't embarrass me and make me leave. No one had told me that I wouldn't be able to attend this historical event. Why else would my father have taken me out of school to come here? My plan was not to ask, just to go into the room and see how things went.

I walked in slowly and confidently, trying not to make eye contact with anyone. The conference room was actually pretty small. The table itself had been set up for eight men only. The other men sat on an assortment of chairs against the left wall and at the back of the room. It was tight, but not too tight to be uncomfortable. Everyone was finally chattering, excited. The fact that General Born waw finally here had broken their reverie. A few were quiet, looking alone and sort of isolated, concerned, and even worried. Clint Murchison was against the left wall with two proteges attending him as usual, as if he were a king.

Lundquist came in alone first, followed by Nesbitt a few minutes later, leaving just General Born and my father to find their places. Another five minutes passed and the two finally came in. Immediately there was a silence that was so intense it was nearly painful.

These men knew the time had finally arrived that no one had believed would ever take place, at least in their lifetime. The man in front of them was about to tell them that the President of the United States is not the most powerful man in the nation; the Joint Chiefs hold the real power.

My father came over to my corner of the room to stand next to me. I looked into his face to make sure everything was alright. He appeared very calm and relaxed, even confident; so, I guessed it was.

Born Gives His Speech

Born had closed the door behind him and taken his place, standing at the head of the table. He made a quick survey around the room, taking a mental note of everyone in the room and the general situation. It seemed as if he looked right at me, but it didn't seem to alert him, so I felt that I was OK. Then, he looked at the men sitting at the table directly in front of him, still not speaking to anyone. Everyone was very quiet. I was still worried that he would remember seeing me and ask me to leave. I desperately didn't want that to happen. I wanted to hear exactly what he had to say and not miss a word.

Finally, he started with shocking words to come from an American Air Force General, "We are no longer going to talk about killing President Kennedy. We are going to kill President Kennedy. The son of a bitch nearly got us all killed with the missile crisis. We came so close to full nuclear war with the Russians that I believed it was inevitable. We cannot trust this son of a bitch any longer or to allow this to happen again, we, now, have to kill him."

He put emphasis on every word in this short statement. It meant the end of President John Kennedy's life. Kennedy was no longer the President of the United States to this man. He was now just a soon-to-be dead man and nothing more. Born had lost all respect for this President, as had all the Joint Chiefs.

He paused then and slowly looked around the room to get a measure of how everyone had just taken his profound words. He moved from face to face in a quick but searching way. I was the last he lay his penetrating eyes upon. His eyes winced sightly when they met mine and he stopped. I was sure what he was thinking. I had heard every condemning word. *Bruce shouldn't be hearing this.*

Even though my father was standing beside me, Born was going to make me leave; I could see it in his eyes. My heart stopped and I held my breath. Never before had I not wanted to leave a room more than now. I knew that if I had to, I would only have part of the story and for the rest of my life, I would blame him for humiliating me and missing making me miss the rest of this monumental event. But Born was determined and quickly looked over to my father, "Orris, will you come up here?"

This confirmed it. But I decided I wouldn't go easily; I would state my position, "I should be allowed to stay. What difference does it make now? I've been listening to them talk about killing Kennedy for over two years. I've just heard you, General Born, confirm it. You're finally going to actually kill President Kennedy."

My father went up to Born and leaned over, so he could talk to him without others hearing. He nodded his head in confirmation and came back to say exactly what I knew he was going to, "Bruce, you have to leave. General Born doesn't want you to hear this."

I started to object, pleading "Daddy, I don't want to go, I want to hear what General Born has to say about this." All he could do was to give me his serious look and say the inevitable, "Bruce, you have to leave the room." I knew it was no good. It was hopeless and I blamed Born.

But when I looked back into my father's eyes, I realized something more. Not only the world was about to change, but my world had already changed. I had heard the truth and they could never alter it.

They could never take this away from me. For the rest of my life, I would know the truth.

I quickly glanced around the room and all eyes were on me. I don't think there was a man in the room who didn't understand me or blame me for wanting to stay. But I was a proud boy, raised by a proud man. I knew how to act in defeat and humiliation. I walked to the front of the room and paused ever so briefly next to Born and looked him straight in the eye. I didn't want him to ever forget this moment when he made me leave.

Without saying a word, I turned to the door and calmly opened and closed it quietly behind me. I knew I was going to miss out on one of the most dramatic moments in modern history and one of the most shocking speeches in the twentieth century. An American Air Force Major General giving the final order to a group of young CIA operatives to assassinate their president.

So, my 'wings were clipped..' I walked sadly out to the reception area where the new receptionist commiserated with me, "Bruce, they do the same thing to me, make me leave just when things get really interesting."

I immediately fell "in love" with her, even though she was probably twenty-six years old. She had a crisp and fresh look, eyes as blue as the morning sky that moved with intelligence, observing and missing nothing. She became my "Snow White."

Then I left for a long walk along the banks of the Trinity River, only a few hundred yards away. After I returned, it was still about four hours before Born's meeting adjourned. They obviously discussed a lot I would regret this for the rest of my life. In retrospect, I realize that if they had let me stay, I might never have turned against them; I might have come to feel like one of them forever.

4

MY FAMILY

My Grandfather, Emmett Delmon Bell

The Big and Little Sandy are two small rivers in Northeast Texas that were known to be excellent trout fishing estuaries in the early 1900s. Orris Bell's ancestors left Mississippi and Tennessee for this area late in the Civil War. His mother's family settling in Fort Worth and father's about ninety miles east in the town of Big Sandy near the confluence of the two rivers.

Emmett – there are several different spellings -- Delmon Bell, Orris' father, was the only remaining son of a large family decimated by the War. He had survived because he was young, all the other males having died fighting for the South. The remaining women made their migration with this one little boy and some of their slaves. Like many Southerners, they kept their slaves despite Lincoln's emancipation orders; owning slaves was the only property right women had at the time.

The death of the male ancestors influenced the later Bell men. Of course, it wasn't only men and boys killed and maltreated in the War; defenseless women and girls, no longer under male protection, were taken severe advantage of and raped, kidnapped, murdered or, at the least, displaced, never to be heard from again.

As a result, Emmett was raised by a group of very disturbed, aging Civil War widows and daughters, leaving him very troubled and bitter about the Civil War and its causes for the rest of his life. And just as now, a Freudian displacement resulted, a displacement of hate and desire for revenge onto the black man, more even than on the politicians actually responsible for the war and the six hundred thousand lives lost. These feelings and attitudes were passed on from generation to generation with tales of the tragedies and losses. Especially, the loss of Southern values and the destruction of their way of life and culture; all because of the black man and the Yankee 'rabble rousers.'

When the family moved from east Texas in the late 1920s to Fort Worth, Emmett prospered. Economically probably because of his bridge-building skills. And politically. becoming head of the local Republican Party, a Grand Masonic Lodge Master, and the White Supremacist clandestine organization, the Ku Klux Klan which had reached a pinnacle in the 1930s with hundreds of thousands of members. And his politically active father, also, became a Fifth Degree Mason in the Order of Freemasons, the largest worldwide secret society in the 1930s.

Fort Worth was a ranchers' supply town, a railway cattle shipping station, a leather industry location, an industrial supply town for the booming Texas oil industry, and the home of Texas Christian University. Most of the best oil land in Texas was west of Fort Worth in the Permian Basin and it was the first large city reached traveling east from the Basin. So, as the oil boom produced overnight wealth, the nouveau rich also came to Fort Worth to spend their money and build new mansions.

Despite the Great Depression of the thirties, the oil business continued growing, producing many men who ostentatiously donated millions of dollars to various civic organizations, primarily the arts and related institutions. One such "needed" enterprise was a Botanical Garden. And because of his distinct interest in Botany, Emmett became the primary promoter of, the Fort Worth Botanical Gardens., enabled in part by the federal government Depression construction grants. So yes, there was a positive side to Orris' father.

Fortuitously, there was an ideal location., one hundred undeveloped acres in the Trinity River flood plain, now dammed by a major Public Works Administration Project. Initially the Gardens, designed by Emmett himself, comprised stone terraces of roses, with fountains at the top, middle, and bottom, and small cascading waterfalls in between. Today, the Botanical Gardens have been developed into one of the most attractive public destinations in the area, the centerpiece of Fort Worth's Arts and Cultural Center, including three major art museums, the Zoo, a public park, the Performing Arts Center, and the Fort Worth Rodeo and Stock Show Emporium.

Unfortunately, it was not until I was twenty-two that I learned about my grandfather's achievement and that only by sheer happenstance. I was there in the original Rose Gardens with a young woman, Kimberly Dudley, and had stopped to read a brass plaque dated 1937. It commemorated a certain Emmett Delmon Bell for his accomplishment in developing the Gardens. This, of course, was, my grandfather.

I was shocked, to say the least. How could it possibly be that I had never heard of this. And to learn about it this way. had lived in and around Fort Worth for sixteen years. Why had my father never told me? For some reason, he apparently didn't feel his father's civic-minded Botanical Gardens accomplishment was that inspiring. Something must have happened for him to dismiss the Gardens as insignificant or maybe it represented some negative aspect of their relationship.

I asked my mother about the Gardens and she confirmed grandfather's role, but she clearly avoided my question as to why my father had never mentioned it to me.

Orris himself, in his older years, became an accomplished vegetable gardener and I never saw him so relaxed, content, and happy, as when he was working in his garden. But, by no means, did I ever see him plant one flower. On the other hand, grandfather would always plant very large flower gardens around his property and took care of them as though they were cherished children. More feelings than he showed his offspring or grandchildren

Orris Emmett Bell; the Early Years

My father, Orris Emmett Bell, was born in 1917 in a log cabin built by his ancestors near Big Sandy. He was from Irish, Scottish, and Cherokee Indian bloodlines on his father's side and Irish on his mother's. His mother was from a prominent Mississippi family and had four sisters and one brother, who all lived in the Fort Worth area, where they also had resettled during the Civil War.

Orris' life as a child wasn't all that bad. He was only the third surviving male Bell bearing the family name since the Civil War, the only one of his generation. Surrounded by an abundance of Bell women, he was treated like a prodigal child, privileged, exceptional, warranting extra care and love. But the rather sophisticated, well-educated Bell women passed their sophistication and love of learning onto Orris, teaching him Southern etiquette and manners, unusual for the rural Texas setting. This exceptional childhood, combined with the love of nature he acquired from the beautiful rural setting, would help him prosper and achieve success, later in life.

But when Emmett moved the family to Fort Worth, Orris and his sister found a different world. It wouldn't be correct to describe him as a country boy, but rather a boy who until this time was raised in the country. And Fort Worth provided him with exposure to a Western city lifestyle combining both a cattle empire mentality and a booming oil industry wealth.

Although the change required some adjusting, it was easy for him because of his outgoing personality and his natural good looks. He became an excellent student, graduating at age seventeen with a straight-A average. Now with the availability of a good library not available in Big Sandy, he developed a tremendous interest in history, any kind of history — American, World, and Ancient. He would read anything and everything he could find, including the American Classics, a good way for him to satisfy his desire for intellectual knowledge.

This enthusiasm for learning, along with his phenomenal memory, would be important in the future, not only in augmenting his own engineering knowledge, but enabling him to fascinate and keep people engaged in interesting conversation for hours.

But his exposure to a twisted view of the world by the extreme conservative influences of his father, shaped his personality. In essence, he had little choice other than to become one of them, a very ultra-conservative young man with a bitter vengeful attitude toward the American black man, Catholics, and Jews. In fact, he became a hardcore bigot. And ultimately, he would even go as far as to become the main administrator/planner of the assassination of a liberal, Catholic President of the United States, President John F. Kennedy.

Orris as a Young Man

In 1939, the Bells -- Orris, his sister, and parents -- moved from Fort Worth to Long Beach in the Los Angeles area. Father Emmet with his experience in building large wooden beam structures made the move to work in the prospering boat building business, making fishing boats up to eighty feet in length. The change was easy for him, what with his talents, unique mind and aggressive attitude toward life and work.

In 1942, with the advent of war, he transferred his talent to the Navy, building wooden boats, up to one-hundred-twenty feet. By 1943, he was in charge of a Navy wooden boat facility, where he continued until the end of the war.

For Orris, California would be a world-changing experience He quickly came to realize that there was a world out there, very different from Texas and the bigoted attitude of most Texans. His personal interest in history took on a new meaning; he saw its influence more clearly here, what with California's diverse cultures; a major difference from the Texas he knew.

He took up deep-sea fishing as a regular pastime. Whenever his father could take off from work, they rented a boat and headed west of Catalina Island and even sometimes, on more extended trips along Mexico's Baja Peninsula.

But Orris would also travel back and forth to Fort Worth because of girlfriends. He was a little over six-feet tall now, with coal black hair, brown eyes, and a dark complexion because of the Cherokee Indian blood. A very handsome man, often confused for Dean Martin; more than once, even in later years, I saw young, giggling women come up to him, asking for his autograph. He always accommodated them and let them leave thinking he was the singer until they looked at his signature. It actually was funny to watch their reaction; he would sign his own name, Orris E. Bell.

In early 1942, at the age of twenty-four, Orris joined the U.S. Army, serving first in North Africa where, at the end of the year, he was infected with malaria. After his Battalion moved to Italy in 1943, he spent a year and a half convalescing in and out of different hospitals. But there were side benefits; he fell in love with Italy once he learned the language from his nurses. When he wasn't in a hospital, he explored Italy, its cities, countryside, and as many of the fairer-sex Italians as he could.

Most Italians, because of what seemed like good Southern Italian looks and his ability to speak their language, readily accepted him. Attractive women, of course. But also several men in the Mafia, met through the women. He learned about the mystic and unusual political beliefs of the Italian Mafia and was intrigued with the smooth interaction between it, the police, and private enterprise. And the camaraderie and dedication of the Mafia was appealing, leading to more involvement and an influence continuing for the rest of his life.

In early 1945, before returning to the U.S., he travelled to France for several months, mostly Paris. The malaria was finally better and he visited the local bars and restaurants with his Army friends, looking for the best French women with whom to enjoy the countryside.

Despite experiencing the horrors of that war, all in all, Orris' war service in Europe was easier than most. He had spent nearly all of his time in Europe in the rear area, recuperating or enjoying what Europe had to offer. And it set the stage for a future lifetime association with Europeans, especially Italians, Italian culture, and eventually the Italian Mafia. He would return many times, especially during the last two years of his life.

Maxine Bell

Because of his Navy connections, at the end of the war Emmett was made an exceptionally good offer to purchase eight sawmills and vast government contracts for timber rights in Idaho and Western Wyoming, All for pennies on the dollar, through closed bidding and all seized during the war for the Navy. So, when Orris returned to the U.S., his destination was Idaho, not California. On the way there, he stopped in Iowa's and a homecoming dance for servicemen.

That was where he met eighteen-year-old Leona Maxine. Max was born in 1927 to Swedish-born parents. Her father, from a wealthy family, immigrated in the early 1900s to buy several large farms in northern Iowa where nearly everyone was of Swedish descent. He built a large stone family house on one of these farms and had four children. Maxine, however was the apple of his eye and was given everything she longed for, including much love and cuddling. She was a pretty, blue-eyed, blond with a warm and loving persona that endeared the to everyone. As would be expected, she was a cheerleader, junior through high school.

Of course, she fell in love immediately with this dashing, dark, handsome and mysterious man, even though he was ten years her senior. Arguably an unfortunate turning point. Otherwise, she probably would have married a local Swedish farm boy with whom she would have lived a happy life. But as fate and young foolish lush would have it, that was not to be. Two weeks later, she announced her intent to marry this man. Although concerned, her father reluctantly agreed to her wishes, as always. As to be expected, a big wedding was held, Swedish style.

To ensure he wouldn't lose his beloved daughter to far-flung ports at Orris' beckoning, her father offered them a large farm of their own as a wedding present. However, as he was about to take his annual summer trip back to Sweden to visit his five brothers and extensive family, the specifics were postponed until his return,

Unfortunately, tragedy struck in Sweden. On the way home from partying with his brothers, all six men were killed in a car-train accident at a track crossing. And unfortunately for his children, his will left everything to their mother until she "passed." Of course, Maxine was destroyed by the loss of her father and became fixated on her new husband who replaced her loving father in her young vulnerable mind.

A Venture With Emmett

So, instead of Orris becoming a successful Iowa Farmer, he decided to try his luck with his father and his businesses in Idaho and Wyoming. Moving to Boise, Maxine and Orris found themselves among rough, radical right-winged Fascists, Militia, and White Supremacists, who had fully infiltrated the timber industry in the Northwest by 1946. Connections he would nurture and further develop for the rest of his life.

And for Max, a difficult relationship with a jealous, dominating mother-in-law. Mabel had spoiled her only son and doted over him as if were still a boy, not accepting his love for his new wife; the stereotypical mother-in-law, dominating and forever critical. And when Maxine gave birth to her first child, Stephanie, this only worsened.

On the other hand, Emmett quickly became very fond of his new daughter-in-law; she was irresistible in every way. So as his wedding present, he gave half of all of his newfound riches to the couple. Unfortunately, this venture with Emmett lasted only two years because the two men could not get along or agree when it came to crucial business decisions.

So in early 1949, the businesses were sold for a considerable profit, split equally between them, and all returned to Southern California.

U.S. Chemical Milling Corp. and Charles Lundquist

Prior to the move to the Los Angeles area, in 1948 Maxine had given birth to her second daughter, Deborah. And unknown to Maxine, continuing his womanizing he had fathered an illegitimate son in Idaho. Now, five more were to arrive: me in 1950, then Stephen, Carolyn, Katherine and in 1957, Stuart.

But Orris had major problems. He liked to live the high life. And that meant gambling and the womanizing; betting the horses at the local tracks and Hollywood starlets. And Mafia types. It was at Del Mar that he would meet men who would play important roles later in his life, Clint Murchison, Sid Richardson and J. Edgar Hoover.

So, in spite of the fact that he had come away from the Idaho lumber business in good financial shape, by 1954 he had gone through most of his money and needed a job to support his increasing family. Luckily, probably through contacts he had made, he started working in 1955 at U.S. Chemical Milling Corp. or U.S. Chem Mill, as it was called by many in El Segundo.

It is probable that the engineers who designed the Atlas Missile, our first viable Intercontinental Ballistic Missile (ICBM), made a mistake by not fully accounting for the space required for the engines needed to provide the necessary thrust power. This was a national security issue because the U.S.S.R. was hot on our heels with their own ICBMs; we could be annihilated if we fell too far behind in this nuclear race.

The only solution was to decrease the thrust power needed by cutting the weight of the missiles themselves. And U.S. Chem Mill was one of the few companies that could help do this; using a new chemical process that allowed the milling of metals and alloys much thinner, while still keeping their integrity and strength. The prior standard process of milling metal with an End Mill cuts metal with a bit, damaging the part.

U.S. Chem Mill had been started in 1954 by a chemical engineer, Charles Lundquist. His process to mill metals; primarily aluminum and titanium, with various acids, revolutionized the aerospace and especially, the aerospace defense industries. The startup of his business was perfectly timed. Within a two-year period, it became the fastest growing U.S. defense industry company. Its value was doubling every few months, making Charles Lundquist a billionaire and one of the most powerful and influential men in the industry and the country. This was, in large part because of the influence of General LeMay, expecting that 'super rockets' armed with nuclear weapons were coming in the near future.

Lundquist had been successful in many other business ventures, in large part because of his personal ties with Richard Nixon, who in 1958 had helped provide him a major, exclusive U.S. Navy contract to clean up and restore the South Pacific atolls that were left radio-active and destroyed from the nuclear and hydrogen bomb testing in the 1940s, 50s, and 60s. He later confided to me that this contract was his most profitable venture.

Coincidentally, Lundquist also happened to be connected to the right wing radical establishment. And U.S. Chem Mill was highly involved with the CIA, working on a number of covert projects.

It turned out Orris was perfectly suited for the sales position he obtained, partly because of his personality, but also his innate understanding of engineering. And almost as important, the contacts he had made with the Mafia and understanding their ways of doing business. His job entailed bidding on government contracts, interacting with aerospace industry customers, primarily engineers and scientists, as well as military officials.

Although what he encountered was already a corrupt system, it was quickly mastered. He would frequently buy these contracts illegally; utilizing his expense account and beautiful women obtained through his Mafia Hollywood contacts; there were always plenty of these trying to just survive. Everything he did was first class, the best restaurants, best hotels, best women. Money opened doors very wide and many men were becoming wealthy and powerful with the right business and political contacts.

Orris quickly rose to Vice President in charge of sales, providing him with an adequate income to finally support his obligations.

My Sister Dies and Orris Takes Me Rabbit Hunting

My earliest years when we lived in a small house with a garden full of flowers, were the happiest. Then all I could smell was the scent of fresh blooms, before my nostrils filled with the stench of corruption and fear. Back then my father seemed happy. His life had not yet slid close to disaster, and he was a free man; that is to say he was not yet addicted to booze, women, and power. Above all, power. But, probably, his 'happiness' was just an illusion.

Everything began to change when I was four and like so much in my life, it was death that began to bring the shadows down. My baby sister Katherine fell sick. I had a feeling, a premonition something tragic was in the air, the kind of feeling only young children can have when their senses are still free of all the cramping anxieties of adult life. This was a tragic event that was to haunt me for the rest of my life, and probably my parents too.

One night this premonition coalesced into a terrifying dream, one in which I woke up to a strange bluish light coming from my sister's bedroom, reflecting off the hall wall. I went out into the hall, and looking into her room I could see a man bending over her bassinet to pick her up. He turned slowly to see me watching.

"I have come to take your baby sister," he said. I took a step toward him, thinking to try stopping him. Then his voice became soothing, like a department store Santa Claus placating a nervous child. "Don't worry," he whispered, "Katherine will be alright." He turned then with her in his arms, walked to a far corner of the room and repeated, "Don't worry, the baby will be alright." Then he ascended through the ceiling, holding her and the light dimmed, leaving the room grow dark.

When I actually woke up, I was bathed in perspiration, my heart beating like a violent monster. I ran to my parents' room to wake them and tell my mother the man had come and taken the baby, but not to worry because he had said, "The baby would be alright."

She ran down the hall, telling me to stay. In the meantime, my father was now awake and followed her. I could hear her crying and knew she had found the baby gone. I stayed in their room about twenty minutes and then returned to the baby's where my mother was sobbing and my father holding my sister, his arms clasped around her like she was a holy relic.

Upset, I went back to their room and then, hearing a noise outside, I went to the window just in time to see an ambulance pulling away. When my parents came back, my mother still crying, they asked me to tell them fully what had happened. I did and then asked why the ambulance had been there. Gently, my father answered that it had taken the baby. Knowing differently, I almost shouted, "No, the man took her. I watched him do it."

A few days later, they took me to the funeral. Still not understanding, I asked them why they were acting like they were burying the baby, when I knew what had really happened. They tried to tell me she had died and the autopsy later revealed she had been suffering from pneumonia.

Afterward, I still refused to accept the death, wanting to believe she was still alive in another world. We just couldn't see or communicate with her in the normal sense we had before.

And my father became a different man, spending very little time at home. He was devastated by the death, but he was also emotionally scarred by my mother's reaction. She seemed to withdraw from him. I don't know if she blamed him. It was just that from the moment after this tragedy, all her emotions seemed to be strongly filtered, like she was holding something back. But as I was to learn later, although he presented a positive façade, Orris' mind was already not in the best of shape because of his war experiences. I could sense this when the subject came up or a war film started on TV.

Now after my sister's death, he, apparently decided I needed to learn what death was, that death is terminal and final. And his way of showing me was taking me hunting for the first time. So, he took me out in the Southern California desert to hunt rabbits with a shotgun. This probably wasn't the most intelligent thing to do with a young child who had just lost a very much-loved sister. I was clearly too young to experience death this way. Seeing these rabbits killed so senselessly and violently left me fixated on rabbits for the rest of my life. Besides, I couldn't relate this tragic slaughter to my sister dying. She wasn't a rabbit; she was my sister. No one shot her with a shotgun; she died of pneumonia.

Why he was shooting rabbits made no sense to me. I actually had the thought he wanted to shoot me; he blamed me for her death.

But there was another consequence to my sister's death, or at least my story about what had happened. My parents had me repeat it to others, including his boss, Lundquist, who was raised in a Scandinavian world of the occult and mystic lore. And this was when began my grooming for a leadership position. And asking my opinion about things what might happen, if they did certain things.

5

THE MOVE TO TEXAS

Dallas/Fort Worth

In 1957, Lundquist asked Orris to move from Southern California
to the Dallas/Fort Worth area which was becoming the leading location
for the growing aerospace industry. First to expand his sales work, but
also oversee the building of a new, large U.S. Chem Mill facility.

Orris and Maxine did not really want to leave Southern California
and its lifestyle. For him it was also partly difficult memories. Lundquist
tried to persuade them by offering a large block of stock in the company,
a house, a new car, as well as agreeing to increase Orris' percentage for
the contract she secured. No one could refuse such a lucrative offer.

The family moved to an area northeast of Fort Worth close to Bell
Helicopters' main assembly plant. Orris leased office space in a new
airport, Amon Carter Field. Because he would now be flying back and

forth between Los Angeles and Dallas, he would be gone from home over half the time.

Orris' first primary job now was to locate a large enough property adequate for the proposed Chem Mill plant, large enough to allow for future expansion. Friends Clint Murchison and Sid Richardson from his racetrack activities, were Texans and became involved in the venture; primarily Richardson, who was very involved in the area's land development.

The plan was to purchase approximately two hundred acres in the middle of a piece of property of several thousand. Richardson and his associates would purchase the surrounding property and break it up into appropriate-size sites, as needed by other aerospace manufacturers who would follow. Orris located two appropriate properties and Lundquist flew out to make the final choice.

They settled on one in Arlington, halfway between Dallas and Fort Worth, close to the new Dallas/Fort Worth Turnpike. Part of the Waggoner 3D Ranch purchased by Angus Wynne Jr., a Murchison associate. (It would eventually become a multi-use Industrial Park, housing an LTV plant and Six Flags over Texas.). Several thousand adjacent acres were available for future development.

Orris had brought Swede Larson, his main man in sales, with him. The two men were interacting with Convair, Chance Vought, Bell Aerospace, Bell Helicopter, and a number of other aerospace, aircraft manufacturers in the area. And all was going well.

Unfortunately, problems developed when one of US Chem Mill's several subsidiaries, Darco Industries Inc., a major revolutionary refrigerated vending machine operation out of Chicago ran up an indebtedness of more than three and a half million dollars. As a result, the SEC required Darco,'s disposal and US Chem Mill faced Chapter X bankruptcy reorganization.

Because of this, the company had to struggle mightily to keep functioning and fulfill orders. Orris and Lundquist did everything they could, but they quickly fell behind on delivery dates to the Air Force and aerospace companies, eventually resulting in severe penalties and fines. To make matters worse, the Government declared that U.S. Chem Mill's inability to deliver on time was a national security issue and forced it to relinquish key contracts to other companies.

U.S. Chem Mill had been like a living entity, itself, in many ways and the effort to keep it alive was like an attempt to resurrect the dead. In fact, when I heard my parents discuss the situation, I interpreted the term "crash" to refer to that of a plane, especially as they were bemoaning the loss of many friends in the company.

This failure in 1962 was too much for everyone, except for Charles Lundquist and his many other ventures. Besides his very profitable work on the atolls, he was able to keep several large pieces of property in Southern California, quickly starting construction on a very large business complex in El Segundo, Continental Development focusing mainly on aerospace and aircraft defense industry corporations and by the year 2000, contained thirty multi-story buildings, the crown jewel of all his properties.

Lundquist continued to be an avid financial supporter and close friend of Vice President Richard Nixon. He contributed money and many other forms of support to Nixon's effort to become President in 1960, when he ran against John Kennedy. And, again in 1968, he would contribute heavily to the campaign against Robert Kennedy. The two men remained very close associates and friends, even after Nixon's resignation.

But important for my story was his continued support of my father and our family. For example, for a number of years he owned the largest personal yacht in Southern California, moored at Marina Del Rey, and which as my sister Stephanie's godfather; he gave her its use as a wedding present.

More important was his involvement in the planning of the President's assassination.

Orris as Troubleshooter for the Aerospace Industry

The collapse of U.S. Chem Mill meant left Orris unemployed. But through his contacts and work there, he had become a troubleshooter for a number of different organizations within the military aerospace industry. He had built a strong reputation with his ability solving problems. And it was this reputation that he now relied on.

For instance, he would be called in on an emergency involving a major aircraft part. This one problem could halt the entire assembly line process, potentially costing millions of dollars a day. Orris would meet with the assembly plant engineers to understand the problem, and then the manufacturing company engineers to determine if they could quickly solve the problem. If not, he would find another manufacturer that could. Of course, a sizable sum of money would change hands to expedite this process.

Orris was perfectly suited for this. He looked and played the part, successful, confident, charismatic, very intelligent. Always dressed perfectly in public, he wore expensive suits, custom-made white cotton shirts with gold cuff links and handmade Italian shoes. All from Neiman Marcus in Dallas or expensive New York, Chicago and

Los Angeles stores. His luggage was tanned leather, custom-made by a Fort Worth saddle maker, who he knew personally. But his tastes were not just for himself, but also business associates and friends. And they extended to the expensive hotels, restaurants, bars and private clubs used to meet his clients.

He would change his persona to meet the situation, even in the most stressful. Special was his wit, able to come up with appropriate "one-liners,." Sarcastic if necessary, but very funny. Always able to break the ice and bring together people who otherwise, would be adversarial. But I could always tell who he actually liked and respected, and who he had to tolerate and make feel special and important. The ultimate diplomat.

With all this, he was a magnet for beautiful women and successful men who wanted to be like him and with him. Charles Lundquist would tell me after his death, "Orris was a man's man."

If you were good to Orris and treated him with polite respect, he would do anything for you. But if you crossed him, he would never forgive you. Never. Thankfully, if you were a family member, a sincere apology would be rewarded with forgiveness, with the issue never being brought up again. At least, that's the way it was before the assassination.

Finally, almost important were his innate understanding of engineering and his Mafia contacts.

The Family 1957 Through 1961

Despite all Orris' business, our home life was fairly quiet, private. My sisters Stephanie and Debbie set the tone for this, never fully accepting the move from California; in many ways they had never left. They restricted their interactions with Texans to school., not even wanting classmates to visit. Maintaining their California identity, they watched the Walt Disney's 'Disneyland' religiously every Saturday night and anything else related to Southern California. This attitude continued through 1962, when they finally began to change their opinions of Texas and Texans

I don't know if Orris bought a horse for Stephanie because of this, but after, her attitude seemed to soften and there were always horses in our life. It found out that as a boy, he had been responsible for taking care of the family farm horses and so, always had a strong association with horses and the men rearing them.

I always missed California, myself, so I could understand my sisters' attitudes. My younger siblings were too young to have much of a reaction to the move.

And then this: There was a tree farm located right behind our first house where Stephen and three of our friends were sexually assaulted in 1958. I witnessed part of this by a man who, seeing me, chased, but thankfully didn't catch me. At the age of seven, this really affected me, making me wary of male homosexuals into adulthood. And I believe it was this assault that prompted our move to another house in Arlington.

However, it was mother who had the greatest difficulty. Before this "incident," she had tried to make the best of her new life in Texas, but there were several other stressors and losses—the move from California, the loss of friends, the final closure of U.S. Chem Mill, which was like family itself, and the uncertainty of Orris' future.

Maxine Attempts Suicide

But the final straw was direct evidence of Orris' womanizing. One of his lovers became angry and threatened to phone my mother about their love relationship. And she did as she threatened, calling one evening just before Orris was due home, "Orris just left me to go home. We have been having an affair for the last year and he's going to leave you for me."

When Orris came in a few minutes later, Maxine didn't yell at him. It was very rare for her to raise her voice, but she was obviously very hurt and informed him about the call. I don't think that anything like this had happened to her before, even though I believe she was aware he had other lovers. After all, his actions must have given it away as they usually do in infidelities. Like being in the wrong place at the wrong time, women answering the phone in his hotel room, lipstick on his collar, and lying with ludicrous excuses. All the usual mistakes that most men make in these situations. I guess even though really disturbed. she felt she had to accept it because of the children – this was a time before equitable divorce.

The next day was a Saturday, so I and my siblings were home from school. Orris had left appearing angry and humiliated by this embarrassing encounter between the two women. Then shortly after, the woman called again. I don't know what was said, but I could see it upset my mother to a degree I had never seen.; she wasn't acting like herself.

After about twenty minutes, she went into a bathroom she never used, locking the door. I became so worried that I went and knocked. No answer, but I could hear the water running. Now I was really worried because she never used that room to bathe. I kept knocking harder and harder pounding and calling her name, trying to get her attention. Trying to break down the door, impossible since I was only eight. Still, there was no answer.

Stephanie and Debbie heard the commotion, came into the hall, to ask what was going on. I told them what our mother had done, that she wasn't answering my pleas. Together we quickly reached the conclusion that it was time for more drastic action.

I decided to go outside to break the bathroom window. I couldn't see through it because the drapes were drawn. So, I picked up a brick from the flowerbed and smashed it. Then pulling back the drapes, I could see her in the bathtub, not responding to any of this.

After yelling to my sisters to call an ambulance, I climbed through the broken window. When I reached her, the water was still running, pouring over the side of the tub. Her nose was just an inch above the water and at first sight, I didn't know if she was still alive. She was completely unconscious. I put my hands under her chin and on the back of her head and pulled her further above the water. She was completely limp, really frightening me.

I reached over, turned the water off and opened the drain. Then I tried to determine if she were still breathing. It was very hard to tell at first because her breath was so shallow. Thankfully, when I felt for a pulse in her neck. she was still alive.

The ambulance seemed to arrive very quickly, and she was taken to the hospital before we could fully grasp what this was all about. What had caused her to go to this extreme and nearly succeed? If she had just slipped down another inch in the water while she was unconscious, she would have surely drowned. For our mother to do something like this was so unexpected. She was always very calm, collected, and an exceptional mother. But we did find a bottle of sleeping pills; along with one of very strong painkillers.

Apparently, she nearly died at the hospital several times, but thankfully they were always able to bring her back in the nick of time. They located our father and he got to the hospital while they were still working on her.

The whole episode had been a very frightening and disturbing experience for all six of us children, especially, the younger ones, who couldn't understand what had caused all this. They needed to be reassured that this would not happen again, but it was hard to convince them because they were so young. When he came home, Orris talked with us honestly about what had caused her to do such a thing, trying to reassure us children, especially the younger ones who were having difficulty understanding anything of this.

Mother returned from the hospital a few days later. I don't think he made false promises to her that he would change his life and give up other women. However, he apparently did take the necessary steps to make sure that this woman would never call her again and that no other woman would either.

Actually, after she had recovered, she seemed fairly content and happy. In fact, she began to function as Orris' secretary, while he was freelancing, a job which she seemed to enjoy. She would come to personally know all the men with whom my father interacted.

***

(After her own mother's death in 1970, she would inherit several million dollars, money to do with as she wanted. Frugal, but also a spendthrift like a child in a candy shop, splurging on a few things such as a Cadillac matching my father's and a three carat, flawless diamond ring – when I told her I was worried she might be killed when someone tried to steal it, she only laughed. And after Orris' death, she handily managed his business dealings.

(In the early 1980s she finally seemed happy, accepting Orris' strange ways. They had money and travelled all over the world together. In 1985, she was celebrated for her life's dedication to the aerospace defense industry when one of the companies created "Max Day" in her honor. Orris' death in 1987 devastated her; she had lost her lover and soulmate. She always maintained she loved him so much, it was worth all she had gone through with him. Refusing to give up her independence, she lived alone in a house she bought in Fort Worth until her death in 1994.

(She loved people and animals, always having birds and at least one little dog which she treated like her own children. Occasionally she would bring home a lost family found through her church or even just beside the highway. Something we children got used to. She would buy them a car and give them enough money to get to wherever they were going, and more.)

Orris' Own Depression

After we moved to Fort Worth, my father would occasionally fall into depressed states, brief but distinct. I don't know if this had to do with moving back to Texas as mother worried, but I do know it got worse after the U.S. Chem Mill failure.

Like most men then in the aerospace industry, he drank a lot, but he was worse when in these depressed states. I don't think I ever really understood these depressed states that seemed to affect him to such a degree or what seemed to bring them on so suddenly.

During these times, he would revisit the local Fort Worth areas he knew as a boy. He would take long, long drives in the country down in the Trinity River bottoms, often with our mother and all of us children in our green Chevrolet station wagon. I don't know how much these trips also reminded him of the Big Sandy and Little Sandy Rivers of his young childhood.

Or if his fascination with the Trinity River was related it being named after the Christian concept of the Trinity, the union of the three entities: the Father, Son, and Holy Spirit. But Fort Worth, definitely part of the Baptist Bible Belt, tends to focus on religion more than most American cities. It seems they have never heard of separation of state and religion.

These trips continued until 1961 and were a time for all of us to be together. Mostly in the fall and spring, when it was storming and the river would be at flood stage. Aa if the storms intensified his depression, something like worrying a sore tooth. There would be tornado warnings with lightning and torrential rain falling and he would say, "Let's all go for a ride along the Trinity River." We never disagreed and went faithfully.

We would have to cross this old rickety steel bridge and many times the water would be so high and raging right under the bridge a few feet below us, I wondered whether we would make it safely. But, for some reason, I loved this experience, it was exhilarating. The storming weather, the lightning, the wind, the hail, and the cold rain that comes with it. To go outside and feel the power of these violent North Texas storms with the wind in my face and the shattering sound of lightening close by; the closer, the better. The next day, Orris would seem completely normal, as if nothing had occurred.

After 1961, it seemed he had no further interest in making these stormy trips. I'm absolutely sure that was because he was now developing his own corporation, U.S. Sonics, Inc. in Dallas, which provided him a new purpose in life. New business and the daily need to travel there from Fort Worth. He literally didn't have time to be depressed. We had also moved further from the Trinity River and his favorite drive along this enigmatic river.

Guns and Hunting

After we moved to Texas, Orris began taking me deer hunt ng with his associates on different ranches, especially one outside San Saba and another near Glen Rose. There was also a twenty-mile long area of the Trinity between Fort Worth and Dallas that one of his favorites where he had hunted with his father as a young man. It was still undeveloped, an area of densely covered river-bottoms, relatively close to where we lived, quickly accessible, and a sanctuary for wild animals and game. It was still beautiful; now it's nothing but Texas-style brick homes and commercial development.

When the river was low, we would go down near an old bridge here to target practice and hunt Water Moccasins. It would be very hot and humid with locusts in the trees continuously screeching their loud noise. It was a lot of fun, but it took excellent marksmanship because these snakes are different from any other I've ever encountered. Not only ugly and smelling bad, they have a terrible bite and can be very aggressive when frightened, so there was an element of danger. They would look at you with an almost human intelligence before they decided what to do; whether to come at you or go the other way. It's all very strange.

It was very difficult to get close without these deadly snakes hearing and seeing you. And to get close enough for a good shot, we would have to get under low trees, where their mottled brown colors and rough scaly skin made it very hard to distinguish them from the tree branches. And when we fired at those in the river, those in the trees would fall out, frightened by the loud bang of a 30.06, and ready to strike. Sometimes, they would actually fall right on someone and try to bite.

They were worse than a den of Rattlers. There could be so many we would have to put down our rifles and beat them off with a stick. Hunting them was really just to keep their numbers below the point they would decimate the fish population. And, of course, they were a serious danger to people, especially children.

The hunting wasn't just limited to Moccasins, we targeted squirrels, geese, doves, rabbits, quail, and in the fall, Canadian Geese. And I had the feeling that even though Orris enjoyed the hunting, the real purpose he spent so much time doing so with me was to teach me to be as good with a rifle as he; his desire was obvious. I think he knew that someday I would need this proficiency to survive. Little did I know then that he was right, that someday this ability would go a long way toward saving my life.

Orris expanded his avid hunting in the fall of 1957 by taking several trips to hunt deer at a private ranch outside Durango and to one outside Ridgway, both in Colorado. In 1958, he and a close friend, Charles Lyon began to cohost trips for Aerospace Defense Industry buyers, officials and engineers. i Of course, these were plush events at a hunting lodge with excellent chefs to cook the best of cuisine, with lots of liquor and beautiful women when not out in the bush. These hunting trips would last seven to ten days and were talked about throughout the industry. And, of course, Orris would receive back twenty-fold in the form of contracts.

The number of men involved quickly increased so that two such hunting parties were required. This also allowed accommodation for men previously excluded because of animosity or rivalry; the competition in the aerospace defense industry is one of the fiercest in the business world. Later, even a third event was arranged, much smaller and oriented more toward serious hunting for six or seven men, as Orris and Lyon wouldn't get any hunting themselves, playing host on the other two trips.

These trips continued until the fall of 1963, when Orris and Lyon didn't go deer hunting in Texas or Colorado, too busy with the Kennedy assassination planning. But yet, Orris would occasionally come home in his field gear; when I would ask him what he had been doing, he would simply reply, "Target practicing." Preparing to change their type of game this year to something much more dangerous, the President of the United States.

6

S.A.C.

Making The Flight to SAC Headquarters in Early 1961

At breakfast one Spring morning, Orris told me he wanted me to go to with him to Air Force Strategic Air Command headquarters in Omaha. The trip was to be in a week's time, and we would be gone for five days. He didn't tell me a lot more, other than a group of men would be going on a chartered American Airlines Constellation plane.

This would be the first time I would fly, and the family made a big deal of it. In fact, he told my mother to buy me a new suit. I was ten years old, and though I didn't know it at the time, besides being my first flight, this would be a pivotal trip for both him and me. This would be a coming-of-age event for me; and my first meeting with the man to be such a major figure in my life and the assassination, General Born. Circumstances dictated that I mature early.

The day for our trip arrived along with a terrible storm extending all the way to Nebraska. Little did I know that meant a very rough ride most of the way. The whole family accompanied us to Amon Carter Field Airport in Euless. But even that drive was impacted by the storm. The normal route was blocked by high water detouring us to Dallas and then to a different road to the airport, delaying us about an hour.

Was this some kind of omen? I only knew that I was getting anxious. But unlike the weather, my personal storm would never end, but only grow much worse as the years passed.

We were well-acquainted with this beautiful airport because we had accompanied our father here many times, admiring its extraordinary gold relief sculpture on the lobby ceiling. It was relatively new and one of only two privately owned airports in the country, developed by friends Sid Richardson with runways long enough to land a B-36 bomber, it would become the base for a group of these in the not-so-distant future.

It was Orris' favorite point of departure because it and the close by Western Hills Inn were owned by friends Sid Richardson and Searcy Dobkins. The airport as an alternative to Dallas' Love Field. This had been the site of his U.S. Chem Mill office. And the Inn housed a private club to Orris belonged, and where he would take us to swim. He also used the hotel and club as a meeting place for out-of-town aerospace industry people.

American Airlines had also been involved in building this airport. And across the street was their training facility for. stewardesses who Orris would use as 'call girls' for clients. For a period of time, I actually thought he was some kind of a strange 'man of the night' and the aerospace thing a side game because I would see so many of these women with him and I knew they were going to his clients.

By the time we finally arrived, the plane had been sitting on the tarmac, engines running for over an hour, and full of men waiting not so patiently. The flight had actually originated at Love Field and for some odd reason, it had taken the short flight here, just to pick up Orris and me. To pass the time, these men were drinking rather heavily and enjoying their young female companions, whom I certainly wasn't expecting. Until now, I didn't know that these 'business trips' were a combination of sex, drinking, and business, all combined to make the United States the most powerful nation in the world.

Because of the storm, the pilots and passengers were very eager to get in the air before the weather got any worse, many being ex-Air Force pilots themselves.

A group of five or six black men were waiting for us to help with luggage, et cetera, men that Orris knew. They had been told we were late and to help us get to the plane quickly. They hovered around the car like a storm of bees.to help the whole family climb out and take our suitcases from the trunk. We all took off in a run, some others simply joining in the excitement for the fun.

It seemed like a mile through the long glassed-in corridors leading to the tarmac. I had played with my brothers and sisters in these corridors many times in the past three years, day and night, so they seemed like home to me. Unfortunately, the days of such simple pleasures at American airports are long gone.

When we arrived at our gate, breathing hard, a huge silver plane sat alone in the cold, hard rain, with its large props turning swiftly. It re-aroused that ominous feeling in me. I just knew that something bad was going to happen. My first air trip and with this storm, I was sure we weren't going to survive.

I looked up at the open rear door where a stewardess appeared, starting down the portable stairs with an eager, nervous look on her face. She introduced herself as Sarah Jane. She was coming for me, to take my hand and guide me into hell or at least, the land of devils and very jealous wives; even though some might think it was heaven.

I turned to my beautiful mother and knew it was time to say goodbye and I just knew it would be forever. I looked her in the eyes and kissed her soft cheek. Then I looked over her shoulder at my brothers and sisters who had excitement in their eyes, to say goodbye forever to them, too. I bumped into my father as I let my mother's hand go and turned back towards the door. I looked up into his face and realized he knew this was the end of my innocence. He pushed the door open for Sarah Jane as she ran up to us.

She reached in, firmly took my hand and asked, "Are you ready, Bruce? Let's go." Her hand felt warm in the cold rain, as we ran across the tarmac to the waiting staircase. I paused to look over my shoulder just in time to see my father bend down to kiss his wife goodbye, also, forever. I turned back to the stewardess who was now soaking wet. Her hand still felt warm, and her beautiful eyes were begging me to climb the cold wet staircase to Hell with her. I knew she didn't want to go alone. So, we started up this very long stairway.

I could see the prop turning rapidly at the front of the wing, blowing cold rain on us. The engine was loud, and I could smell the burnt fuel coming from the exhaust, mixed with the smell of the rain. At that instant, lightning struck the tarmac right in front of the plane. The blinding flash of light stroked through the turning prop. The deafening crash of thunder caused us both to freeze in place and cringe down several inches.

Waiting for the light to stop flashing through the prop, it seemed as if it were actually hit, and the world was about to end. Her hand tightened over mine and I knew I would love this beautiful woman forever if we actually survived. It seemed like a full lifetime passed as we both stood frozen, attempting to recover from this obvious omen. Should we turn back and be saved from this silver monster on its way to destruction? Or should we continue on and let fate take its course?

Somehow, we recovered from the lightening crash and headed up the rest of the stairway. Stepping through the door, I had no choice but to accept there was now no return from our perilous destiny. Suddenly a loud cheer sounded, and I turned to see who, what, and why. I realized it was for little me. Twenty-five men and to my surprise, twenty-five young women, took to their feet, smiling, and applauding.

I turned back to the stairway and found Orris just mounting the bottom steps. And through its rain-drenched windows. I could see our family in the airport corridor, smiling and watching my now wet father climb the stairs to this ship of fools. As he entered the doorway, I stepped back with Sarah Jane and a cheer louder than that for me, pierced the damp air.

There were two other stewardesses standing close to us and a tall, beautiful, blonde young woman a few feet back. Orris turned to this woman who, as she took one step forward and he one step back, put her arms around him and kissed him hard on the lips. Another loud roar reverberated through the plane.

Instantly, I was flooded with confusion and confusing emotion. I glanced at my mother, a mere seventy feet away, still looking at the plane's doorway. Could she possibly see her husband kissing this woman? But then I realized he was conveniently standing just one step from the door, just one step out of my mother's sight.

Then the memory flooded back, of saving her from suicide about a year earlier when she had found out about a woman with whom he was involved. Was this woman the same one? After a minute of silent shock, I realized I was going to have to let go of Sarah Jane's hand, and forced myself to proceed, not showing that shock. She smiled at me and motioned toward the front of the plane.

But before I started up the aisle, I wanted to have one last good look at my mother to make sure she hadn't seen the kiss. When I stepped out into the open doorway to look through the rain to the now fog-laden corridor windows, I could just barely see the family. I waved to them, and my mother vigorously waved back, hands above her head. At that gesture, I felt relief, she was alright and more likely than not hadn't seen my father indulge in his devilish behavior.

I turned back to Sarah Jane, and we headed up the aisle together at the head of a procession of three other stewardesses and then Orris and his adulteress. As we did, the men and some of their young women smiled and nodded to me, some extending their hands to shake mine. I recognized many of these men as my father's business associates, some of them quite well. I also knew some of their wives and children.

I looked back at Orris and watched him as he came forward to shake hands and have a few brief words with the entourage of engineers, salespeople, vice presidents, and plant managers, mainly from Dallas/Fort Worth aerospace companies. His girlfriend trailed, quietly smiling at everyone as she walked to take her place on the throne next to him at the front, the queen of the entourage.

The back hatch of the plane closed, and it began to move forward even before we had reached our seats. I sat where my new-found friend indicated, the front seat on the left side, next to the window, a seat of honorable recognition in Air Force circles and standards. She reached down to strap me in and seated herself next to me, fastening her own. I didn't know it yet, but she had been handpicked to be my personal companion for the entire week of the trip. She would accompany me everywhere and before the week was gone, I would come to know her quite well.

Orris and his girlfriend took their seats directly behind us. Shortly, we reached the end of the runway, turned into the wind and started forward. Once in the air, we climbed steeply to our cruising altitude, the plane buffeted violently through the thunderstorm. Long before we had reached flying altitude, the stewardesses unbuckled and started bringing more drinks to everyone. This seemed to be just as much a party as a business trip. The men were loud, and the girls were laughing.

When we finally reached flying altitude and the plane settled down in its flat trajectory toward Omaha, I unbuckled my seat belt and turned around to have a good close look at Orris and this woman he had kissed in front of me. As my eyes met his, I couldn't help but see an uncomfortable reflection about how I would accept such a flagrant act of infidelity. He damn well knew that I had saved my mother's life only a year earlier; a tragedy caused by this blonde wretch sitting so close to him and in plain sight of his wife's favorite son.

I tried to bury my contempt for her and turned my gaze from my father's guilty eyes to hers. She was a beautiful woman now that I could see her closely, but she reminded me of a living Barbie Doll with a much too perfect face. I could see why Orris had chosen her above the rest. She was a status symbol, a prize that said in his world, "I'm top gun and I have this woman to signify it." She was a political ploy and a toy to him, all five feet and ten inches.

I'm positive he knew I could see right through everything he was doing. This would be a new world for the two of us, the beginning of a relationship where I would be the keeper of his secrets and therefore, someone he could share other secrets with. He would use me in a way extremely unusual for any father and son. And Orris being the man he was, would use every advantage he could to reach his personal, extremely high goals in life. Somehow, I gleaned that I was to become his personal, not so secret weapon, in his secret world of deceit and tyranny.

So, playing his game, I smiled at the blonde tightly holding my father's arm and said, "Hello," to her. She looked straight at me, and I knew she realized that she was no competition at all to me. Her eyelids fluttered and she turned to my father without uttering any response whatsoever to me. I was my mother's child, and she was demonstrating contempt and, at the same time, jealousy for me. She knew my father loved me deeply and that love came from his for my mother, in spite of his infidelities. She could not bear to even look me in the eye because of this. She disliked me because she hated my mother, and I reminded her of my father's love for his wife.

I had offered my glove to her, in spite of the fact she had turned it down so stupidly. We all make mistakes, but few make such obvious, unfortunate ones as this. I was willing to turn my cheek, give her a chance, and try to see her side. But now it was too late. It was done. I looked back to my father and I'm sure he could realize I thought him a fool to choose such a stupid woman, even if she did look like a Barbie Doll.

I turned away, thinking this was the first time a grown person had intentionally ignored an effort on my part to befriend her, and she had done this so callously. I lost respect for my father's judgment of women and knew that if I could see the contempt and falseness in this woman so easily, then he and others could also.

About the time we reached the Oklahoma/Kansas border, we hit a severe wind shear. We had already put on our seatbelts because it had begun to get rough again. The other stewardesses were still standing when suddenly the plane fell straight down a few thousand feet, throwing them up to the ceiling where for several seconds they appeared to be stuck. Just as suddenly as the plane bottomed out, they fell to the floor, hard. It was like falling in a wild rollercoaster, only I was sure for the moment that the plane must have lost its wings and we all could have died. The fact that they were still attached gave me newfound respect for the aircraft engineers on board.

Finally, the weather improved over Kansas. We had briefly broken through the storm. The moon and stars were out, and it was beautiful. Everyone seemed to relax, and Sarah Jane guided me into the cockpit. They were obviously expecting me, as the co-pilot got up and after introducing himself and the captain, left. The captain then invited me to take the co-pilot's seat and showed me how to make the plane climb and descend and how to bank left and then right by turning the yoke. He then said he was going to let go of the controls and allow me to take over.

Obviously, this was an exhilarating experience for a ten-year-old boy. He told me to slowly push forward on the controls and then to slowly pull back. As I did, I could feel the plane move downward and then back up. It was very interesting and fun, and a lot easier than I would have thought.

After about twenty minutes, Sarah Jane came back with the co-pilot and we returned to our seats. I glanced at Orris' girlfriend as I was sitting, and she still refused to acknowledge or return my simple smile and "Hello." But this time, I think I was sort of playing a game with her, taunting her; I knew she wouldn't say hello to me, I knew she never would.

It was still another thirty minutes before we reached the Omaha runway. When we did, it was about ten o'clock, dark, and we were two hours late. Suddenly everyone pulled themselves together and seemed to sober up.

In Omaha

Disembarkment was quick and orderly, in an almost military procession; after all, nearly all had been in the military. Sarah Jane took my hand as we started down the aisle with everyone else. We were the last to disembark, Orris and girlfriend right in front of us.

It was still drizzling a cold, bone chilling rain bouncing off the dark tarmac About fifteen Air Force automobiles with a lieutenant or captain in each, sat waiting.

Orris and girlfriend followed an Air Force Captain who had greeted them at the bottom of the stairs, strongly shaking Orris' hand. Obviously, they knew each other. Everyone else boarded cars in a hurry, loudly slamming doors. The four of us and the captain got in our car which took the front of a procession across the tarmac, out of the airport, and quickly on to our hotel.

We pulled up to our hotel in about twenty minutes. When Orris got out, we followed. He took control, putting the group in order. I had never seen him like this; it became very clear he was the undisputed leader. In a matter of seconds, we were all assembled in some kind of rank; the leading men closely behind him and the rest, at the rear. The women, all but Orris' girlfriend who stayed close with him, fell to the far rear. Then, suddenly, as if on command, we moved forward up the stairs.

The four of us, Orris, his girlfriend, Sarah Jane, and me, went through the doors first into a very large lobby. A group of Air Force Generals and Colonels appeared from the doors of the bar at the back of the lobby, led by one who I would come to know as General Born. They appeared to have been waiting impatiently for us and filed straight toward Orris. The three in front, all shook hands with Orris. Then Born suggested that since it was so late, they all meet in the bar for a few drinks to decide how to proceed.

Orris turned to me, "Bruce, Sarah Jane is going to take care of you while we're here. She will take you to your room now and I'll see you later before you go to sleep. OK?"

After affirming I understood, Sarah Jane and I started down a long hall. I looked back over my shoulder to see Orris and Born lead the men towards the bar. A concierge appeared in front of us from what seemed like out of nowhere to lead us to our room deep in this cavernous hotel.

When we arrived at my room, Sarah Jane informed me she was in the connecting one on one side and Orris' was on the other. She came in with me to do her best to make sure I was comfortable. She then turned to leave, saying, "Goodnight, I'll see you in the morning. Just knock on my door and I'll take care of whatever you need. Your father will come to see you before you go to sleep."

And sure enough, later that night the door to Orris' room opened and he walked in. As I peeked into his room, I saw his friend getting ready for bed. She looked up at me, sitting on the bed, taking off her stockings. Her eyes met mine and she actually gave a little sly smile, not for me, but for herself and her accomplishment of being able to control my father in this sexual way.

This was a good beginning for her. She would eventually have two children with Orris and he would take care of her for the next twenty years, before their relationship finally ended.

Orris asked if I were alright and seemed sincerely concerned about me and my psychological comfort. He instructed me to just knock on his door if I needed anything, then kissed me goodnight.

The next morning, we all went down to the hotel restaurant for breakfast. The rain had stopped, but it was still cold and partly cloudy. It would stay like that all week long. Afterward Orris left with his entire entourage for SAC headquarters and left me in Sarah Jane's care with the use of an Air Force car to go wherever we wished.

That night, Orris had dinner with the SAC Generals and his Air Force associates. The next day, he took me to SAC headquarters. This wasn't the first time I had been on an Air Force base with him, but this was different. The longer we were here, the more I realized he was the most important, influential man in this group of aerospace people and was sought after by the Air Force officers for his attention and opinion.

They took me on a tour of a small museum, located in a hanger on the base. It displayed nuclear bomb delivery systems and various nuclear bombs and detonation devices, all of course inactive. Outside were several of the latest nuclear bombers, one of s which, a B-58, they let me climb a ladder into and sit in the pilot's seat. This was an aircraft I knew my father had been involved with in a major way, at Convair, General Dynamics, in the late 1950s.

On our third day, Sarah Jane and I visited the Omaha Zoo. The rest of the week, we toured the various interesting places around the city. It was fun to be with her because she liked me and tried her best to keep me interested. But I couldn't help but notice that she seemed depressed and preoccupied with something. Every now and then, I would catch her looking off into the distance in deep thought, not even hearing me say her name. And oddly, even though before this week would be over we would come to know each other very well, after the trip, I would never see or hear anything of her.

I would eat at least one meal with Orris and his friend each day. But for the most part, he was off with his Air Force people and I really didn't see that much of him. She continued not to say one word to me, even though I tried to be as nice as I could under the circumstances. When I smiled, she would look the other way, refusing to even acknowledge my efforts.

The week passed quickly, and it was time for us to leave. The same men and women assembled in front of our hotel, and boarded the same Air Force cars to move quickly across Omaha in the same military procession,. When we arrived on the tarmac, our aircraft sat, shining silver, waiting for us to board and return us to Dallas/Fort Worth. At least, the weather was dry and much better than on our trip a week earlier and I no longer had any fear of flying.

When we boarded, Sarah Jane again took my hand as we moved to the same seats at the front with Orris and his girlfriend behind. The return trip was uneventful until when we crossed the Red River on the border of Texas and Oklahoma, about forty minutes from hugging my mother at Amon Carter, Orris asked me to join him at the rear of the plane. There, he asked me to take a seat next to him. He looked at me seriously before saying, "Bruce, you know you can't mention the woman I've traveled with to your mother. Don't you?"

I reassured him, "Don't worry about this, Daddy. Have you already forgotten that I was the one who saved her life last year because of the same woman? Do you think I would do anything that might cause her to try again?"

Orris looked at me with eyes that couldn't hide his feelings. If it were anyone else he was talking with, he might not have been able to believe what he had just heard. Coming from me, his loved and understanding son, he could only turn his head in shame and realize he had made a big mistake to have exposed his girlfriend to me so blatantly. I knew he wasn't worried about me ever saying anything to my mother, he was worried I would never forgive him for this seemingly barbaric, unnecessary display of disloyalty to not only my mother, but to me, also.

Our plane landed smoothly, and we taxied to our disembarking location, where only Orris and I would leave. I could see my mother and siblings through the same windows as a week earlier. Orris' girlfriend and he had moved to the rear of the plane to kiss and say goodbye, which I felt was another insult to my mother and even to me. Sarah Jane came back, gave me a kiss on the cheek, and said goodbye to me before I started down the stairs. I looked back at my father hiding out of sight from my mother before I left the plane. he seemed like a child not wanting to get caught with his hand in the cookie jar.

After climbing down the stairs, I stopped and looked back at this huge plane sitting in front of me. I realized this trip had changed my life forever, but I wasn't sure at all that this change was for the better. It certainly didn't feel better standing there, knowing that my father was in the back of the plane kissing this strange woman, while I had to turn around and smile and wave to my mother and siblings and act as though all was well and I had had a good trip to Omaha with my father.

Because of this trip to Omaha and SAC headquarters and my exposure to Orris' girlfriend, he realized he could trust me completely to keep a secret. I know now that it signaled the beginning of his new, successful business venture, U.S. Sonics, as well as his very prominent role in one of the most important events of the twentieth century, the assassination of the president. And at the same time, it signaled the beginning of my own involvement and with so many repercussions.

7

U.S. SONICS, INC.

The Beginning

While he was 'free-lancing' as aerospace consultant after the demise of U.S. Chemical Milling, Orris continued his contacts with Charles Lundquist and General Born. But true to his nature, he wanted something more for himself, and so met with the two men to discuss options. What could they invest in, together with their time and money, that would be profitable for them all?

The Cold War necessitated constant readiness. This had resulted in the Atlas and Titan I Missiles to carry nuclear weapons. There were several hundred of these missiles sitting on launch pads and in silos across North America. It was essential they be able to fire at a moment's notice. Ideally, they could sit already fueled., but they burned a cryogenic propellant, liquid oxygen, an extremely low temperature product and a hydrocarbon fuel similar to kerosene.

Unfortunately, the liquid oxygen would deteriorate very quickly and cook off, so the rocket fuel would have to be changed several times a day, or they could pump fuel through the rocket engines continuously. Either way, it resulted in varnishing and corrosion, meaning they had to be periodically removed and cleaned.

So, the three men turned to setting up a business to do just that. Luckily because of their own influence and that of Curtis LeMay, acquiring a contract was just a formality. And so, U.S. Sonics Inc. was born in 1961. Orris E. Bell would be President; General Charles F. Born, Vice President; Dallas attorney Edwin A. Nesbitt, Corporate Secretary; with Charles H. Lundquist, a de facto owner.

These men would all make a financial investment in the startup; Lundquist the largest, followed by Orris, then Born, and finally, Nesbitt. Clarence Bentley was a fifth, smaller investor, a member of the corporate board who would later be bought out by the others. Two of the board of director's members had been previous deputy district attorneys.

The first thing to be done, even before the legal measures, was to find an adequate location for their new facility. Dallas was the logical place; Orris was in the Dallas area already, as was General Born, working with Texas Instruments. And as already stated, these two men along with Charles Lundquist, had a great deal of influence in the aerospace industry in the Dallas/ Fort Worth area.

They didn't need a large structure, as they planned on limiting work to this single Air Force contract. They found a location on Parkhouse St. near downtown at the very southern edge of the industrial district off Industrial Blvd. Very close and accessible to the Stemmons Expressway, and fortuitously, less than half a mile from Dealey Plaza; one could nearly throw a rock from the Plaza and it would land squarely on what would be its porch.

Orris would still live in Fort Worth, commuting nearly daily. He didn't mind that; he wasn't about to give up his beloved Fort Worth for Dallas. He could visit daily to get his fill of Dallas sophistication.

My father started taking me to U.S. Sonics, as soon as they leased the building, so I saw it before it had anything in it. During this period, I would usually go there on a Saturday and occasionally on a weekday, until school was out for the summer, at which time I would usually go there, at least once during the week as well as on the weekend.

The building they had leased was a shell; everything would have to be built from scratch. Time was of the essence, as the Air Force had been warehousing these Atlas and Titan I engines for some time and needed their cleaning to begin as soon as possible.

Orris had someone in mind to oversee the construction, Norris Lawrence. Norris had a background in construction and had become a trusted and respected friend. He was a Navy man who saw a lot of action in the South Pacific during World War II. I liked him very much; he was very kind and always relaxed in an otherwise, hectic atmosphere; so when I was there, I would always spend time with him.

Orris had been introduced to him by his wife, June, an American Airlines stewardess, whom he had met while at his U.S. Chem Mill office at Amon Carter Field. She had frequently been his stewardess on his business flights, and the two became good friends, including an affair. She taught a few classes at the American Airlines Stewardess College and would provide the women Orris used for his clients. She would become a very close family friend.

June was truly beautiful in every sense of the word. She had a doll face and body with black hair, blue eyes, and a very fair complexion. She wasn't a fussy woman though, just natural; not wearing a lot of makeup or spending hours every morning getting ready for the day. She used no hairspray on her curly hair, in a day when women's hair was usually perfectly fixed in place board. rigid. She had a great personality and was in no way hung up on her beauty, being one of those rare, attractive women who act as though they don't even know how attractive they are. I don't believe I ever heard her raise her voice, other than to laugh often at life and the amusing side of it.

The U.S. Sonics plant would encompass four basic areas: Receiving, Prep, 'White Room,' and Shipping, as well as an office area. Temporarily, they put up the basic layout and had the phone system installed. All of the offices were easy and fast, done within a month.

But the 'White Room' was a different matter and took several months, longer than they had anticipated. The rocket engine components would have to be cleaned in that kind of environment, but also had to be assembled and sealed there to prevent contamination. The need for it to be temperature-controlled and completely germ-free required an air filter system to remove fumes produced by the cleaning process, while still keeping the environment sterile. And outside air would have to be cleaned, temperature-controlled, and filtered before being brought in.

Knowledge of how to build such a room was difficult to locate then, as were the necessary components. Eventually, realizing they needed expert technical advice, they hired a consultant from NASA and subsequently a firm that had worked with NASA. And by late 1961, after five months of arduous work, it was up and functioning, and they were well into the process of cleaning the rocket engine parts.

Norris became the Facility Plant Manager in charge of receiving and shipping, along with a number of other basic facility functions. Because they needed someone with experience with these engines, they hired a woman engineer/scientist brought from Rocketdyne to be in charge of the actual cleaning and assembly of the engine components. All of the employees would have to have a security clearance, but the Air Force required this person to have a very high special one.

The Trinity River and its Levees

U.S. Sonics was the last building on what was then a dead-end street, relatively quiet and placid with little or no traffic. Many years earlier there had been a large city park across the street. The only remnants of this once beautiful park were about a dozen huge, old Live Oak trees lining the north side of the street and which stayed green all winter long, looking completely out of place in this sterile, industrial area.

These trees broke up the view of a big electric substation that served a big portion of downtown Dallas and consumed the entire area where the park had once been. This substation, with its huge transformers and high-tension lines, gave the park a mysterious and ominous feeling.

A few hundred yards down the street was a levee that kept the river from flooding parts of downtown Dallas and the industrial area alongside the river during the rainy seasons of spring and fall. Until they built the levees and dams on the upper river in the 1930s., the river could become a mile-wide, raging torrent, a dangerous problem.

I had full freedom to go anywhere I wanted at U.S. Sonics, including and most importantly, outside. When I become bored, I usually crossed the street to sit on the curb under the Oaks, observing everything going on.

Of course, the fact that I could observe everything going on from this vantage point meant I could also be observed. Anyone watching U.S. Sonics would see a young boy, coming and going from this business.

The idea was that if anyone got wind of something suspicious, this could throw them off.

So, I would come to spend an immense amount of time sitting outside of the U.S. Sonics plant, partly as decoy, and partly out of boredom.

U.S. Sonics: Hotbed of Anti-Kennedy Hate and White Supremacy Rhetoric

Kennedy's becoming president upset not only the principals of US Sonics, but also its employees. These men, like most in the aerospace industry were all ultra-conservative, right-wing fanatics, radical white supremacists. With strong connections with the still prominent Ku Klux Klan.

So as to be expected, the common rhetoric there toward President Kennedy after his election was bad enough. But as his policies became more obvious, especially his 'equal rights' efforts and what he was doing with his brother, Attorney General Robert Kennedy in the South, their mistrust and hatred only worsened. Eventually turning to the talk about actually killing him.

Over time as these discussions gained in momentum, they weren't restricted to him alone, beginning to include Robert and Martin Luther King. The talk increased to a point of fervent, fanatical slanderous remarks, with such maliciousness, it really disturbed me. At this point, it didn't make a lot of sense why they felt so strongly about the Kennedys and King; it was confusing.

And it wasn't just the people at the business. I would overhear my father in nearly every conversation on his office-phone talking about it; all over the country in both the aerospace industry and military. And not just on the phone; there were also constant remarks with visitors to U.S. Sonics. This bothered me because he was talking with such a zealous attitude toward murder so openly. I began to worry that something could happen to him because of all this.

At this time, I was attending elementary school fairly close to our house and very much enjoying my social and educational life at this basically middle-class school. This area of Fort Worth had no minorities, so I was never exposed to any during my education. But we did have Black maids who came to the house, cook dinner, and do basic cleaning for our mother, since there were eight in our family.

U.S. Sonics: CIA Front

From the very beginning, U.S. Sonics was designated a CIA front company. Even before construction had been completed, it would operate as such for several other projects. Born, Lundquist and Orris already had a vast background with The Agency.. Probably, its first operation was in the planning and implementation of the Bay of Pigs invasion. It also played a role in the Cuban Missile Crisis.

And because the international influence of Texas, specifically Dallas, was growing and Dallas was a hot-bed for ultra-conservative fanatics, it was a perfect company for the planning of the assassination of a president. Dallas' right-wing citizens passionately hated Kennedy and would shed not one tear over his death; they would throw a Texas style barbeque party, complete with the true Texas spirit of hate.

The CIA could not have asked for a better set-up. Born, Orris, and Lundquist would be the three main forces and decision makers. Of course, the CIA advised them and went over every aspect of the planning with them. U.S. Sonics was perfect because it was small, it was located in a very inconspicuous location, and the vice president was an Air Force General, close to the CIA and General LeMay. He was also a rabid Republican and had a long, influential history with Texas.

Orris, a man who just happened to be in the right place at the right time, was the perfect man to oversee it. He had the ability to organize as well as interact socially and easily with all the very different parties to be involved. He already had vast associations with the right people, most importantly those in the aerospace defense industry and military, as well as men in the Mafia.

He was politically right, an active member of the Republican party and an ultra-right-wing conservative. And, most of all, he could be completely trusted to get the job done and in the way the CIA wanted. The CIA and LeMay had known him before and trusted him to run this side of the Kennedy assassination. Orris would make this happen as smoothly as possible. And now, the anti-Kennedy rhetoric that had been brewing at U.S. Sonics intensified.

8

THE EARLY ACTIVE PLAYERS

The Richardson-Murchison Team

Clint Murchison Sr., Sid Richardson, and Orris were all born and raised in East Texas, which naturally brought them closer together as friends, but most importantly, as sharing the same mindset of the ultra-conservative Republican, passionately hating communism and liberal America. Orris had met Sid and Clint in 1954 at Murchison's Del Mar, a California racetrack, and close-by resort, El Charro. Many of the players had met there, including LeMay and Hoover. Orris would eventually introduce Clint and Sid to Charles Lundquist and General Born.

Clint Sr. was one of the richest men in the world, making most of his money in oil production. He had immense power, not only in Dallas where he lived, but throughout Texas and the entire nation. LeMay brought him into the assassination to play a leading role because he was able to control all the necessary entities, including the Dallas

Police Department, District Attorney's Office, and Mayor. He also had relationships with a number of Mafia leaders. So he brought together the consortium of players needed, while facilitating the assassination in many other ways.

Cliff Sr. had originally been close to, and had a lot of power over, Vice President Ly, but the two men had had a major falling out when Lyndon decided to run as Kennedy's V.P. candidate. because he had such disdain and hate for JFK, the whole Kennedy clan, and their liberal politics. In fact, he had refused to talk to Johnson over the three years since, even when Lyndon called a number of times.

However, his son, Clint Jr., owner of the Dallas Cowboys continued a working relationship with Johnson, and was the one who helped convince Lyndon that the President's assassination was the only viable way to end his insane reign.

Sid Richardson, Murchison's closest friend, and also a wealthy oilman, but from Fort Worth, was the 'point man' in the Murchison/Richardson team, dealing with Orris, Born, and Lundquist. He had been active with Orris in the effort to locate the right property for U.S. Chem Mill and the two had become very close friends.

After his untimely, very disturbing, fatal heart attack in late 1959, Murchison and his son naturally gravitated closer to Orris and his group.

H. L. Hunt

Hunt was a close LeMay friend and a CIA operative. They were introduced by another Texas oilman, D. Harold Byrd, involved with the General in the Texas and Louisiana Air National Guards.

He played a back role in the assassination compared to the Murchisons, also providing funding, but not nearly as much. I saw him at U.S. Sonics on several occasions and listened to my father talking with him on the phone a number of times during 1963.

I thought he fled the country on the morning of November 22, 1963 with several of his Dallas partners, flying down to his Mexico ranch on his private airplane and not returning for several months, until all was under control and clear. However there has been some speculation that he may actually have been present in Dealey Plaza on that day.

Ed Nesbitt

When Orris, Born, and Lundquist set up U.S. Sonics, they brought in a prominent Dallas lawyer as Corporate Secretary, Edwin Nesbitt. Nesbitt had a lot of political influence in Dallas and connections with many very dedicated, powerful friends. He had previously served as a Dallas County assistant district attorney. He was well-liked and Orris' personal lawyer, very close friend, and confidante.

Ed was a member of the Dallas Athletic Club; he played racquetball and handball religiously. (Jack Ruby also was a member of the Club.) He was referred to as 'The Judge' by friends because of his close relationships with the Dallas judges and his ability to control them and their legal decisions. So, he would help take care of local Dallas and Texas problems involved in the assassination.

Ed would become the *de facto* president of U.S. Sonics after the assassination and would continue in this role until its closure in 1965.

David McCord

Ed Nesbitt's often business associate, legal partner, and close friend was a man named David McCord, equally connected with the Dallas court system and police as well as the Mafia. So, he was instrumental in working with Nesbitt to help control the Dallas political, judicial, and law enforcement scene.

Frequently the two, Ed and Dave, would visit U.S. Sonics together and, sometimes, I would have lunch with all of them and hear them discuss the assassination.

McCord was an interesting handsome man with a good personality, wit, and charm. He and Orris were close friends and Orris had used him as a lawyer several times. He was also a close, trusted friend of General Born.

I knew he was involved with the Mafia because I heard his opinion being sought about sought about Joseph Civello, Carlos Marcello, Santo Trafficante, and Sam Giancana. He knew Jack Ruby well and associated with a number of his partners in organized criminal activity, men such as the Fox brothers, mysterious Mafia figures expelled from Cuba.

He and Orris remained close for many years after the assassination.

Charles Lyon

Charlie Lyon was a buyer at Ling-Temco-Vaught (LTV), an aerospace company that built military aircraft, with a large assembly plant in Grand Prairie. A business associate, Orris would pay him illegally to give him and the companies he was representing, contracts for aircraft parts, a common practice. He was also one of Orris' closest deer-hunting partners and co-host of the Colorado hunting parties. Orris took me to LTV to meet him in December, 1962.

Charles was a very important player in the assassination. My father trusted him completely and chose him as the number two shooter. He was someone Orris could fully depend on, with no doubt that he would do his job well on the day of the assassination.

Charlie had motivation to participate in the plot, beside his political views and friendship with Orris,. He had grown up on a farm outside of Waxahachie, twenty miles southwest of Dallas. After going to college, he thought he was finished with farming and headed for the bright lights of Dallas. But, after getting married and two beautiful children, he and his wife became disenchanted with city life, deciding that farming was in their blood after all and decided to try to buy a farm back in Waxahachie. The only problem was that property values of farms were escalating faster than they could afford; it seemed impossible for this hard-working couple to ever be able to afford their dream.

Of all the men involved in the Kennedy assassination, I knew Charlie better than any of the others, with the exception of Norris Lawrence. The two men were both trusted friends, perhaps more like surrogates at times for my father. At any rate, I knew he would trust them with me in any situation.

It was difficult not to like him, a man usually pretty serious, but one who could also be very friendly and down-to-earth with an amusing sense of humor. I hunted with him many times between 1958 and1968, so personally knew his capability with a rifle; he was an exceptional marksman.

He was a man who demanded respect, but I must admit that for some reason I lost some of that respect after the assassination because

I expected something more of him than to be like Orris. It felt like he had fallen a long way from the tree when he joined Orris and the band of assassins.

Jeffrey Miller

Jeff Miller was always something of a mystery to me, but then my father had many mysterious men and women in his life. He was a friend of Ed Nesbit, with an office in the same building, the Kirby Building in Dallas. I would see him quite often with my father from 1958 until his death several years later, He was referred to as my Godfather, but I never understand clearly how this happened or exactly what this actually meant. I never really liked him or honestly, appreciated anything about him. To me, he had a superficial character, but I could have been wrong and just prejudiced against him for personal reasons.

He married a wealthy woman, a very close friend of Lyndon Johnson and Lady Bird. Her father was from an old Texas family with strong political ties to Johnson and the Democratic Party; he interacted with Lyndon on a regular basis, advising him on Texas politics and greatly helping him, using his own money and influence. So, his daughter hated the Kennedys because they were so cruel to Lyndon and Texas in general. She was a woman from the old Texas establishment and aristocracy who felt they were above and beyond the United States and the Yankee ultra-liberals.

Jeff was a half-blooded American Indian. At five foot eleven and a little heavy, about two hundred-ten pounds, he carried his weight well and never would have been considered fat. He had graying, kinky, short hair that had been black. He was a handsome, unusual looking man in a rugged way, with a somewhat dark complexion. And very intelligent, talented, poised, and educated, having received a degree from Dartmouth in Mining Engineering. Sophisticated and well-read.

He just liked to play, and he was a player, somewhat flashy, but tastefully so. His was a style acceptable in Dallas in his circles. He drove a very expensive Cadillac Eldorado convertible. Wore a large diamond ring of several karats. Dressed impeccably in clothes bought at Neiman Marcus.

Before the Kennedy assassination, he mainly stayed with mining investments and interests. Along with his wife's money, which padded his pockets well, he was never left without money. After, he became something of an entrepreneur in areas besides mining.

Orris had met Jeff through Nesbitt, and had many things in common with him; mining and oil, investing in Mexico and South America, Mafia associations, and partying wherever they were. Both had Hollywood connections, including Jewish players and many starlets. He introduced Orris to Zsa Zsa and Eva Gabor and their Hollywood group. Orris likewise introduced him to his own Hollywood friends.

Jeff played a very strong role in the assassination, in Dallas and wherever else needed. He was basically Orris' right-hand man in the planning and organizing. I saw him constantly during this time at U.S. Sonics and his and Ed Nesbitt's offices.

He was eventually killed by Dallas Mafia people in 1982, after taking advantage of them, scamming money from them. Jeff had done this periodically, finding it amusing. My father had warned him that they would finally have enough and kill him. Jeff obviously felt otherwise and paid with his life for screwing them one too many times.

Searcy Dobkins

When I was seven, Orris began taking me to meet Searcy Dobkins. Although he was referred to as my 'uncle,' to me he was strange and mysterious. All I knew about him was that he was a rancher and I had access to his ranch whenever I wished, a haven where I enjoyed fishing in ponds stocked with bass. The ranch was several thousand acres between Dallas and Fort Worth, north of the turnpike, one of the most valuable pieces of property in the area, and which

But more important, he was a successful banker, part owner and board member of the First National Bank of Euless. He had developed the private club in the Western Hills Inn which Orris utilized. That was also where Lundquist would stay during his frequent trips to Texas. And a place where I and my siblings would swim and play, while the two men talked.

Dobkins and my father had a very close and unusual relationship, unusually close and secretive. Although it was obvious Orris fully trusted and confided in him about everything important business-wise, I always felt that there was some hidden topic they weren't prepared to share in front of me. This despite my father sharing nearly everything assassination related with me elsewhere.

I did know however, he had some involvement in the assassination planning because I saw him at U.S. Sonics several times in early 1963.

9

THE MAFIA AND ITS ROLE

The Mafia

The CIA and primarily through it, members of the 'Military Industrial Complex,' have carried on a secret and extensive relationship with the Mafia since the CIA's inception; both the American-Italian and the World Italian Mafia organizations. The American public knows little about this and, even if it did, would have trouble understanding the complex interaction between these two very secret organizations. One such example was the Agency's utilizing Mafia figures in the attempt to remove Castro, something that Kennedy was aware of when he took office.

Ultimately, the CIA and the Mafia set up a hugely profitable secret organization to launder billions of dollars through a number of semi-legitimate corporations, profiting from a multitude of government contracts.

111

Both, the Mafia in Italy and that in American would eventually become involved in the Kennedy plot. The effects of his assassination would cross international boundaries, influencing markets, political relations, defense positions, economics, and even social relations with allies and enemies alike. The world Mafia organization could help smooth this impact.

During the Eisenhower administration, prosecution of key Mafia figures was basically non-existent. To a large degree, the Mafia had cleaned itself up so to most Americans, it was something of an accepted evil. J. Edgar Hoover and his FBI had turned a blind eye and wanted to continue this approach, because it actually was in his own best interest. So, now he strongly disagreed with Robert Kennedy's tactics against it. And so, now the Mafia had a strong relationship with both CIA and FBI.

In early 1962, Orris had been talking for several months with a number of his white-collar Mafia contacts who were becoming nervous about the public scathing that Attorney General Robert Kennedy was giving it. With the apparent blessing of the President, he was holding Justice Dept. investigative committee hearings resulting in a number of warrants to prosecute mid-level and even some high-level, Mafia figures. If this continued, there could be irrevocable damage done to the Mafia in America, which in turn would greatly influence the World organization.

The Kennedys were damaging the hard-earned progress made in the public's perception of the Mafia. What was puzzling was the motive for all this, because the Kennedy family had a long history of interacting with the Mafia. In fact, patriarch Joe had originally made the seed money that enabled him to become very wealthy by creating an immoral alliance with it during Prohibition, importing Canadian liquor and distributing it with their help.

And Joe had used his relationship with the Mafia to purportedly help his son get elected in an election deemed very close. The larger states were spread evenly between the two parties, so the outcomes in a few of the smaller electoral states could make the difference. Two of the states Joe was focusing on were West Virginia in the Democrat primary and Illinois in the actual election; in the end, these two states made the difference.

So, why the Kennedys would attack the Mafia, and so extensively, seemed illogical. And then to continue after these hearings had long since shown they were hard on organized crime. After all, this had not been an issue during the election and there had been no recent public outcry.

But importantly, one of the most dangerous things when dealing with Mafia issues, was to use them and then attack them. Vendetta is their law. And certainly, the Kennedys could not be naive about this. Maybe, the attacks were compensation for their father's immoral behavior. But whatever the reason, it would end up coming back on them with a relentless vengeance.

So, if a Mafia-assisted assassination of President Kennedy were successful, not only would the recent persecution of the Mafia end, but it would firmly secure its functioning position. It would gain control of alcohol, illegal drugs, prostitution, gambling, and other vice-oriented operations. Most importantly, it would have the help of the federal government to pass supportive legislation for these ventures, like lotteries and semi-legitimate front companies such as Indian reservation casinos. And even control of professional sports teams themselves.

And the Mafia would be allowed to launder money by setting up semi-legal corporations that manufacture Department of Defense parts and weapon systems. Similar corporations would profit from infrastructure construction projects and everything from school food suppliers to prison systems. This is basically free, giveaway money from the government, as long as the CIA and other entities get a cut of the profits.

But the involvement of the Mafia in the assassination could be something of a double-edged sword. There was potential for it to lose most everything if its involvement were exposed publicly. In fact, the Mafia's possible involvement would be exposed when Jack Ruby, a known Dallas Mafia drug dealer, and pimp, would kill Lee Harvey Oswald.

But the Mafia stood to gain greatly, and in reality, actually had little or nothing to lose. If John Kennedy would have been elected to a second term, he and Attorney General Robert Kennedy would possibly achieve their goal of eliminating both Mafia and CIA. So, its leaders were more than willing to discuss with Orris and his associates, its potential involvement in the assassination.

In the end, the Mafia's participation would extend much further than just one local Dallas Mafia pimp and drug dealer. It would be used for most of the 'hits' after the assassination. At least six hundred people would be murdered in order to hide the truth of who actually assassinated the president. Anyone, who knew too much and was expendable.

As the planning for the assassination progressed and I became aware of the Mafia's involvement, I became more and more bothered, knowing how violent these people could be. I had innately never liked anything about them, had never bought into the somewhat romantic image that has sometimes been promulgated. I felt they were a scourge on American society that should be eradicated; so, my own thinking was really akin to the Kennedys'.

Orris Emmett Bell Himself

Orris himself had a long-standing relationship with the Mafia, dating back to his time in Italy during World War II. Then, in Southern California in the 1950s, there had been the Mafia association involving gambling at the horse racetracks. And his Mafia friends, associated with Hollywood, who provided him with young starlets for the buyers in the aerospace-defense industry.

He was not a Mafia member before the assassination, despite his obvious connections to it which I witnessed. But after, I would many times see men bow to him in public, even at very good restaurants and bars. Some would actually try to kiss his hand; he would always pull it away and look at them as though they should never attempt this in public. I never asked him, but I seriously wondered just how powerful he was with the national Mafia or that in Italy, for that matter. I was worried because one of the rationales for bringing the Mafia into the assassination was to take any heat off the real players in the inevitable investigation. But his easily discovered association with the Mafia could be problematic.

However, Orris' easy relationship with the Mafia was just one of the reasons he would be designated as the leader in the assassination planning.

Johnny Roselli

Johnny Roselli, a primary Mafia figure, was the main go-between for it and the CIA. Roselli and Orris were best of friends, going back to the L.A. days when he was the man supplying Orris with those promising Hollywood starlets for the businessmen he was entertaining. The film industry was dominated at the time by the Mafia. He would also introduce Orris to many heads of the Mafia from around the country.

The two would respect their individual and even different positions in the plot to kill the president. And their friendship would continue for a long time afterward.

Important now was that Roselli had always played an unusual role among the various American Mafia factions. He, if anyone, could work between the different regional groups with their history of mutual distrust, to bring them together for the betterment of the entire Mafia organization. Therefore, he was able to convince them it was in their own interest to be involved in the Kennedy assassination, rather than die at the hands of the Kennedys.

So, beginning in March of 1963, when the Italian American Mafia began its involvement in the assassination planning, his name was often spoken around U.S. Sonics. I saw him there and elsewhere on at least six occasions, including once when Orris and I went to lunch with him and the two of them discussed the assassination. I also frequently heard Orris on the phone with him.

He was involved all through the planning because the CIA had a good and trusting relationship with him. So, he was present at Dallas meetings with the CIA men on a few occasions, the only Mafia individual so allowed.

Johnny Roselli would be assassinated in 1975 by the CIA after being called to testify before the Church Committee, the House Select Committee on Assassinations. because he had become too much of a risk to the security of the true assassination players. There was a concern that he might break and talk about his role and others'.

His body was found floating in an oil drum in the Miami Bay. He had been stabbed and strangled; legs and arms cut off; and stuffed still breathing, into the drum along with his severed legs and arms.

The Dade County Coroner's office reported the cause of death was suffocation. He had 'suffocated' in the oil drum, staring in the dark at his severed legs and arms. Killing him in this Mafia gang style sent a strong message to all others who knew too much. Talk and you will die, and in a very bad way.

Carlos Marcello

Carlos Marcello was one of the most prolific and powerful Mafia figures in the American Mafia and had a personal vendetta against the Kennedy brothers, John and Robert, hating them passionately and more than willing to do whatever he could to help with an assassination. In 1962, Attorney General Robert Kennedy had him charged with fraud for using a false birth certificate stating Guatemala as his home of origin, whereas he had actually been born in Tunis, Tunisia. The A.G. then ordered the FBI deport him to Guatemala.

Of course, he simply returned to the U.S. with the help of his lawyers, but with a promise to get even one way or another. (Interestingly, he would be acquitted on the false birth certificate charge in November 1963.) On his return, he resumed his position as head of the New Orleans Mafia, whose district actually included East Texas and Dallas, meaning that he issued orders to the Dallas Mafia, including Jack Ruby.

I began hearing his name at U.S. Sonics in March and more and more frequently as the months progressed. Also sitting in his office, I overheard my father's phone conversation with him, learning his association with the Mafia. And surmising from Orris' reactions, that he was considered something of a "nut," a "hot head."

During the summer, their interaction concerning the assassination would be extensive, but mostly about Oswald then in New Orleans, even though Marcello wasn't Oswald's primary handler there. Orris spent a considerable amount of time in New Orleans then, and a lot of this was devoted to interaction with Marcello.

Santo Trafficante

Trafficante, Florida Mafia boss, lived in Tampa Bay, but would often travel to Miami to meet with Orris in the summer of 1963. Miami was one of two acceptable alternative cities being considered as the site for the assassination, if Dallas should fall through as first choice. Upon occasion, Orris also traveled to Tampa Bay to meet him in his hometown.

I began to hear his name at U.S. Sonics, in conjunction with Marcello's in April, and for a while the focus moved from Marcello to Trafficante, and then back again as the summer wore on. Trafficante also came to Dallas and U.S. Sonics, where I saw him before having lunch with him and my father, listening to them talk about the upcoming assassination.

Sam Giancana

Sam 'MoMo' Giancana was a major figure in the Chicago Mafia in 1962-63. I would meet him with my father at the end of the summer. This was a high point of the assassination planning for me because I knew of his prominence in the Mafia. I knew what he looked like before meeting him because I had seen him on television several times as well as his photograph in the newspapers. I had read a lot about him and was in a way fascinated by this man who could function somewhat openly as a Mafioso, how he played his role.

He seemed more cautious than the other Mafia figures I met, but very willing to listen to the plans to assassinate President Kennedy. And in the end, he joined fully in this effort.

Later, in the early 1970s, he would be forced to leave the country, going to Mexico City. The FBI would subsequently bring him back in 1975 to testify before the House Committee on Assassinations, as it was investigating the President Kennedy and other political assassinations, reviewing new information.

He was to be a main witness, so it was eager to question him. But he would be murdered the night before he was to testify, shot in the back of the head and then several times around the mouth, an obvious message to anyone considering telling the truth. He had apparently agreed to do just that.

Joseph Civello

The first of the Mafia characters to appear on the scene in Dallas, I first met Civello at U.S. Sonics in late January 1963, where he was active in the assassination planning. He was a handsome man and seemed very sophisticated. In fact, I didn't know he was associated with the Mafia or that was the head of it in Dallas, although answering to Marcello. So, when I first met him, I thought he was in the aerospace industry.

In the beginning, he seemed very active at U.S. Sonics for a little longer than a month, then faded as the higher Mafia figures began to play an active role.

He didn't disappear altogether, as many men seemed to in the very beginning of the planning. It was just that his presence wasn't as often, and his name wasn't floated around as much as time passed. But he was there until the end in November 1963, just in and out, but never gone forever. I actually went to his house once.

That period between December 1962 through February 1963. That was the busiest time at U.S. Sonics, as far as the number of bodies present, especially December 1962; when, at times, it even seemed crowded at U.S. Sonics. I would see many men once during December and not know who they were and never see them again.

Jack Ruby

Jack Ruby played multiple roles in the assassination planning from shortly after the beginning, right up until he killed Lee Oswald. But, as with most of the assassination planning, there were layers and compartmentalization; a 'need to know' strategy, so only a few knew the whole plan. And Ruby was not one of the few. And to my knowledge, he never came to U.S. Sonics.

I first met him in January 1963. He was always lurking in some dark hidden corner and his name was as frequently heard at U.S. Sonics as was General Born's . His eventual act is well-known; the real reason he killed Lee Harvey Oswald has been speculated on many times. In the beginning, Ruby himself stated he killed Oswald for Jacqueline Kennedy, so she would not have to suffer through what would be a lengthy, heart-breaking trial of Oswald.

That would be a strange alteration in character for this despicable man, who sold heroin in bulk to Dallas Police Officers, who would then distribute it to multiple mid-level dealers. A man who ran a string of whores for years and was rumored to have the best stable in Dallas; it made no difference whether you wanted a ten or twenty-year-old girl, he had them. He provided them with heroin and amphetamine. A man with no morals and no ethics, like most Mafia individuals. Why would he care so much for Jacqueline Kennedy's feelings? He wouldn't and didn't. He just needed a cover and that was the ridiculous cover he came up with; quite a creative guy.

Ruby killed Lee Oswald for one reason and one reason alone, he was ordered to do so by Sam Giancana, which meant that he had no choice. It was that simple; Ruby knew that if he did not follow this order, he was simply a dead man himself. This had been planned before the assassination; an alternative if Oswald had not already been killed.

Most of the men I met with my father had some sophistication, came across as normal with normal families. But there were also men like Ruby. I could immediately tell the difference.

10

OTHER PROMINENT FIGURES

J. Edgar Hoover

J. Edgar Hoover would visit the El Charro Resort and spend time at Del Mar Race Track several times a year, with Clint Murchison and his ultra conservative friends. Hoover was a race-horse lover and regular gambler at a number of tracks around the country. Whenever he came to Southern California, he would bring his lover and second-in-command at the FBI, Clyde Tolson. He felt free to express his open feelings toward Tolson there, without concern for his public image.

This brought fellow racetrack enthusiasts, Orris, Lundquist, Born, LeMay, Murchison, and Richardson together with him on a semi-regular basis from 1955. Both these hugely powerful men, Hoover and Tolson, hated President Kennedy and the liberal views he stood for. Perhaps, even more than they hated communism. They would come to interact directly with the Dallas FBI men under them to aid the assassins in any way possible, both, prior to the assassination and after.

George DeMohrenschildt

George de Mohrenschildt's surname was originally von Mohrenschildt. He had had several careers early in life, and migrated to the U.S. from Poland in 1938. Because the British informed the U.S. government their suspicion he was working for German intelligence, he had been disqualified from joining the OSS in 1941. But, apparently after 1947, he developed several CIA connections, including J. Walton Moore. He worked for Clint Murchison as a petroleum geologist and belonging to the Petroleum Club, apparently counted among his good friends oil barons, Murchison, H.L. Hunt, and Sid Richardson.

I first started hearing his name at U.S. Sonics in May 1962 and always had problems pronouncing it. I had lunch with him and Orris in that July. After this, he was somewhat of a regular at U.S. Sonics for the next several months. I regularly listened to my father talk to him on the phone until he eventually left Texas for Haiti in 1963.

From our first meeting, he gave me the impression of a strange person, who felt he was some sort of royalty and deserved to be treated as such. He paid no attention to me, as though I wasn't even there; just fine with me because I didn't like him and didn't hesitate to let him know as much. I thought he was ridiculous.

Because of his Russian heritage, his connections with Texas oilmen, including George H. W. Bush, and his then long-standing relationship with the CIA, he was brought in by CIA agent J. Walter Moore to be Lee Oswald's first 'Handler' in Fort Worth/Dallas. Moore had previously introduced the Oswalds to Ruth and Michael Paine.

My father assumed this role of 'handler' in early December 1962, after De Mohrenschildt's relationship with Oswald became a bit strained. Lee was jealous of the attention the local Russian-speaking community was lavishing on Marina and it had been DeMohrenschildt who had introduced her to this group and kept it going with lavish dinners in her honor and gifts that Lee couldn't have afforded. After the handover to Orris, DeMohrenschildt stayed involved with the Oswalds for several months, mainly to deal with Marina, until he left the Dallas area shortly after Oswald botched an assassination attempt on a General Walker.

Interestingly, he and I would share the same psychiatrist in Dallas in 1977 before DeMohrenschildt committed suicide, knowing he was about to be called to testify before the House Select Committee on Assassinations. This Dallas psychiatrist strangely disappeared from Dallas immediately following the xfsuicide. It was later discovered that this psychiatrist had falsified his own records when he applied for a license to practice psychiatry in Texas.

Michael and Ruth Paine

In early September 1962, my father took me to Bell Aerospace, a subsidiary of Bell Helicopter in Fort Worth, where he had a number of associates. On the drive over, he explained whom we were going to have lunch with Michael Paine, an old friend, an aerospace engineer with. When we arrived, he told me to wait in the car while he went in to get him, it wouldn't be very long. But it turned out to be about thirty minutes.

Physically, Paine was non-descript. And at the nearby restaurant, he was unassuming, a little shy, and quiet, but interesting. He had a strong interest in the John Birch Society and had attended meetings of that right wing, ultra-conservative organization. During their conversation, I heard my father mention John Kennedy, Lee Oswald, and DeMohrenschildt several times.

Apparently, Orris was really interested in Paine's wife, Ruth, and for several reasons. She spoke Russian, was a 'Quaker' and was very conservative as well. And she had connections to the CIA, through her father and sister. At the end of our lunch, arrangements were made for my mother, Ruth, Michael, and Orris to have dinner together Friday night at the 'Farmers Daughter', a Five Star, formal Fort Worth restaurant. Obviously, this was well before General Born would give his infamous speech in November and clearly meant that they, the assassins of President Kennedy, were doing the preemptive work, well before the final decision would be made.

Even though I wouldn't meet Ruth until 1963, my parents and my father's co-conspirators mentioned her several times in connection with a Marina and Lee Oswald, names I had not heard before. Before I met Ruth, I formed the impression that she was an unusual, interesting woman, particularly from my mother. Over time, she would have several pivotal roles in the assassination plot, but like most of the participants, her knowledge was limited to a 'need to know' approach.

My father would repeatedly praise her after the assassination and especially after its investigation. Quaker Ruth Paine was perfect for the cover-up role. I believe she was the person who would spend the most time in the 'hot seat' before the Warren Commission. Testifying along with Michael, she was her slightly nervous, slightly confused, perfectly articulate, deceptive self. And did an amazing job of keeping her cool, while lying so convincingly. Orris described her as fabulous to be able to do all this, and under such immense pressure.

He continued a close relationship with her for many years and continued to have nothing but good things to say about her and her

Quaker religion. So devoted to the effort to kill President Kennedy and always be trusted to do her part. Of note, Richard Nixon was also a Quaker.

I for one, never bought into the confused innocence that was sold to the public. The poor lost, good Quaker just trying to do good for Marina. I actually wondered if Orris wasn't having an affair with her. He stayed in contact with her for years after, always referring to her as an 'amazing woman', even though she wasn't hardly as attractive as most of his women. With her, I don't think this would have mattered to him.

The Fort Worth Petroleum Club

Orris, Lundquist, and Jeff Miller, all had a strong interest in the oil industry and interacted on a regular basis with men involved in it. Many were friends. And all of the Dallas/Fort Worth influential assassination players, with the exception of the Mafia men, belonged to the Fort Worth Petroleum Club. If there were any one organization the Texas players could be tied to, it was this club. Orris Bell, Jeff Miller, Ed Nesbit, Clint Murchison, Clint Murchison Jr., Searcy Dobkins, Michael Paine, De Mohrenschildt, Dave McCord, H. L. Hunt. Many others were members. Even George H. W. Bush.

11

OTHER DYNAMICS

The Role of Religion; Abraham Vereide

In the days before John Kennedy's fateful 1963 Dallas trip, thousands of fliers were distributed in downtown Dallas, depicting him in a mugshot-type photo, headlined, "Wanted for Treason." Among the charges were "He has consistently appointed Anti-Christians to Federal office…Upholds the Supreme Court in its Anti-Christian rulings."

Such a slander was very much in line with a 'Christian' group founded in Seattle in the mid-1930s by Abraham Vereide, Abram. Known as 'The Family', the group was designed primarily to influence America's business, political, and governmental leaders. It operated primarily in secret, initially adhering with biblical admonitions against public displays of their 'good works.'

Originally from Lutheran Norway, Abram had spent two years at a Methodist seminary in the U.S. During the 1920s, he operated Goodwill

Industries in Seattle, organizing nearly fifty thousand housewives to collect used goods for distribution to the needy. Yet, despite performing this charitable work, his underlying belief was that those who sought assistance from Goodwill were unwilling to work for their own success, observing that, *"Promiscuous charity pauperizes."*

Regardless, this charitable work gained him positive notoriety and after moving to Boston, then-New York governor Franklin Roosevelt asked him to organize relief there. This prompted him to resign from Goodwill in 1934, and later embark on a new career, a ministry. On his return to the West Coast, he encountered explosive labor strife, he 'ministered' to businessmen, not the strikers, conducting regular prayer meetings and then prayer breakfasts called 'City Chapel.'

A critical concept of Vereide's philosophy was that of 'public justice'; God could pardon people of their sins without punishment, and still maintain a semblance of divine justice. Another major tenet was his nuancing the word, 'meek' to mean "humible," implying "successful" so the New Testament declaration came to mean, the strong shall be the inheritors of the world. Justifying his true philosophy that it was 'the strong' he intended to minister to.

It was 'the strong' that he saw in the history of the early White American settlers; a merging of Christianity and the country's business community, irrespective of the indigenous or the use of slaves. Similar to the rejection of non-whites understood within the concept of Manifest Destiny.

And as an admirer of those in power, Vereide made no secret of his regard for Hitler, who was modeling his 'lebensraum' after 'Manifest Destiny' to master contiguous territories to promote racial unity. This obviously required identifying a group, race, or peoples of a contrary faith, e.g., the Jews. It seemed to matter little to Abram what the international consequences were of Nazi fascism, brutally imposed upon those it conquered as well as Germany's own populace. Or the massive loss of life during World War II. All that mattered was Vereide's drive to influence the religious, business, and political power elite, to be anti-union, and anti-socialist.

So, a prime characteristic of his group was an evident fascination with fascism and a fascist version of 'America First', as a counter to Communism, and similar to the regimes in Italy and Germany. And similar to the latter, the enemy also included Jews. And like Hitler, Vereide also embraced many beliefs of German philosopher, Friedrich Nietzsche.

In 1944, recognizing that Germany was on the verge of defeat, he founded the International Christian Leadership (ICL), apparently with the goal of it being sufficiently influential in Europe to combat Communism once hostilities ended. And in 1946, the U.S. State Dept. sent him to post-war Europe with a letter of introduction, to contact Nazi war criminals and determine the 'good' ones willing to plead allegiance to the United States.

Abram conducted this work in Berlin in secret, viewing secrecy as success, necessary for diplomatically sensitive political missions. To this end he adopted a 'cell-like' compartmentalizing structure. Coincidentally, he was in Germany at the same time as former OSS officer Allen Dulles, was conducting his similar 'Operation Paper Clip.'

By now, he had organized his breakfasts in major areas such as San Francisco, Los Angeles, Chicago, St. Louis, New York, Philadelphia, several Florida cities, and Washington D.C. They became 'rites of passage' for power elites, including politicians and businessmen around the country. During the early 1940s, he had already, developed strong political connections in both Houses of Congress and in 1945, held his first joint Senate-House prayer-breakfast, creating a new elite power group. Referred to as "The Family," it would come to include government officials, corporate executives, heads of various religious and humanitarian organizations, as well as high-ranking politicians from across the world.

A number of U.S. Senators and Representatives publicly admitted to working with this group in passing or influencing various pieces of legislation. It was described as one of the premier politically, well-connected, and secretly funded organizations in the country.

However, what the organization accomplished out of public view may be far more consequential. For example, in the early 1950s Abram and Billy Graham were seen standing 'shoulder to shoulder' with a Kenneth M. Crosby. This former FBI agent in Latin America during World War II, was now a stockbroker representing American business interests in Havana and apparently, a CIA asset. But Crosby established prayer cells for Abram of which he routinely briefed the CIA, including Dulles. One prayer-cell included American embassy personnel, representatives of American banks, and the United Fruit Company, a Rockefeller business.

In conclusion, Vereide's viewed those in power as the inheritors of God's preordination and His permission for establishing and maintaining control over the people. And according to Doug Coe, who headed up the group upon Vereide's death, this redefining of biblical imperatives was, and remains, an important aspect of power in America.

Billy Graham

America's most famous evangelist, Billy Graham, was crucial to The Family's goals and operations and the creation of a new order of

Christianity. Sid Richardson had befriended him, not because of his religion, but because both held a common faith in free enterprise. Richardson, along with Clint Murchison and H.L. Hunt, became patrons, offering whenever help was needed. Importantly, Richardson introduced him to a number of Texas political and business leaders, including Lyndon Johnson and John Connally, and eventually Dwight Eisenhower, to help recruit him to run for president, as a Republican.

Graham had become a national icon in 1949, when he held a number of evangelistic meetings in Los Angeles. William Randolph Hearst, America's most powerful newspaper mogul, viewed him as a potential political star after attending one of these in disguise. Hearst instructed his underlings to shower the preacher with media coverage, creating a celebrity-like status for him and even more media exposure.

Early in 1951, Abram Vereide helped further Graham's growing popularity within the Christian community by having some of The Family's representatives coach him in the various mannerisms and niceties of educated society, which then armed Billy for whatever his future held, and for the Family. Graham would cloyingly be referred to as 'America's Pastor' when, in fact, he was more the High Priest to the power elite, particularly the oil industry. Graham, himself, termed his alliance with the country's oil barons, as his 'oil period.'

Graham was The Family's point-man in establishing what eventually evolved into the annual National Prayer Breakfast, a highly visible annual event in Washington D.C. In 1953, after he was elected President, Eisenhower, with the help of Graham, agreed to attend Vereide's first Presidential Breakfast at the Washington Franklin Hotel. The event, later renamed the National Prayer Breakfast, has been attended by every President since.

Graham was deeply anti-Semitic, consistent with Christianity's historic struggles with the Jewish faith. Nixon's Watergate tapes revealed Graham saying about the Jews, *"They're the ones putting out the pornographic stuff…"* He further voiced that the Jewish *"stranglehold has got to be broken or the country's going down the drain."* During the meeting, Graham observed that he had many Jewish friends who gathered around him, because he was friendly with Israel, *"But they don't know how I really feel about what they are doing to this country."*

His relationship with John Kennedy did not begin well. On August 18, 1960, he held a 'secret' meeting in Montreux, Switzerland for some twenty-five Protestant leaders, in an effort to stop the Catholic Democrat from becoming president. Dr. Norman Vincent Peal led it and when the media discovered some of the particulars, he bore the brunt of public scorn. The upshot was Kennedy forcefully and directly confronting the anti-Catholic bias by publicly declaring that the Vatican would have no impact upon his presidency, whereupon the issue of Kennedy's Catholicism dissolved.

The two interacted several times. At one point, Kennedy asked him the difference between the evangelist's religion and the Catholic Church. Somewhat evasively, Graham essentially argued that the need to evangelize was prevalent within the tenets of all Christian religions, including Catholicism.

A curious situation arose in November 1963 when Graham sought to meet with Kennedy to warn him that he had a 'foreboding' of tragedy befalling the President during his upcoming Dallas trip. But he was unsuccessful in either meeting or speaking with him. One could speculate as to whether this foreboding may have been because of his close alliance and association with the Texas Oil Barons.

I really don't know how much influence The Family or Graham had on the assassination conspirators, just that their tenets were so similar. And that Graham's home church was in Dallas, because of his association with the oil barons, while his residence was in North Carolina.

The Role of the Occult

Perhaps surprisingly, symbolism and the occult played a key role in the lives of many of the Kennedy assassins, including Orris. And many Mafia, CIA and high government officials are steeped in the occult, and the same beliefs and religious practices. Although the religions overtly practiced may be quite different -- Baptist for Orris and Catholic for the Mafia -- the underlying similarity may be one of the foundations for the close alliance of the CIA and Mafia. Many believe there is power in evil and that worshipping it is sometimes necessary to achieve a positive goal.

In this, there is a striking resemblance to Vereide's philosophy. Of course, the KKK utilizes the occult, what with its Grand Dragons and symbols that have supernatural meaning and powers. And in many ways, there was a strong association with the occult practices of the 'Masons' and its lore. Orris' father was a fifth degree Mason and also deeply involved in the occult.

These men were steeped in secrecy by their very natures and unusual mix of Christianity and the occult. In their strange form of Christianity, they worshipped not only Christ and God, but also the Devil and Evil, essentially equal in power and necessity.

They believed we all have the Devil in us, and to ignore and not exploit this power is itself a weakness, while to admire and utilize it, a virtue. So, it could often be better to ignore the obviously moral, but likely unsuccessful route, in favor of the immoral.

This way of thinking could not be exposed to 'normal Christians'; therefore, they practiced their beliefs in complete secrecy. But they did attend Christian church upon occasion as a camouflage to hide the practice of this occult religion.

These beliefs were family beliefs, not just of the men. For instance, a young lady, I would be involved with much later, the daughter of one of my father's 'group,' was a 'Devil worshipper.' Her parents had no problem with this; it was normal to them. They had even sent her at the age of ten, along with her sister, to a private school in Salem, Massachusetts that taught 'Devil Worshipping' as its religion. I believe a number of other children of CIA-employed parents attended this school.

These men also placed great emphasis on belief systems of the ancient Pharaohs who found power in worshipping evil. Different animals represented powerful gods and assumed certain meanings. Hawks, falcons, snakes, geese, cranes, and many others. For instance, the hawk was considered the most powerful god, Osiris. The snake represented a form of evil. Geese represented good and prosperity. And the eagle and 'birds of prey' were messengers with supernatural powers and also symbols of control and sanctity.

It is interesting that the eagle became an icon of both America and the CIA. And its symbolism is why Orris would have the 'eagle' on his headstone, along with Isaiah 40:31, *"But those, who hope in the Lord, will renew their strength. They will soar on wings like eagles; they will run and not grow weary, they will walk and not be faint."*

Also included by these men, Greek and Roman mythological figures such as the horse, often winged. Some of these figures were complements to those of Christianity. For instance, the four horses of the Apocalypse.

And color has significance; for instance, the four horses of the apocalypse represent four attributes: white for conquest, red for war, black for famine or fear and pale green for death. In fact, the CIA's color is black, fear being something I believe they want to provoke in the American people. Orris would choose a black marker for his headstone.

Finally, I believe that the name 'Orris' is actually derived from 'Osiris, the Egyptian god' represented by the hawk. This name can be found in the southern U.S. states associated with the Masons and their occult. And variations, such as 'Oris', coincidentally the spelling of the name of another man involved in the assassination.

The Role of Racism

The beginnings of U.S. democracy incorporated the idea that majority rule requires inherent protection of minorities and individual rights. Of course, the Constitution was really only referring to white, male landowners. But history from long before also belied that as colonial governments paid fifty British pounds for an adult Indian male's scalp, twenty-five for an adult female's, and twenty for childrens'. And in 1763, the British Army's Commander-in-Chief wrote in praise of using smallpox-infested blankets to "extirpate" the Indian race, which had no immunity to it. Similarly, the Spanish forced native Americans to live on mission land in California, exposing them to malaria.

The subsequent multitude of wars fought between the Europeans and the Natives from the time of the earliest colonial settlements in the seventeenth century until the early twentieth is well documented. But the 1830 Indian Removal Act authorizing relocation from their ancestral homelands resulted by default, in further ethnic cleansing as sixty thousand walked the "Trail of Tears."

But just as egregious was the slavery of Africans. Of course, slavery has existed throughout history; even Native Americans had slaves. But what occurred now was not benign like that which may have existed in Greek and Roman times, but a very brutal one. And while it's true there were African slaves in pre-colonial times, particularly in the Spanish empire portion of what is now the U.S. Southwest and parts of Florida and South Carolina, the English colonies normalized slavery to build a successful capitalism.

Slavery was enforced by the Fugitive Slave Acts. The first signed into law in 1793 by President George Washington, himself a slave owner. And the second in 1850 by President Millard Fillmore who, while opposing slavery, viewed it as an "exiting evil, and signed the law to preserve the Union. After complaints by slave owners about the consistent flow of slaves seeking freedom in northern states, frequently by the "Underground Railroad" created by abolitionists, he vowed to use federal troops to enforce it.

Laws were passed authorizing local governments to seize and return escapees, and imposing penalties for aiding escaping slaves. Thus abetting pervasive slave hunting and culminating in frequent lynching, something that was to last long after Lincoln's "emancipation", even to recent times. It is estimated that more than four thousand were victims, largely ignored by state and federal officials.

Blacks in America were accustomed to the system being utilized to control them. But they were not the only ones to be stigmatized. Mexicans in the Southwest. Immigrants, such as Chinese in California, Irish in Boston, Italians in New York. But of course, those doesn't compare. And discrimination is elsewhere, of different religion, ethnic heritage, and especially those with different sexuality.

So, discrimination and racism in America have a long history. Furthered by America's concept of Manifest Destiny, coined in 1845, which like Vereide rationalized any move warranted if it furthered one's interest. But one must also label the affected people as inferior. Sometimes that is relatively benign, such as the patronizing proselytizing by missionaries or the "evangelicals."

12

THINGS BEGIN TO CHANGE

The End of U.S. Sonics as a
Functioning Business

The Atlas and Titan I ICBM systems were killed by President
Kennedy in 1962, to be replaced with Titan II and Minuteman 1
systems. The new systems were actually a great improvement. The Titan
II used a stable liquid fuel that did not cook off or contaminate the
rocket engines and it wasn't constantly pumped through the engines.
And the Minuteman I used solid fuel. So, there was no need to clean
the engines of either missile.

At the same time, the Joint Chiefs and the CIA did not want
Kennedy to eliminate the original missile systems so abruptly. They
felt this would seriously damage their position in the nuclear missile
race with Russia. After all, these systems were proven and reliable.

Although it would take a full three years to completely phase out these missile systems, the Air Force had sufficient numbers in inventory to last through the down phasing. So it no longer had any need for U.S. Sonics' service.

This meant potential financial disaster for U.S. Sonics, 'cover', but lucrative business. They had not developed a contingency plan because no one would have believed back in 1960 that Kennedy would do this, and against the wishes of the Joint Chiefs and the CIA. In fact, the Air Force had assured them that this contract should run for at least ten years.

They first tried to rally the Air Force and a number of conservative politicians to at least keep part of the Atlas and Titan I programs alive. But, to no avail. Kennedy wanted these programs dead, and he got his way this time.

Fortunately, General Born was able to use his influence to at least take up the slack temporarily by having U.S. Sonics awarded a contract cleaning parts from other Air Force aircraft. This was no way as lucrative as the original contract, and unfortunately was only viable for a year or less before it would be pulled by an Air Force auditor, realizing just what it was, a giveaway to U.S. Sonics. After all, this compensatory work did not need to be cleaned in a 'White Room' under quality-controlled condition; an Air Force maintenance shop had previously cleaned these parts.

This was one more reason for the people at U.S. Sonics to hate President Kennedy. He had unknowingly rung the death-bell for U.S. Sonics as a viable business.

One day after the work had stopped, I was in the shipping room by myself, where I saw a batch of these other rocket engine parts, so unlike the beautiful precision parts they had cleaned before. These were steel braided, flexible hydraulic lines cleaned by dipping their ends in a liquid plastic, leaving them somewhat soft after drying, and sealed against contamination. They were for movable aircraft parts, such as the ailerons and rudders.

I saw that on a number of these cleaned lines, the steel braiding had frayed from rubbing against something while in use, and were in such bad condition, that their use could result in a failure cause an airplane crash. To me, this amounted to gross negligence, and I knew they were about to be shipped.

So, I went to my father to show him the frayed steel braiding. He reassured me that these damaged parts would never be used on a flying aircraft and told me to pick out the worst ones, which I did. He them threw them away in a trash bin. When I returned to U.S. Sonics a few days later, the first thing that I did was go over to 'Receiving' to make sure that there were no more bad parts waiting to be cleaned.

U.S. Sonics had only employed twelve people to run the cleaning process. As long as it had the primary contract with the Air Force, the overhead was very low and the profit very high, once they had absorbed the cost of the 'White Room.' It was never meant to grow into something like U.S. Chem Mill had.

But still, unfortunately this downturn for U.S. Sonics meant a drastic loss of income for Orris. And although he stated that our subsequent move to a house in Meadowbrook in east Fort Worth was because of commuting distance, probably the lessened income was a factor. Of course, the less expensive house also provided a lower level public profile, while he was masterminding the assassination.

During this time, he was still able to finance his luxurious travel expenses through expense accounts he was receiving from other corporations that had kept him on their payroll, in case they suddenly needed his services. And he was also able to support three other households related to his extra-marital affairs: one in Dallas, one in Idaho, and one in L.A. In other words, Orris' own lifestyle didn't change much.

Further, he need only ask, and Clint Murchison and the other financial supporters of the assassination would provide him with whatever funds he might personally need.

U.S. Sonics After General Born's Speech

But U.S. Sonics had further changes. After that fateful Speech directing the cabal to assassinate President Kennedy, there was a seriousness in everyone's attitude. Gone were the open jokes and criticism of the Kennedys. The threats on the President's life that had been so common and spoken so openly for all to hear, were a thing of the past now. They still talked about killing him or about 'Pandora's Box', as they referred to the assassination. Only now this was in hushed tones behind closed doors. The attitude had gone from one of, "We don't care who hears us talk about killing Kennedy," to one of caution and secrecy.

At the same time, it was a hot bed of activity. When I was there, which was three and four times a week, I couldn't believe how busy the place was, despite that the only real function of U. S. Sonics, the Air Force contract, was finished. For now, although the regular employees were still busy continuing the outward signs of business, they had been joined by CIA men, ten or so who had attended Born's speech, plus as many as ten to fifteen others irregularly. Plus three or four secretaries.

Literally, it was so crowded at times, I could barely work my way through a room. And the chatter was loud, very loud.

The non-regulars came and went so fast, I had no chance of finding out who they were and what their position was in all of this. I would see the same man once or twice over a two or three-day period and never see him again. It was a huge 'jigsaw' puzzle for me. I was left alone to put it all together.

It was physically fast, too. Men were moving from office to office and the phones in between, as though it was the New York Stock Exchange and the Market on a bull run. They were upbeat as well, not really excited, but engaging with each other, as though they were really into what they were doing, and they needed it done as fast as possible. I believe that most of these men were CIA, laying out the basic planning for the assassination and trying to cover all possible bases and leave no rock unturned.

My father would answer my questions about something I didn't understand, but I usually had to wait until we were on our way home, and sometimes I couldn't remember exactly what it was I was going to ask.

This activity went on until Christmas, every day of the week, Saturday and Sunday no different; the place was as busy as ever. After Christmas, this frenzied activity fell off steadily and then like a hammer dropping, on January 1, it was all over, U.S. Sonics was quiet, as though it had never happened.

During this time, because of his visible status, Born limited himself to interacting with Orris alone as much as possible. In case of subsequent investigation, the position would be that Born, albeit vice-president of U.S. Sonics was unaware of its role in the assassination. Of course, he continued as an active participant in the planning and assisting wherever needed and visiting several times. And he continued his role as conduit to the Joint Chiefs of Staff and the other instigators. He was a natural leader, something that men felt intuitively, so his presence was always reassuring. As a hardened military man, he carried out his orders, but he certainly could voice alternatives to his superiors.

New Secretaries

One of the first changes that General Born and Orris made was to replace the secretaries with new ones from Air Force Bases in Texas This had actually been done before Born's speech, while he was still active with the Cuban Missile Crisis. They all had top-secret clearances, so they were well-known to Born and Orris, who knew without question, they could be fully trusted, even in this extremely unusual situation of planning the assassination of the President of the United States.

Not yet knowing about the planned assassination, I had wondered why they had replaced their secretaries; it seemed strange. But it was that day I first met one of these ladies, my Snow White that I fell in love with.

These same secretaries stayed at U.S. Sonics through the entire planning of the assassination, a full year. I got to know them quite well. Very few people could have imagined that girls who appeared to be so nice, could have been involved in such a dirty deed as a president's assassination.

Daddy Brings Home Lee Oswald and Family

In June of 1962, the final decision to kill Kennedy hadn't yet been made. But as the CIA does everything, a 'contingent plan' of assassination was being put in place. A first step was to bring back a sleeper agent, Lee Harvey Oswald from Russia to Fort Worth.

It was a cold winter night in early December, one of those North Texas nights when the temperature was about twenty degrees and the humidity above ninety per cent. For some reason, I recall that our Christmas tree was not up yet. I was in the television room with my brothers and sisters, watching the Walt Disney show. My mother came up behind me, put her hand on my shoulder, and motioned for me to come with her, but to be quiet and not arouse the others. She said my father had brought home some people from Russia, who he wanted me to meet. I hadn't heard him come in, but I followed her into the foyer where stood a man and a young woman, holding a baby.

The man was about twenty-eight and the woman twenty-four. They were all bundled up because of the cold outside; the baby was swaddled and all I could see was her face. They looked a little confused, as though they weren't quite sure why they were here or meeting this young boy. My father introduced them, "Bruce, these people are from Russia. This is Lee Oswald, his wife Marina, and their baby, June." I shook hands with Lee, bowed my head to Marina, and bent over to see the baby, who was asleep.

This was the first time I had met someone from Russia, so I was excited and enthralled about this surprise as my father expected. Something I would never forget. For years, I had been fascinated with that country because of my unusual exposure to the Cold War and the missiles and military aircraft associated with it. And I can't count the number of times I had to 'duck and cover' under my school desk, due to those Communists' relentless interest in killing all of us Americans.

Yet, they looked so innocent. It was obvious by the way that my parents interacted with them that they knew them fairly well, and had for some time. And that he had specifically brought them home to meet me. Of course, he had his own deceptive agenda for this. One I never could have imagined in a million years. I thought he was just being nice to me, when in reality, it was another step in his plan for my involvement in the assassination of the President, with or without my consent.

We all went into the living room where I looked closely at Lee and said, enunciating slowly and clearly, "It's very good to meet you. I've always wanted to meet someone from Russia." Of course, I had no idea that he was actually an American who had defected to Russia and was now returning.

I had a million questions for him about Russia and he tried to answer them the best he could, patiently and carefully, but without a Russian accent. He came across as intelligent and articulate, but in an unusual and almost eccentric manner. He would always seem a little confused and lost to me, as though he were somewhere else, in deep thought about something other than what was going on around him.

I asked him why they had come to the United States and he answered, "I reached a conclusion that I did not agree with the political position that Russia was taking toward the United States. and the rest of the world in general. I felt it was time to leave Russia and return."

"What do you mean by return to the United States? Have you been here before now?"

"Yes, I used to live in the United States before I defected to Russia several years ago."

This struck me as rather odd, but I knew I shouldn't pursue it any further. Perhaps, Orris would clarify it later.

Then, I turned to address a question to Marina, but he interpreted because she could not speak any English and acted as though she couldn't understand what we were saying.

After spending about twenty minutes with me peppering Lee with questions, but definitely not long enough as I could have gone on for hours, my father said they had to go. They were on their way to Dallas, where they were now going to be living. They bundled up June and themselves, and prepared to leave with my father. Little did they know that this man, Orris Bell, was planning to destroy their lives; to set Lee up and have him killed in order to place the full blame on him as the one and only assassin in President Kennedy's assassination, about a year later.

I would see Lee briefly in passing at U.S. Sonics two more times in December. And many times in 1963. We would have lengthy conversations about Russia and other subjects. I got to know him quite well and came to like him. I actually thought he was older than he was because his face had more character than someone his age. What I didn't get to know at this time, was his actual history; for instance, he never mentioned being in the Marines.

What I would find out later was a very complex story. Lee Oswald was a perfect candidate for the type of work he would be engaged in with the CIA. He had been through a lot, a rough childhood, and a somewhat crazy and impulsive mother. He was moved around constantly and never had a solid father figure. He joined an extremely conservative youth military organization when quite young, to be very influenced by it. In fact, he was quite racist, and I would hear him telling and laughing at racist jokes.

This led to him joining the Marines, the most conservative and rigorous American military organization, where and when the CIA got their hands on him. Considerable time and effort were spent grooming him for his future role. I know now that the military is the primary recruiting ground for the CIA and many of its covert programs are formed through the military.

They first sent Lee to a school in Japan to learn Russian, which he did in record time. They then instructed him how to get discharged from the Marines with a hardship discharge, and had it approved, so he could be available for the CIA's next task. After a short visit to Fort Worth, he was sent to Finland, so he could defect to Russia as a covert CIA agent.

They weren't certain what they would use him for there; they were just planting one more CIA agent, as they had done many times before. How he would be used would be dictated by how well he would assimilate himself in Russian society and how well and to what degree, the Russian government would accept him as an actual U. S. defector and not another CIA plant.

So, his return to the U.S. was a continuation of his CIA activity with actually no personal feelings about Kennedy, just operating under orders portraying him as a communist 'sell-out.'

The Rifle

Days after the formal ending of the Cuban Missile Crisis and a few before the infamous General Born speech that set everything into action, my father arrived home one evening right after me. It was early for him to be home, and I ran into him just as he was coming through the front door. He told me that there was a new rifle in a box, along with another box, in his car trunk. He handed me his keys, asking me to bring them in. I rushed to do what he asked;. I was always ready to see a new rifle.

And sure enough, when I opened the trunk of his canary yellow Ford Galaxy 500, there were two boxes wrapped in Sears Roebuck paper, from the catalog department. In 1962 Texas, you could purchase a rifle through the catalog without giving your name or any form of I.D. So, if you paid cash, there was no way to trace the purchaser. And there were no security cameras. The serial number on the rifle was registered as a Sears purchase, but no one would know who actually purchased it.

The rifle was in the obvious "Remington" box. The other, about two inches square and fourteen long, had a picture of a riflescope. I carried them into the living room and Orris who could tell my excitement and told me to open them.

First, I opened the rifle box. It was a Semi-Automatic 30.06, different from any other rifle Orris owned. The other contained the scope for the rifle. I was confused about the whole situation because he used 'peep sights' on the Springfield 30.06, bolt-action rifle he used for hunting. Because of his attitude against using a semi-automatic rifle with a scope to hunt deer, I didn't understand why he had bought this rifle; I certainly didn't think he had changed his opinion about this.

Orris could tell that I was puzzled. For a moment, he looked like he wasn't prepared for any questioning. But finally after thinking about it, he said, "This rifle is for my father, your grandfather. He can't see well anymore, and he'll need this scope." This sounded strange because my grandfather was nearly completely blind in both eyes from glaucoma and cataracts. The scop wouldn't help him see a deer any better; it would still be very blurry. Besides, he hadn't hunted in years, and was not in any kind of physical condition to do so, especially in the Colorado mountains in its cold weather.

But I knew better than to question my father about this. So, I was left with the question as to was why he really bought this rifle. And why wasn't he telling me the truth about it.

It would turn out, this was the rifle he would use in the Kennedy assassination, he just didn't want to tell me that he would be one of the actual shooters, although he knew that I would probably figure it out, or find out at some point during the next year of preparation and planning. I did, of course.

The three rifles used in the assassination by the actual three shooters, were identical Remington with scopes. All purchased in the same manner, with cash at Sears Roebuck catalog departments, Orris' in Fort Worth and Charlie's in Arlington. I don't know where the third was purchased.

The success of the actual assassination of President Kenney to a huge degree, would be Orris' responsibility; that is why he chose himself as one of the three actual shooters.

Orris' General Dynamics Gunsmith

About a week after Orris brought the Remington home, he asked me to accompany him on a visit to his gunsmith to check the rifle out. I agreed, still very interested in the real story behind it.

The gunsmith's house was close to Carswell Air Force Base and General Dynamics. I had never met him before, but Orris seemed to know him quite well. He apparently worked for General Dynamics as a machinist. A big, well-spoken, polite man in his late thirties, early forties.

He was standing out in his front yard waiting for us, and greeted Orris as if they were old friends, then shook hands with me. He had a beautiful little house and nice yard with large, broadleaf Maple trees beginning to turn colors, due to the recent cool weather.

After my retrieving the gun and scope for my father, we walked back to his shop in the backyard. Once inside, the gunsmith looked the rifle and scope over closely, and then began explaining what needed to be done to have it work properly. He knew this Remington well, having worked on many. It was a long standing, tried, and proven rifle known for its quality, reliability, and accuracy.

However, his assessment was that the factory spring for the bolt was too weak, so needed replacing. He would also rework the trigger squeeze, so it would be the way Orris liked it, very light. He would mount the scope, a good choice for this rifle. And, finally, he would go out to the rifle range, sight the scope in, and make certain everything was working perfectly. That was it, there wasn't a lot needed to be done. Orris pick it up in a week.

So, a week later, Orris and I returned. Once again, the gunsmith was waiting in the front yard and greeted us the same way as before.

He was a congenial, regular kind of guy, obviously liked his work, took great pride in it, and apparently was excellent.

He explained exactly what he had done. The rifle was sighted in and was working perfectly, no flaws; it should be good for several thousand rounds before anything else would be needed done.

About four days later, Orris and I went out to a place on the Trinity River where we commonly went to shoot. First\, he took some shots, then he let me. It felt like a happy privilege, however not used to a scope, it was strange the first several times. It had a butt-pad to lessen the shock against your shoulder but to an eleven-year-old boy, it still fired very hard. I enjoyed it, though; firing high-powered rifles when you're eleven years old is a lot of fun. Something like riding a wild rollercoaster, with an anticipatory buildup but ending with an ear-deafening bang.

By the middle of December, I knew Orris was definitely going to be one of the three primary shooters in the assassination. And I had also found out that Charles 'Charlie' Lyon was also to be one of the three. From their hunting trips together, they trusted each other immensely; they both knew the other could be completely trusted to do their job in the assassination.

Orris took me back to the gunsmith to have him do the same retrofitting for Charlie Lyon's Remington, identical to Orris' in every respect, same scope, same trigger squeeze, everything. We picked up this second rifle several days later and Orris immediately gave it to Charlie.

This same sequence was repeated with a third rifle, initially for Clarence Bentley, but that plan would later change. When Orris and I picked up this one, it was the last time I saw the gunsmith. I don't know that this gunsmith knew, at that time, what these rifles were to be used for. But, if he didn't at the time, he probably figured it out after the assassination.

But he did seem to know my father quite well and probably something about my father's political convictions. And would have realized that these three rifles were for more than just shooting deer. And it would not be unexpected for him to have been on the inside with the assassins; General Dynamics was rife with radical individuals who hated President Kennedy, probably more so than any other large aerospace company in the area.

I believe Orris taking me with him to the gunsmith's was the beginning of his using me as a cover. He had taken me with him to meet with Walter De Mohrenschildt and Michael Paine earlier in 1962, July and September consecutively, perhaps that was actually the beginning of his using me as a cover.

Oddly, for Christmas, he would give me a Remington 22 semi-automatic rifle also with a scope and another rifle for deer hunting, a 30.30 Winchester. In Orris' mind, as weird as it may appear, giving me this rifle and scope had to have had some relation to the upcoming assassination. As it was, at the time I would only use the Winchester and that only for hunting deer.

After the assassination, the Remington Orris used to shoot President Kennedy disappeared. When I asked him what happened to it, he said he had given it to my grandfather. But when I then asked my grandfather about the rifle, he said he didn't know what I was talking about. However, the rifle appeared in a group photograph of my grandfather with eight CIA conspirators taken a year after the assassination, in the fall of 1964 in Colorado. When I would later see this photograph in 1998, I recognized these men.

I later found out that the rifle was actually being loaned out to many people in the aerospace defense industry, who were using it for hunting and target practice. It became a thing of pride for these ultra-conservative men.

When I finally did see it at my father's house in 1970, it was worn completely out. The bluing on the barrel worn off to expose the steel to rust, the stock marred and rough with all the varnish worn off, the bolt loose in the seating, and the bolt spring worn completely out. I could work the bolt mechanism with my little finger too easily. I could hardly believe this was the same rifle, but it was without question.

We would move to a house very close to several hundred acres of open virgin woods, where I began to use the Remington 22. These woods became a place where I could escape alone and think about the repercussions of the assassination. For the next five years, these beautiful woods were my own personal sanctuary.

Lyndon Johnson's Role in Securing the Date

Johnson was being judged by the Texas political and business elite as having failed in his primary function within JFK's White House, to protect this Texas constituency. While he had entered the 1960 presidential contest with a nearly swaggering self-assurance of the effective political insider he was, little did he realize how his power would be nearly depleted. JFK's move to close tax loopholes, particularly the oil depletion allowance, would cost this business cartel millions.

Compounding all this, was a major scandal involving his political protege, Bobby Baker. LBJ had failed so dramatically, Texas was deemed lost for the Democrats in the upcoming election. Furthermore, it was known that Johnson wasn't to be on the re-election ticket in 1964.

Of course, Dulles was well aware of these obvious reasons for Johnson to wish the President harm, and gain the lost presidency for himself. But the primary price would be catering to the Military Industrial Complex by continuing the Vietnam War, despite Kennedy's memo establishing its end. He would also be under the influence of the CIA, and have to follow the advice of J. Edgar Hoover to stop Robert Kennedy's efforts to eradicate the Mafia. So, Dulles was able to bring Johnson into the plan.

Fortunately, he wouldn't be impeded from his forward-looking civil rights and socialist-like actions such as Medicare. Maybe these would be his way of compensating for his participation and forced acceptance of the radical right's influence.

An interesting situation was that because of her relationship with them, Jeff Miller's wife became the initial contact between the Johnsons and the Dallas planners. In January of 1963 or perhaps earlier, I had heard Orris specifically talk about her visiting with Lyndon and passing information concerning the assassination to him. She also involved Lady Bird, who hated Jackie Kennedy. But after she made several trips to the Johnsons' ranch in January and February, Orris and the Dallas group moved to a more direct form of communication, using Clint Murchison Jr.

So, Johnson had full knowledge of the planned assassination and agreed with it. And, in fact, he would be instrumental in getting the President to come to Texas in the fall of 1963 and on to Dallas, lobbying Kennedy in late 1962 to begin consideration of such a trip. And as early as December 1962, the group at U.S. Sonics seemed to be fairly confident they would be able to get Kennedy to Dallas in the fall, utilizing Johnson's influence.

The tactic was for Johnson to tell Kennedy they couldn't win the up-coming presidential election if they didn't go to Texas and campaign together. Texas support was wavering badly, so Kennedy must show his face there and put down the growing allegations he was a coward and a Communist. And this had to happen as soon as possible to start the momentum going.

However, Kennedy was receiving strong advice from his staff to not go to Texas at all, and if he did, to not even consider going to Dallas because of the open threats there against his life; no matter what Johnson said about the people of Dallas seeing him as a coward if he didn't.

But the planners weren't that concerned about this advice from his staff, given the pressure exerted by Johnson and because a bypass of Dallas would definitely mark him as a coward. They were convinced that Kennedy would understand Johnson's simple basic philosophy and come to Texas in the fall of 1963.

And they were right. Kennedy was persuaded by Johnson's political savvy and agreed to go. He met with Johnson and Texas Governor, John Connally on June 5 at the Cortez Hotel in El Paso; specifically to discuss a future visit to Texas. At this meeting, the three agreed it would be in late November. The original plan called for a quick one-day visit to Dallas, Fort Worth, San Antonio, and finally, Houston. And so resolved the final hurdle for the planners.

In September, there would be even better news. The President decided to extend the visit to Texas to two days, November 21 and 22, the latter being when he would be in Dallas. And, on October 4, a decision was made to allow Connally to plan the actual events that the president would attend.

Lee at U.S. Sonics

It was in December when I first saw Lee Oswald at U.S. Sonics, and I wondered why he was there because I knew they weren't hiring anyone. But maybe, he would work with Norris on the parts they were now acting as if they were cleaning. I didn't get a chance to talk with him then, even though I wanted to continue our conversation about Russia. He had come in without my seeing him and had gone back to my father's office to briefly talk. I only caught him when he was leaving and all I got to say was, "Hello, Lee," before he was out the front door and gone.

I didn't know he was going to be involved in the assassination, or that Orris was now acting as his handler, his go-between with the CIA, after deMohrenschildt had left He was clearly a willing participant in whatever role he was to play. Of course, he did not agree to act as a 'Patsy' or to give his life for the cause.

Oswald needed a job in order to show an income, that he money to pay his bills, buy his rifle, handgun, and scope, as well as cover gunsmith costs. But it would have to be tight, and had to appear there was no outside financial help. That would have implied a conspiracy; this was to appear a one-man job.

I believe Orris initially instructed him to apply for jobs close by on Industrial Blvd. I remember seeing him come and go for a few days, wondering why he was walking and where he was headed; I later learned he didn't know how to drive. Eventually, Orris and Born arranged for him to be hired by Jaggars-Chiles-Stovall, a map-making firm doing a great deal of military work and a little further away on Industrial Blvd. It is curious that no one has questioned why he would take a job near minimum wage, and so far from his home.

How complicit this firm was in the assassination, I don't know. If they weren't involved, my father and U.S. Sonics would have come up in the FBI interrogation of the owners, after the assassination and during the Warren Commission report. These men testified, but the fact that Orris frequently picked Oswald up there was never revealed to the FBI.

13

JANUARY 1963

U.S. Sonics in January 1963

So, by January things at U.S. Sonics calmed completely down. Everyone working on the Air Force contract, except Norris Lawrence, had been laid off. But that period, December through February was the busiest time for the assassination planning. It was amazing how this company could transform itself so quickly from a company cleaning Air Force parts into one with a single motive goal, assassination.

A cover operation was put in place, meant to give the appearance the company was functioning normally. The delivery and shipping trucks still came and went on time, twice a day as usual. Norris would offload parts shipped from the Air Force in the morning and then move them untouched to the shipping area to be trucked back the next afternoon. Similarly, the new secretaries arrived and left at the appropriate times. Men in suits still came and went, but they were different men with a different agenda and purpose.

Orris was continuously traveling around Dallas and indeed the whole country, meeting with contacts and associates in the assassination. But, often they would come to U.S. Sonics, especially Miller, Nesbitt, and Born. All three came and went freely in and out of Orris' office; Nesbitt for ten minutes, Miller fifteen, Born twenty. Someone like Lundquist from out of town, sometimes for hours. I too would come and go freely.

Orris also had many meetings away from the company, at a club, an apartment, someone's office, a restaurant, a hotel suite, and so forth, but rarely the same place. And when I went to Dallas with him now, two or three times a week when he was in town, I went everywhere he did, playing the decoy role. The men we were meeting seemed to become comfortable with my presence, talking in front of me seriously about killing the President and the problems needing to be addressed.

Sometimes, they would even invite me into a meeting room to ask my opinion, something usually concerning the public and how I might react. They seemed to value what I had to say, and took me seriously, even the CIA men. Although, all this was very serious, it was sort of a game for me, a strange game, piecing everything together.

I continued sitting in on the meetings that the CIA men had either at or away from U.S. Sonics. All of their full meetings now took place away from U.S. Sonics, those at U.S. Sonics were limited to two or three men. Their occasional questions continued to usually concern my opinion on some social issue I might have a clearer view on as a child. I only knew the men by their faces and personalities, but I was getting to like them. Different, more sophisticated, and to the point. Where Born always seemed nervous, they seemed confident and relaxed. And if he were at U.S. Sonics when they came, no one had to tell me not to come into a meeting. I knew my place with all the different men and how to treat them appropriately.

My father very rarely asked me to leave. The rare times he did, I left quietly, saying only, "Yes, sir." I knew my place and usually was rather formal about it in front of others. I was at U.S. Sonics so often that I became a 'picture on the wall'.

When he was meeting with someone who didn't know me, my father would usually introduce me saying, "This is my son, Bruce. It's alright to talk in front of him." This was usually enough to cause the person to relax and accept my presence.

Naturally, Orris would remind me from time to time not to mention one word of what I was hearing or seeing to anyone, and to report anyone or anything suspicious. I was constantly asked if anyone had approached to question me about the Kennedy assassination or anything related. He seemed especially concerned about someone approaching me at school. This was another reason for my presence at U.S. Sonics in the decoy role; I was a draw for anyone who might be suspicious, and after seeing me there with my father, would most likely approach me when I was not at U.S. Sonics. Of course, I would answer 'no', report this breech back to my father, who would then have this problem eliminated.

When Lundquist didn't make his regular weekly or biweekly trip, Orris would fly out, to solve some of the ongoing problems together. In a way, I believe my father used the trips to L.A. as an excuse to get away from the extreme pressure involved with this difficult undertaking. After all, L.A. was his old playground, with old friendships.

When in town, Lundquist would still stay at Dobkins' Western Hills in Euless, just as he had several years earlier, when he was planning the new manufacturing plant in the area. And I would still go there with my father to see him, and go swimming as I had done there for years. They would sit by the pool drinking, while I swam, one experience I still treasure for some reason. I think it reminded me of when I was very little in California. Even though Lundquist was here to discuss assassination preparation, I still enjoyed his company.

The Inn was a key meeting place for the conspirators away from U.S. Sonics. Sometimes, there would be ten or twenty men there or, sometimes, just Lundquist and my father. As time passed, the meetings with CIA men became fewer and fewer, until by mid-summer, there were none.

Security at U.S. Sonics

I was always very concerned that Orris, people working at U.S. Sonics, visitors and everyone involved in the assassination planning, would talk so openly and freely about it. When I occasionally expressed these concerns to him, he just told me not to worry. They had it under control and would know if there was a problem.

This isn't to say there wasn't significant security, there certainly was. The receptionist knew everyone involved in the assassination, and on the rare occasion someone came through the front door who wasn't involved, she was to immediately notify Norris Lawrence. Norris was always there to immediately and politely deal with the situation. Such a person was usually someone who had the wrong building or was lost and just looking for directions.

In fact, at least every two weeks, a team of CIA people, specialized in security and debugging, would visit. Sometimes they would arrive unannounced four or five days after their last visit, to catch people off guard. They would go through the building from top to bottom, every room and area. Physically looking and using electronic equipment to locate any listening device. They would also secure the telephones with electronic equipment to ensure they weren't being bugged. Outside, they walked the building perimeter, performing the same tasks.

In early December, they had placed a new silent alarm system on all doors and windows. They also checked the cars used by Orris, Born, Nesbitt, and Miller, to make sure that they were clean of any bugging devices. To my knowledge, nothing was ever found out of order. But in spite of witnessing the CIA do their inspection on several occasions, this didn't answer my concern that everyone spoke so openly.

Thankfully, they changed how they spoke in public, something very noticeable to me. So, anyone else would have no idea what was being discussed.

Rather, it would sound like a common business or social conversation. They never used Kennedy's name, but referred to him in the third person, as "him,," "the subject," or simply "he." The assassination was "Pandora's Box'" or simply "The Box." For example, they might inquire, "Is everything going OK at U.S. Sonics?" The reply would be, "The Box is fine," meaning the assassination planning was going well. They never used the words "kill" or "assassinate," and certainly never the names of anyone involved. I could always follow their conversations though and know exactly what and whom they were talking about.

But despite all these precautions, I was still constantly worried about something going wrong and that someone might be listening that shouldn't be.

My Personal Life

In January, we moved to a house on Montclair St. in the Meadowbrook area of Fort Worth. A beautiful, older area on the far eastern side of the city, very close to the Dallas/Fort Worth Turnpike. There may have been several reasons for the move, but Orris said it was because of its proximity to the Turnpike, cutting twenty minutes of travel time. He was so involved in the assassination planning, I really don't think he cared what house he lived in. But it was adequate for his family temporarily; that was all that mattered.

Meadowbrook was an area very familiar to him from his childhood. He didn't seem to be overly bothered by the move, once it was completed; he seemed even happy with it.

The move was in the very early part of spring semester, so I was late enrolling. I would be in the sixth grade at Meadowbrook Elementary, a beautiful old two-story, red brick building, kept in excellent condition. The grounds were heavily surrounded by large old trees and lush grass. There were big playgrounds in the back with no fences.

Unfortunately, because I was spending more time at U.S. Sonics with my father now, I was skipping school more than attending. For some reason, neither of my two main teachers seemed to care or questioned me why. I always brought a note from my mother saying I had been ill, something they never challenged.

Thankfully, I was still able to make good grades and pass, but I couldn't form close relationships with any of my classmates. In fact, they felt like strangers. I had always been a very social child and I missed those relationships. I think this was just fine with my father, he didn't want me to form close relationships with anyone for the obvious reasons; probably he would have preferred me to have no relationships at all. Maybe this was another reason for our move to Meadowbrook, to break all relations with the past.

But, I wasn't about to give up girls, and became close to one, Suzy, a very pretty blonde who lived on Meadowbrook Drive, a few blocks from school. When I actually attended school, I would walk her home. This was in an old, well-kept area, with many old, large houses. The setting was beautiful and typical of the South. They lived in a large colonial-style house with a raised, wooden front porch and swing which we would use until well after dark. I got to know her parents and got along with them pretty well.

I Meet Jack Ruby

Since the age of nine, I had been collecting match covers from my father. He smoked and would bring home covers from all over America and, sometimes, the world. I would take them from his coat pockets to put in a big gallon jar; I had a few hundred.

In 1960, he had started bringing home the most beautiful match covers I had ever seen; they became my favorite. They had a striped, bright pink silk background, front and back. On the front was a raised carousel with horses embossed in gold. And on the back, also in gold, it read, "The Carousel Club Downtown Dallas," with phone number and the same carousel. They really stood out from my others. I had probably ten of these matchbooks at any one time, but had no idea whose club it was, certainly that it was a Strip Club, or for that matter, what a strip club was.

This obviously meant my father knew Jack Ruby long before 1963. Probably not well, but he had at least met him, given Orris' propensity for women and strip clubs, not to mention the Mafia. In fact, as often as the Carousel Club matches would turn up in those suit pockets in 1960-61, I would say that he visited the Carousel Club on a semi-regular basis. Probably because it was close and convenient, less than a mile away from U.S. Sonics, both coincidentally only a few blocks from Dealey Plaza.

I first started hearing Ruby mentioned in 1961 by my father and some of his friends, such as Jeff Miller, Dave McCord, and Ed Nesbitt. I knew he had connections to the Mafia; I had overheard that in a conversation between Orris and Jeff. Only later would I realize he was the owner of the Carousel Club of matchbook infamy and was to have an important role in the assassination.

The first time I met him was in January 1963. At his South Dallas apartment. I had no idea of who we were to meet or why, although I assumed it had something to do with the assassination. The routine of my father taking me out of school was still relatively new.

It was a cold, foggy, drizzly day. The exit off Highway 75, a major highway running through South Dallas, is also the exit for the Dallas Zoo. One reason I remember the visit so well is because I had gone to the zoo several times and recognized the highway exit sign. I also remember the particulars of the drive, crossing over the freeway, turning north on the access road and then shortly turning into his place. Orris made no reference to a map, so he had obviously been here before.

We got to Ruby's apartment about ten. I remember it being on the second floor of a three- or four-story building with a dark red brick facade on three sides and which appeared to have been built in the 1940s. There were two wings with a courtyard in the middle. Entry to his apartment was from an inner balcony walkway.

George Senator, Ruby's right-hand man, answered the door, "Come in, Mr. Bell, Mr. Ruby is waiting for you." Telling me he was subservient and not the man we had come to see. And, also that this was the Jack Ruby. I remember Senator as being tall and thin, about fifty to fifty-five years old, and a little balding. He seemed a pleasant, quiet, calm man, who knew how to treat and act around men he was to serve.

I could tell from the way he and Orris looked at each other, this was not their first meeting. they were comfortable with one another. I would see him again on a number of times in the following months and he would always be very polite toward me. He must have been a good housekeeper because although the apartment was cluttered and cramped with a lot of furniture, it was reasonably clean, although fairly dark. Not large, but sufficient and efficient.

I was used to meeting strange men with my father by this time, and most were distinguished and normal with normal families. But occasionally there would be a Mafia guy, and I could immediately tell the difference. But men like Jack Ruby were rare and as a matter of fact, there had never been anyone before quite like him. Regardless, Ruby and Mr. Senator didn't faze me too much.

George Senator led us from the entranceway to a small living room, where Ruby was siting.at a dining table. He seemed to have just gotten up, being in his robe and slippers, probably because he worked late at his club. Senator seemed to be a little embarrassed by this and quickly asked us if we wanted something to drink; I asked for a Coke.

Ruby rose to shake my father's hand and told us to sit down. Orris introduced me to him, and he said hello. His two dachshunds, which had made no fuss when we came in, came over to greet me, and I bent over to pet them.

The two men began making small talk and although I wasn't really paying attention, Ruby didn't seem to be comfortable with me listening and politely asked me to go down and walk his dogs for him. He directed Senator to leash them and show me where. This was fine with me, I wasn't enjoying his cramped, dark apartment anyway and I liked his Dachshunds. Senator took us downstairs to a grassy field beside the apartment complex, where the dogs and I were to wait until 'they' were ready.

I was there enjoying the dogs for about an hour, maybe more, before Senator finally came back. We went back upstairs where Orris was standing, getting ready to leave, but still talking to Ruby. They said goodbye and shook hands, Ruby thanking me for walking the dogs and saying he would call Orris again. The subordinate Senator did not offer his hand to my father, who of course understood the ways of the Mafia, but instead, said goodbye in a polite and respectful manner to the two of us.

I never went back to Ruby's apartment again. The next time I saw him was about two weeks later in February. After I had made my favorite walk along the Trinity Levee, Orris took me back to Southeast Dallas. An area where Orris rarely ventured, it was where both Ruby and Oswald lived. We met Ruby at a Dobbs House restaurant, an early 1960s national chain, popular at the time. He was already there, waiting at a table without George Senator. They shook hands and we sat down. Ruby said, "Hello," to me and even called me by name.

We ordered an early lunch, and they began to talk. The restaurant wasn't very full, but was starting to get the lunch crowd. We were far enough away from anyone who might overhear their conversation. Ruby was again hesitant about talking in front of me, but my father reassured him, "Jack, don't be concerned about Bruce. He knows what's going on. He's here for a reason."

After that, they talked openly, but quietly and of course, as in any public conversation, never using John Kennedy's name. I always knew who they were talking about, because that was all they talked about at first, the President or his assassination. Except General Born's interest in killing a General Edwin Walker.

Because Ruby was a go-between for the Mafia, later discussions involved passing information about progress or changes in the plans that could affect the Mafia. Getting information to other Mafia figures like Carlos Marcello, Santo Trafficante, Johnny Roselli, and Joseph Civello. Sam Giancana was a primary topic because it seemed he wanted reassurance the plot would be successful.

By this time, Ruby didn't seem to mind my presence any longer. And they began talking about a Lee Oswald and how things were progressing with him. New Orleans was mentioned several times. Once Orris would start going there in May to meet directly with Carlos Marcello and others, Ruby's role as communicator diminished, especially as Civello became more involved.

During their conversations, I acted as I was always supposed to in a public setting. As though I had no interest in what they were talking about and instead looked everywhere else other than at them; out the window or around the room. I wasn't supposed to enter into their conversation unless I was invited or asked a question. But, of course, I was riveted to every word.

I never saw Ruby at U.S. Sonics and I don't believe he ever was. I think they didn't want his presence there because they felt he was too recognizable, especially as his club was so close, and men who worked nearby on the street might have patronized it. But, I saw him at least four other times in March, April, and May, always in public at restaurants in or at his Carousel Club.

Between June and August, I saw him at least three times. Orris and Ruby were discussing Orris' flying to meet with Mafia leaders in different parts of the country. One late afternoon in mid-September, Orris and I went to the Club, an old brick building. I think it was open because he left me in the car and there were other cars in the parking. I was waiting for about an hour, while people came and went through a back door.

After August, I saw him a number of times. And he became very familiar with my being with my father and relaxed with my presence. But then he seemed to become more and more nervous as the assassination date approached, overly worried, concerned about something I didn't understand.

Lee's Shooting Skills

The next time I saw Oswald was middle January, a cold rainy day, not freezing, but bone chilling. After the other kids had left for school, Orris told me to put three rifles in the trunk of his car, his Springfield 30.06, a German Mouser 30.06 completely rebuilt into a perfect hunting rifle, and the new Remington semiautomatic. I hoped this meant we were going to go shooting later that day. I should have known better because by now, so much of our routine had been altered.

When we arrived at U.S. Sonics, he asked me to bring in the rifles and put them in a corner of the meeting room, next to a military case of 30.06 ammunition, about three hundred rounds. I did as asked and then was left to spent two hours or so, walking on the levee.

When I got back, a little before twelve, I sat down on the curb in front of the building. It was still drizzling and cold, but I was dressed for this weather and was fairly warm. When I looked up the street toward Industrial Blvd., I noticed a man walking toward me. In all the times I had sat here, I had never seen anyone walking on our street. I looked intently to see if I knew who it was, realizing somehow, he looked strangely familiar. As he got closer, I realized it was Oswald, appearing rather odd, emerging out of the cold rain, a man walking alone.

He wasn't particularly well-groomed and was dressed a little sloppy. I got up and walked up quickly to him, asking questions as usual. As he answered, I was glad to see he remembered my name. He told me then about his job, where and what it was, and that he had taken the bus to our street. When I asked him if he was going to go shooting with us, he said no, he thought he was going to go shooting with Orris, alone. Disappointing, to say the least. We walked the rest of the way together, quietly through the rain.

Inside, Lee asked the receptionist if Mr. Bell could see him and she answered, "Go right back, Mr. Oswald. He's expecting you." Lee did, while I went into the meeting room to wait patiently, knowing he would have to return to the meeting room, as my father dressed to go shooting. This would be my chance to corner him to ask him all the questions about Russia I had thought of since our last conversation. Becoming impatient, I went back to the receptionist to find out what was taking so long.

When Lee came back to the reception area, I asked him again if he were going to go shooting with us later that day. Avoiding my reference to myself, he replied, "Yes, I believe your father and I are going to a rifle range later today." Somewhat disgruntled, I started a conversation again about Russia. He always seemed to enjoy talking about that, answering my questions without hesitation and elaborating with lengthy responses. He never seemed to have anything negative to say about Russia. And he surely didn't seem violent in thought or otherwise.

About one fifteen, the usual lunch truck pulled up in front and honked its horn. Since we hadn't eaten yet, we went out to get something, joined by Norris. From the way, the two men greeted each other and started talking easily, I realized Norris already knew Lee pretty well. I would come to know that when he came to U.S. Sonics, Lee could usually be found in the back area talking with Norris. Then the two of us went back into the meeting room to eat and resume our discussion.

About two o'clock, Orris came out and told me to put the rifles and the ammunition in the trunk of his car. Even though he, himself, wasn't specifically requested to help me, as if naturally following orders, Lee came with me over to the corner where the rifles were. I handed him a 30.06 to take out, loaded the other two rifles in the car, and then retrieved the case of ammunition.

It was still another twenty minutes before Orris came out in his beige khakis and officer's Army boots and I thought we were finally ready to go. He knew I had been patiently waiting for him the past three hours, but that didn't seem to matter because he then informed me, "Bruce, you can't go with Lee and me today. I want you to wait here with our receptionist and I'll come back and get you later."

I obviously had no choice and was more than disappointed. I couldn't help but wonder why he had brought me along with him today, just to carry the rifles to the car? But like the good little soldier I was, I didn't make a big deal about it, knowing this had something to do with the assassination and my position in that. I understood I wasn't supposed to cause waves, but just do as I was told. It was like a military operation with rank and file and orders to be followed. But still, I couldn't see how my going along would have made any difference.

The two left to the rifle range and I stayed with my 'Snow White', as I was told. I took my chair next to her. and once again she cheered me up with her understanding and smile. Around six o'clock after everyone else had left, it got very quiet, just the receptionist and me. I walked down to the 'White Room' to have a see at what had been going on there lately. It was completely shut down, the stainless-steel vats empty and clean, with heavy plastic wrap and tape around most of the technical equipment. All real work at U.S. Sonics had long since ceased.

Orris and Lee didn't get back until nearly ten that night. We took Lee to his South Dallas house, the first time I had been there. We went in briefly and I got to see Marina and the baby for the second time. We then left for Fort Worth, after a disappointing day for me.

As it turned out, it was also a disappointing day for Orris. In the next week, I heard him say many times that despite his Marine training, Lee was a terrible shot and just didn't have the ability to calmly and accurately shoot the President. He didn't have the personality, demeanor, or nerve. So, Lee was eliminated as an actual shooter, that would have been a disaster. But that was hardly necessary, and it actually turned out better in the end.

At this stage, the planning was an evolving process and changes were frequently being made. So, this didn't eliminate Oswald as the 'fall guy', his primary role from the beginning. A 'patsy' as he, himself, would put it to the media after his arrest. I believe he understood and completely agreed to this, being promised a different outcome than would eventually befall him.

In the meantime, an entirely different group of men were being readied to be the actual shooters. Men with that natural ability with a rifle and nerves of steel; it wouldn't be easy to deal with the pressure of shooting the President, especially the last few seconds before the trigger was pulled, requiring supreme focus and very steady hands.

But even after assessing Lee's shooting skills, Orris continued to take him to shooting ranges around Dallas. Not to improve his skills, but to create an image of a 'Communist Lone Nut' with one primary goal in life; the killing of President Kennedy. Lee was instructed to shoot at the target of the person next to him, and when this person approached Lee to complain, he was to say things like, "Oh, I was picturing that Son of a Bitch Kennedy." This was so off-the-wall, that the average person would remember it, and report it to the authorities after the assassination, when they saw his face in the media.

Immediately after the assassination, a number of different people did actually come forward to the FBI and the Dallas Police to report Lee Oswald as being seen at these rifle ranges, making slanderous remarks about Kennedy. And the media quickly picked it up.

In keeping with this strategy, Oswald was told to order his Mannlicher-Carcano rifle in a way easily traced back to him. As an effort to make it appear he were trying to hide his identity, but knowing they would be tied to him, he used a number of aliases, but his own post office box. He is Lee Oswald, at some times, and A.J. Hidell, Aleck James Hidell, Alek Hidell, Lee Osborn, Leon Oswald, and O.H. Lee, at others.

These was just a few of many efforts to make him look like a 'lone nut', who, if not insane, was confused and generally out of control. His history was another contribution to this picture. He joined the American Marines, then defected to Russia to become a Communist, then returned to America to be an American. In return from Russia, he goes to the Dallas/Fort Worth area, then moves to New Orleans and then returns to Dallas, all for no obvious, apparent reason.

And importantly, both a conservative General Walker and liberal President Kennedy would become his targets. He tells some people he likes Kennedy and others, he hates Kennedy. Later when in New Orleans, he will be pro-Castro and anti-Castro. He loves Marina, but also beats her. Everything about him is confusing and contradictory. Multiple Oswalds. This 'Shotgun Effect' is meant to confuse the public and authorities enough that they are sidetracked, confused, and eventually lose interest in really solving the assassination.

Lee at Jaggars-Chiles-Stovall

The next time I saw Oswald was about a week later, when my father first took me to where he was working. It was obvious that Orris had been here before by the way the men in the front office greeted and treated him. We picked Lee up and took him to lunch, after which we took him back to U.S. Sonics. He and Orris spent about forty-five minutes alone in my father's office and then Lee left, I assumed to catch a bus back to work.

By this time, I had gotten my composure and self-confidence in dealing with Lee, just as I had learned what was expected of me and how to act in general. Between January and April, I saw him somewhere between sixteen and twenty times. Sometimes on the weekend, but usually during the week at Jaggars and Chiles, where I would lead the way in with Orris, as if we owned the place.

They were very tolerant of our intrusions and interference with whatever work Oswald was actually performing. They were also very friendly with me. While Orris usually stopped out front to talk with the owners a bit, I would go ahead to the back to find Oswald in the actual mapmaking area. The light was dim, but the multiple drafting tables and their maps were brightly lit by hanging lights. Because our visits were always timed at lunchtime, Lee would be alone, waiting to quickly wrap up whatever he was working on. He and I would head to the front to go for lunch with Orris.

Afterwards, back at U.S. Sonics., Lee usually wouldn't stay as long as he did on the weekend. But he usually wouldn't go back to work, although sometimes we would take him back. Other times, we would take him home or drop him off someplace to catch a bus.

Every once in a while, Lee would appear at U.S. Sonics after four o'clock and my father and I would have an early dinner with him at one of the more casual restaurants, often a barbeque place or an out-of-the-way steakhouse. On the weekends he came to U.S. Sonics, he would be there for several hours and seemed to have free range, aimlessly wandering around. In and out of my father's office.

It was obvious Lee Oswald had a role in the assassination because he and Orris often talked openly about it in front of me, sometimes intensely, but without the detail as with Born, Lundquist, and others. So, I just wasn't sure what his role would be, and it seemed they wanted him to know as little as possible of the real plans.

And when Orris was with Lee and me, they seemed to talk more about his Russian experiences, Marina's background, and his life, when he was younger. For my benefit, or distraction? Sometimes when we would take him home, we would go in and talk with Marina, or rather we talked to her through Lee because of her very poor English.

The assassination was never brought up in her presence. So, I don't know if she knew anything about it. But I can't imagine her not being curious and suspicious why Lee was spending so much time with sophisticated men like Orris and DeMohrenschildt. Lee was something of an intellectual and for many years had interacted with like individuals, but this was different. Their secretive manner must have piqued her.

Roscoe White and J.D. Tippit

It was early March when I first saw police officers Roscoe White and J.D. Tippit. Returning from one of my walks along the Trinity River levee, I looked over at the U.S. Sonics building. M'God, there was a Dallas police car in front. I immediately thought that the assassination planning had been discovered and they must be here to arrest my father and everyone else.

At first, I didn't know what to do, I was nearly in shock. I hadn't been prepared for this. I had thought we were all safe, here in Dallas, at least at this point. I tried to calm myself down and think of what to do to save my father. First, go over to assess the situation up close; I had to move quickly, or it would be too late, and my father would be arrested and probably hung.

So, I ran down the side of the levee and across the field, watching for other police cars or policemen, trying to stay low and out of sight; difficult in the open grass field. When I got there, I ran over to the police car to confirm it was, in fact, an official police vehicle. I then cautiously worked my way up between the cars to the front stairs and up to the front glass door.

There, I could see the backs of two men, both in police uniform, standing inside with their backs to me. I wanted to run and get away before they got me, too. But I resisted that urge, thinking perhaps there was some way I could help my trapped father. Then when I looked closer, I could see he was standing in front of the officers with Ed Nesbitt, Norris Lawrence, and Jeff Miller. Moreover, I could now see and hear through the door, that they were laughing.

Obviously, the situation wasn't as dangerous as I had first thought. But nevertheless, the situation warranted further detective evaluation, so I continued to watch and listen before finally deciding that these officers couldn't be here to arrest my father; not if they were all laughing. But I still wasn't completely sure, so I hesitated a short while longer, confused.

I finally decided that everything was calm enough, I could go inside to hear what they were talking about, why they were even here. Cautiously, I opened the door to see what would happen. But both officers, their backs to the door, heard me, jumped slightly and instinctively dropped their hands to their guns. Startled and obviously nervous and anxious -- but no more than me -- though they were trying to appear relaxed and professional. So, they didn't so much look at, but around me, checking through the door for anyone else coming in.

But once they realized that I was a child, their hands left their guns and they returned full attention to my father and the other men, ignoring me all together. Still, I was watching them closely, ready to bolt back through the door, if anything suddenly changed.

I moved over next to my father, for a better look at them. I still didn't understand why these two officers were standing in U.S. Sonics. Surely, they were our enemy. Was this as dangerous as I first thought? Probably not because there was absolutely no tension in the air and everyone seemed completely relaxed, laughing at a story my father was telling about President Kennedy. So, I could relax a little.

But what was really confusing was Orris even mentioning anything to do with the Kennedys to these officers, even if it were just a funny story. In fact, they stood there talking and laughing for another five minutes before the one whose nametag labeled him 'Officer J.D. Tippit' said, "Orris, I'll call you tomorrow and we'll go from there." Whereupon they all shook hands and the two officers left.

It turned out that the second man, labeled 'Officer Roscoe White' was wearing a uniform, but wasn't actually a Police Officer; he would join the force when it became necessary. My father had needed these two men to do something for him requiring uniforms.

Orris looked over at me, as soon as they had disappeared. We were so in tune with each other's feelings by this time, we could understand each other's thoughts without having to talk. So, he could tell instantly by the look on my face that I didn't understand what all of this had been about. After all, I had been warned over and over again never to talk with the police about any of this.

Turning to go back to his office, Orris started to clarify for me, "Bruce, I could see that those police officers frightened you when you first came in." After I told him what I had first thought, he told me not to worry about them, these two officers were different. They were on our side, and I would be seeing them here again. I accepted this, but it continued to confuse me, so I would always be wary when I saw them. Something about having Dallas Police Officers around, when they were planning to murder the President of the United States, just didn't sit too well with me.

I later learned that Lee Oswald, Roscoe White, and J.D. Tippit had served in the Marines at the same time and in the same unit in Japan in 1957. It was a small unit with a Top-Secret status, functioning as a radar unit for the CIA, the Air Force, and the Navy. Tracking the spy mission flyovers of the U.S.S.R. in U-2 aircraft in the late 1950s and early '60s.

I saw the two men about two weeks later. This time in casual civilian clothes. They still paid no attention to me, and no one introduced us. I continued to be curious as to why they were actually here, two police wandering around the company rather freely. It really worried me that this could lead to disaster.

I saw them there at least four more times. and since it continued to make me uncomfortable, I tried my best to avoid them, and they seemed to do their best to act as if I weren't even present. When I finally asked my father what they were actually doing at U.S. Sonics, he simply told me they were helping with the planning. For some reason, this was a relief, even though. I had obviously figured that out. I just wasn't certain how. I would later learn that they were CIA assets, more so than actual agents.

The last time I would see the two at U.S. Sonics would be in late October. I overheard Orris talking to them and someone else about their involvement. Lee Oswald had been told they were there, in addition to other duties, to help him with his escape after the assassination. In reality, nothing would be further from the truth.

14

SPRING 1963

The Attempted General
Walker Assassination

General Born had one major rival for the leadership of the military industrial complex private sector in Texas, another hard-core conservative whom he hated, an Army General named Edwin Walker. Despite President Kennedy having demoted Walker recently for 'crossing the line' by giving speeches urging military members to join the John Birch society, he continued as a broker for military industrial transactions and was still very influential with the Military in general. A number of military officers and enlisted men still followed his life and had great respect for him.

This vitriolic competition was well-known and documented. The public doesn't know or understand how much competition and incompatibility exists between the different military branches and their leaders. Many strong enemies are made while competing for influence and money in Congress. General Walker was Army and General Born, Air Force.

Now, having Lee Oswald under his control provided Born the ideal opportunity he had been waiting for. And it fit in perfectly with the plan to make Oswald look like a Communist not only sent back to the United States by Russia to kill President Kennedy, but also other targets, not Democrats or liberal. So, a right-wing, ultra-conservative Republican like General Walker would make a perfect target. And if there were some exposure of those behind this plan, there would be the question, why would ultra-conservatives kill one of their treasured own.

Finally, the assassination of General Walker would serve as a good rehearsal for the Kennedy assassination.

I first started hearing talk about killing Walker in the middle of March, about three weeks before the attempt was made. I heard about his history, why he had been demoted, and why Born hated him so much. But I was still confused because Walker was a General and supposedly active in much the same interests as the conspirators. A very conservative Republican and even a member of the John Birch Society. So, an attempt on his life didn't make good sense to me.

When it came to the actual planning of it, Born's special interest was obvious. He was very involved and usually present during the discussions. Although I heard it all, I sort of dismissed it, worried that an attempt on Walker's life might jeopardize their real goal, the assassination of President Kennedy. They would have to let Walker live and deal with him another way.

Then about ten on the evening of April 10, watching television with my mother, there was a news flash that someone had shot at a General Walker, but missed leaving him unscathed. As soon as I heard Walker's name, I knew without question, it was Born and my father. And even though I had heard them talk about it for the past three weeks, I was still shocked seeing it for real. In fact, it scared the hell out of me. The fact that I knew they were planning to do this, and here it was now on the news. And they had obviously failed.

I didn't know they were going to make the attempt that night, but I believe my mother did, because she was paying unusual attention to the story and the look on her face told it all. We both stayed up to hear the late newscast, not only to hear any updates, but also to see if and when my father would come home. I was very worried about him, but finally fell asleep before he did.

I got up early to see if his car was in the driveway and then found him sitting at the breakfast table, having coffee and reading the morning newspaper with my mother. At least, he had made it home. I went in and sat down. Surprisingly, he lowered the paper and looked over at me with penetrating, focused, angry eyes and said in a very stern, serious voice, "Bruce, I want you to go to Dallas with me today."

All I could say was, "Yes, sir." I could tell this wasn't a day I would be looking forward to. I didn't want to go, but I had no choice. I knew they would all be mad as hell. These men didn't fail very often, and now they had done so badly.

When we left the house, he was in a mood that I had never experienced before. He was never like this. He didn't say one word all the way and I didn't either, because I didn't know what to. Normally, he listened to music, but today he went from station to station to find the news about the attempt on Walker's life. It was still the lead story.

In Dallas, Orris didn't go directly to U.S. Sonics, but first stopped at a restaurant to phone the receptionist to ask if the coast were clear, no one unusual had showed up. She said everything was normal and alright. He then called Ed Nesbitt who would move first to cover them with his Dallas Police contacts. We then went straight to U.S. Sonics, only long enough for him to make several more, quick phone calls. Then we went to Jeff Miller's office, where Ed Nesbitt joined us.

Orris' anger continued, only worsening as the day progressed. And throughout the day, in contrast to what would normally happen, I wouldn't be invited into the offices we would visit. So I didn't overhear conversations or phone calls, except for bits and pieces about this tragedy, while he and the others were going to and from the offices. They were trying to find out where the police investigation was going, so they could intercede and get control of it, without exposing themselves to the wrong people. Obviously, this was touchy. It was obvious they weren't really prepared for this problem because they hadn't believed there was a chance for failure.

Once we were in Miller's office, I could hear he and my father talking about what had gone wrong with the shooting. Orris described about how he and Oswald were in the alley behind the house about nine o'clock. A dog was barking loudly, so they had to hurry and didn't have time to get into the positions they wanted. Lee went ahead and fired at the General from over the back fence, through Walker's study window, as he was sitting at his desk. The shot had missed by an inch. The dog's owner came out on his back porch because of the barking, but probably also because he had just heard the gunshot seconds before.

Orris had his car idling in the alley behind them. And now this man was telling the media that he had seen two men get in a cream-colored Ford Galaxy 500, and speed down the alley. He had got a pretty good look at the car and its taillights and there was no mistaking it. I knew as well as Orris and Miller, that this man was right. There was no mistaking Orris' car. Only the Ford Galaxy 500 had taillights like it and under the streetlights, the yellow car looked cream-colored.

My father was so angry, angry at himself for allowing Oswald to attempt a shot which wasn't difficult, even though they weren't in the planned position. With only very minimal training, the fifty-foot shot at Walker was so easy, anyone could have made it.

Obviously, right now my father felt safer here than at U.S. Sonics. The three men got on the phone again and began working the problem. Orris first made a call to General Born, but closed the door after about a minute, so I didn't hear the conversation. The three men were then on the phone with others for about an hour.

After, we drove up to North Dallas, Orris listening to the news. They didn't seem to be saying anything new. We parked at a house I had never been to before, where my father asked me to wait in the car. I wasn't about to ask him whose house it was, because his anger precluded that. But it turned out to be Clint Murchison's and Orris was there for about thirty minutes before he came out and we headed back to downtown Dallas. He stopped at a restaurant again and made another call to U.S. Sonics and another to Miller.

We then went to the German restaurant, where we had eaten so often before, and where we met Miller and Nesbitt for lunch. We left the restaurant about two and Miller, Orris, and I went back to Miller's office. Joe Civello showed up fifteen minutes later and all three men went into Jeff's office and closed the door. It was over an hour before we all left in different cars; my father and I meeting Jeff at his house this time. I was invited in there, and they soon got on the phone again, talking to several people in Dallas as well as General Born long distance; I've wondered if there was a reason he wasn't in Dallas at this time.

The gist of all these conversations was what to do now that General Walker was still alive. They seemed to be concerned that he could possibly find out who had tried to kill him. The FBI was already investigating and Orris and his group needed to get control of that investigation before it went too far. It was well-known that Walker and Born had problems, so they were concerned that the investigation would lead to Born and U.S. Sonics.

Now that Walker was still alive, they would have to ensure that none of what they were doing would get back to him. And it would be too risky to try and kill him again. But, because Walker seemed to have many other enemies, they felt that the chance of the investigation leading to Orris, Oswald, or Born was slim with what little evidence had surfaced. Except for the description of Orris' car.

It was after five when we left Jeff's. It had become apparent that Orris and everyone else felt that it was better for him to avoid going to U.S. Sonics. I was surprised that he had gone there at all that morning, once I realized what was going on. But now, he apparently felt they had gotten control of the situation to some degree, and he was comfortable enough to return to check the situation in person.

We were only there for fifteen minutes, when we finally left for home. Before we got on the Turnpike, driving seventy miles an hour, he was again trying to find the news on the car radio. When he found it, the first story was about the attempted murder. I don't think he even realized I was in the car with him. He hadn't talked to me, when we were changing locations. He hadn't said one word directly to me all day long, other than, "Come with me," "Sit here," "Let's go."

I tried not to look directly at him, as he was still so mad it scared me to even chance a glance. But when I did, his face was nearly red. I realized that this wasn't the same man I knew as my father. I really didn't know him at all. The first time I had felt this way about him, and it would turn out not to be the last.

He wasn't the only one so upset about the failure. I had never seen these men like this before. They were usually upbeat and in a good mood. But utilizing Lee Oswald in this shooting attempt had been impulsive and a terrible mistake that could have potentially cost them dearly. They had risked not only the exposure of Oswald, but also that of U. S. Sonics and everyone involved.

They had failed and this seemed to make it even worse to me, personally. Not that I personally wanted this man, Walker, dead, but that their failure made it unquestionably more dangerous for my father. A dead man can't point fingers at anyone, but a live General Walker might point his finger at U.S. Sonics, General Born, and my father, if he were smart enough to figure it out.

However, they were still able to manipulate this attempted murder to their ends. They had always planned on pinning Walker's death on Oswald after Kennedy's assassination. But it didn't really matter if it was successful or not, Oswald's participation was still evidence of him being an assassin. A photograph was taken by Orris, not Marina as some have supposed and Marina stated, of Oswald in his backyard, holding his Mannlicher-Carcano rifle and handgun, alongside a newspaper article about the Walker shooting; to tie Oswald to the attempt. They were expecting that ballistics would prove that the same rifle had been used in both assassinations. And, in fact, much later it would be determined that bullet fragments would match the ammunition used by Oswald in the President's assassination. Oswald was also instructed to leave handwritten notes on the Walker attempted murder in his diary.

In the end, hard lessons were learned, and they wouldn't make another mistake like this. They would be much more careful and cover all possibilities before they made any move. And a few days later, Orris was back to himself and had put the General Walker failure behind him.

His attitude toward Oswald was different though. He wouldn't make the mistake of fully trusting him again. And there was some question that couldn't be ignored, that possibly Oswald had intentionally missed the shot at Walker. But, most importantly, a clear conclusion had been reached that Oswald couldn't and wouldn't be one of the three actual shooters in the Kennedy assassination.

What was amazing was that the yellow Ford Galaxy 500 was never tied to Orris, despite the fact that he continued to drive it daily around the Dallas/Fort Worth area, in plain sight.

And on my end, imagine my swinging on my friend Suzy's porch the night before the attempt on Walker, then back the next night having dinner with her family when a news report about the attempt comes on the TV. And Suzy's father commenting, "Who would want to shoot this General Walker? There's something rather strange about it." Imagine how I would feel at that moment, knowing what I knew, siting with this upper middle-class family, leading two separate lives.

Oswald leaves for New Orleans; Clay Shaw

The planners had long planned that after the initial work with Lee was done, he should leave Texas. He was likely to be a distraction from the other work needing to be done; and that prediction had been borne out. Only to be amplified by the botched Walker affair. So, not sure how far the expected investigation would go, and not wanting anything to interfere with their ultimate plans for him in the assassination, they decided they should implement that plan earlier; he would disappear for a while in late April, instead of June.

I had listened to Orris talking on the phone to Clay Shaw in New Orleans several times before about miscellaneous matters. But now it was all about this. I thought he was a smooth, calm guy, soft-spoken, articulate, and sophisticated. Well into September, his name would be as common around U.S. Sonics as mosquitos down by the Trinity River; but by the way he was talked about, he seemed like one strange guy.

(I was also hearing the name, David Ferrie, a man who has been implicated by others as involved in the assassination. But I honestly don't know what role, if any, he played.)

Clay had been chosen to be Lee's handler in New Orleans. He was a good friend of Mafia boss Carlos Marcelo who would also be involved. Besides these creds, he was a well-known, respected businessman with strong ties to the local government and police. Perfect for the role he was to play.

And he obviously did a good job, because I only heard praise. But his job essentially ended there. He would be the defendant in the only trial by New Orleans D.A. Jim Garrison, attempting to prove a conspiracy in the assassination. But acquitted by the jury; a very guilty man.

The day before he was to leave, Lee had been at U.S. Sonics with Roscoe White and J. D. Tippit, I had never seen the three of them together before and they acted like good friends; it was a strange gathering. Afterward, l overheard Lee and Orris talking about meeting at the Carousel Club later that afternoon. And about two o'clock, Orris took me there for the first time; it wasn't open yet, so I was allowed in. Ruby, Tippit, White, and Orris were having a going-away party for Lee.

This was the first that I realized that Ruby was the owner of the Club. The staff was getting ready for the night; I think it usually opened about four or five. The others were already there and sitting at a big round table in front of the high stage to the right, against a brick wall. Orris joined them and I sat down at a table nearby. There was no one else in the actual room.

George Senator, whom I had come to know quite well by this time, came over to take the men's drink orders, and then to me for mine of a Coke. The lights were on, but dimmed a little. I could clearly see costumed women moving back and forth in a hall behind the stage. They would pause and look through the open door, curious to see who Ruby was entertaining at this time of day. They didn't stay long in the door though, as if told to leave him alone and not stare at his guests. Other staff was bustling around; it reminded me of a Broadway show getting ready for opening. Ruby would get up, attend to something and return every ten minutes or so.

Orris and I stayed about an hour and a half. They were all drinking hard liquor, whiskey. This was one of the few times I saw my father drink liquor during the assassination planning, but he wasn't drinking as much as the others, who were obviously enjoying themselves and planning on staying awhile longer.

Oswald in New Orleans

In early May, I asked my father about Lee having gone. He knew that I liked him and was curious about whether I would ever see him again. I was told he would be in New Orleans for a while, but would probably come back next fall. This seemed a long time. I knew the move had a lot to do with the Walker shooting problem, but it seemed rather an over-reaction, not knowing they had planned such a move all along, only later during the summer. Marina moved to the strange city of New Orleans to be with Lee, a few days after he arrived.

It was a long, hot, humid summer in New Orleans. There were two objectives for Oswald's time there, besides keeping him out of sight in Dallas. First, they had to keep him focused on his position in the assassination and confident that he would survive it. Second, they needed to continue the propaganda campaign portraying him as the Communist 'nut' assassin, which they did in a rather circuitous route.

They had him join an anti-Castro group and then placed him on a busy street passing out pro-Castro literature. It wasn't long before the anti-Castro group showed up and created a problem; physically attacking him and calling him a spy. The police arrived and arrested Lee for creating a public disturbance. The next day, after he bonded out and paid his fine, he was interviewed by a local New Orleans television station, where he supported Castro's Communist regime. They now had documentation supporting the story that Lee Oswald was a Communist come back to America to assassinate President Kennedy. But also, his behaviors were erratic and contradictory.

New Orleans happened to be a long-time stomping ground for Orris. In the late 1950s and early '60s, he would attend the Mardi Gras nearly every year. And now he stopped there frequently to visit with Clay Shaw and Carlos Marcello. on his many trips to Miami and Orlando visiting Santo Trafficante. But most importantly, New Orleans was to help keep Lee focused and assured that he would be well-cared-for.

The Third Shooter Problem; Tom Lawrence

The planning had reached a high point at U.S. Sonics in March, April, and May, with a flurry of activity involving the key planners. But others would show only once to meet with them and never again, and functionaries like Roscoe White and J.D. Tippit, would only show occasionally, and usually elsewhere, like the Carousel Club.

My father continued to be very busy in May. To me, his activity seemed more intense. He had more direct interactions with national Mafia figures, Mafia bosses, as well as others. In addition to more meetings in Dallas, there were the frequent trips he was making.

At the same time, "business" business at U.S. Sonics was slower. Orris had turned what remained of the daily functions of the company over to Ed Nesbitt and Norris Lawrence, when he wasn't in town or too busy with the assassination.

And they now had the basic plans for the assassination in place. There would be three real shooters, in addition to Oswald's role as decoy; it having been long ago determined that he wasn't capable of doing the actual lethal shooting. Two of these would be Charles Lyon, his hunting buddy, and Clarence Bentley, who had originally been on the U.S. Sonics board. It was deemed important that only local people that Orris knew personally be used, so that they could only be tied to him in the case of an investigation. Orris and U.S. Sonics would have to take all ultimate responsibility, not the actual instigators.

In June, things got quiet there, partly because of Oswald's move. Clay Shaw came at least once and Orris actually drove Oswald back a few times for a day or two.

Initially, I knew that Orris would be at the assassination site, but not necessarily as a shooter. Rather, I saw him more as someone continuing to play the same role that he was now playing, one of organizer and overseer; he would be at the assassination site, overseeing. I obviously didn't want to deal with the possibility that he could actually be one of the three men pulling the trigger and, in fact, killing the president. This somehow seemed worse than organizing the event.

But of course, I was just lying to myself. It was as plain as day Orris was going to be one of the shooters. something that I would come to accept. It was all very logical. He had bought the new Remingtons. And he was an excellent marksman, not just at a range, but off, where there is a great deal more to shooting a rifle at an animal, especially a human being -- let alone the president of the United States -- than shooting at stationary targets.

And besides, he had a tremendous ability to make quick decisions about whether to make a shot or not. He had remarkable eyes and reflexes. All this wasn't just the opinion of a proud son, but that of all his hunting friends. The fact in World War II he had actually shot men further made him the ideal assassin.

But the plans had to change. I was standing in the receptionist area one day in late May with Nesbitt and Norris, when Orris came out from his office and announced with a shocked look on his face, changing to anger, "That son of a bitch, Bentley, has backed out as being a shooter. I just got off the phone with him."

As Orris explained, he didn't try arguing with Bentley. This wasn't a job you wanted to have to talk a man into. He either wanted this very dangerous job or he didn't, and Bentley had decided, for whatever reason, he didn't. Lawrence, Nesbitt and I all looked at Orris in disbelief. How could Bentley do this!

Orris had long felt the crucial problem of who the three designated shooters would be, was resolved. So, this was a serious problem with many more implications than just having to replace Bentley, which would be difficult enough. A sniper team trains together and becomes a group functioning as one. They have to know each other, trust one another, and know how the others think and will react in different situations.

As I have said, they ran the assassination as a military operation and when one man breaks rank and bows out, it is a serious problem.

In fact, these three men had already spent many hours practicing with targets moving at the anticipated speed of the presidential limousine. And from a number of angles, unsure yet the route of the anticipated parade.

Orris discussed the problem of replacing Bentley with several people he knew he could confide in. It was Norris who quickly resolved the problem, "Orris, my brother, Tom, might be interested in taking Bentley's position as a shooter." This was not what Orris had planned; to use only local people that he knew, but time was getting short.

But Orris had a lot of respect for Norris when it came to matters of weapons, knowing his experience in the military. So, he could assess whether a man had not only the proficiency, but also the bravado necessary to fill the position of third shooter. Norris reminded him that Tom had served in the Navy in World War II, and had been decorated several times for his bravery. He appeared to have the personality and nerve needed for this job. And as important, he could be completely trusted.

Orris knew Tom already, having met him several times before, and liked him. So, relying on Norris' judgment, the two called him to fly to Dallas as soon as possible. This obviously wasn't a position to leave vacant very long, but they shouldn't tell him why, until they had a chance to get a feel for him.

I believe Tom lived in South Louisiana at the time, near Houston. Like a good brother I guess, he agreed to come, and arrived a few days later. Still without revealing anything about the assassination, Orris invited him to go shooting with him, where he quickly satisfied Orris with his proficiency, with a 30.06 and scope. So, the next thing was to outline the assassination plan and put the question to him, would he be willing to be a shooter.

Tom didn't have any love for President Kennedy, as they already knew, being an ultra-conservative Republican, like all the players. After discussing what he could financially and how he would be protected after, it was agreed that Tom would replace the lost third shooter.

Orris helped him get a job at a Dallas Lincoln Mercury car dealership, I believe on Turtle Creek Blvd. I accompanied my father there several times, and we also had lunch a few times together, between September and November. I remember the dealership very well and walking around the lot by myself, looking at the new Mercurys and Lincolns, while my father and Tom were talking together inside. I also saw him at U.S. Sonics several times.

The resultant three primary shooters practiced at a ranch about sixty miles west of Fort Worth, just west of Weatherford and Mineral Wells and about two miles south of Palo Pinto, off Highway 180. Easily accessible from the Dallas/Fort Worth area and at the same time providing adequate privacy for practice shooting. The Brazos River ran through the middle, creating a beautiful setting. It had an old ranch house that sat close to the river, used only by visitors.

For many years after the assassination, I would visit this ranch, still attempting to work out my ambivalence and problems that had arisen for me. It was one place I strongly associated with the President Kennedy assassination. In 1965, I deer-hunted there with my father and a buyer from General Dynamics, Inc.

Jack Lawrence

Everyone knowledgeable about the assassination is familiar with another man named Lawrence; a Jack Lawrence, who would briefly be interrogated by the FBI about a possible role. He had only been in Dallas approximately one month, too was employed by a Lincoln dealership. I remember going there to visit him with Orris who had arranged for the job, walking around the lot looking at the new Lincolns and Mercuries while the two men talked inside. And the three of us having lunch several times.

I believe he was a multi-task person involved in the assassination, but not a shooter. His character, demeanor, age, and eyesight problem all negate that. His background with the Air Force as a patrolman leads to a strong possibility that he could have become involved with 'Intelligence' and the CIA, just like Oswald, Tippit, and White, and was used to communicate with participants they didn't want to know about U.S. Sonics.

At any rate, there is circumstantial evidence of his involvement. He sold no cars and many of the fellow dealership employees were suspicious of his activities. He frequented the YMCA where Ruby hung out and, according to stripper Beverly Oliver, he was a regular at the Carousel Club. And he was a known friend of George Senator.

On November 2, he stated he was going to drive a car to L.A. but couldn't recall the name of the 'Colonel', who went with him to pick up the borrowed car from the dealership – was this General Born? He called the FBI to report Oswald's test drive, (Ruth Paine had been giving driving lessons to Oswald), apparently reluctantly because no one else would.

One assassination investigator places him on the Dealey Plaza grassy knoll and it is reported that the 'borrowed car' from the dealership was found behind the picket fence, possibly as a get-away or backup for the assasins. So, despite his protestation, he was involved at some level, if only a diversion.

Orris and Me

In the morning on the way to Dallas, Orris and I rarely talked very much at all, unless there was something he wanted to discuss with me first. I knew he would like to take this time to think about what he had to deal with that day and not answer my inquisitive questions.

And during the day at U.S. Sonics, I usually didn't question him about things I heard but didn't fully understand. But if we had lunch together alone, I would often use that opportunity to do my enquiry. Or I would wait until the drive home. The subject was always the assassination in one respect or another and he would answer almost all the questions, trying I think to not be obvious about certain evasions.

It may seem strange, but we were like a team. Orris depended on me for certain functions and expected me to deal with the situation almost as if I were as dedicated to the project as he. He expected me to understand the scope of it all and my position in it. And I did function like that because I really had no choice. I was my father's son, and he gave me none. I was told I was going to be involved. I was never asked if I wanted to be.

My father seemed to really need this involvement with me. He continued to want to have me present to talk to, to be something of a sounding board, so he could work through the various day-to-day problems he encountered by bouncing them off of me. It wasn't so much my opinion he was seeking, if at all. Rather my innocence or lack of opinion. It didn't really matter what he said to me, because I was never going to object to what he was saying, as Lundquist or Born might do. I was a confidant for him. There was no one else to fill this place during the day but me, unfortunately – I obviously don't know how much pillow talk with my mother occurred, but as I was later to discover she had to know most everything.

Most of the men, who were close to my father and understood him, clearly acknowledged this need, and never objected. They had also known me for years and understood I could be trusted with anything without talking. So, most of them would never object to my presence. They knew that, in fact, in many circumstances, I knew more about the upcoming assassination than they, because I was privy to most of it while their knowledge was usually limited to their basic functions.

Of course, there were some exceptions to this basic trust in me. And when I was in the presence of someone who didn't know my father that well and me at all, then that person might question my involvement. On these rare occasions, I would be looked at as though it were impossible that discussions concerning the assassination of the President were occurring in front of this little boy who should be out playing baseball and not listening in on such a dangerous discussion. I could always sense when that was happening, and if possible, would usually move away to make him feel more comfortable.

Sometimes, I couldn't help but find this all very amusing; to see these men trying not to stare at me or look at my father, as though he were crazy. But they were usually subservient and aren't do or say anything that might offend. So they, like me, had no choice.

Everything in my life had to be secondary to the assassination, as it was for everyone else. Before school, before all social functions, before girls, before friends, before everything, this effort to assassinate the president came first. Not once did I ever say, "No," to my father or "Daddy, can I stay home today? I don't want to go today." Not once did I ever say, "Daddy, can I just go swimming today? It's 103 degrees outside." Not once did I ever say, "No," about anything to my father. I never complained. I understood how important this was and what my position in it was. My father had enough on his shoulders and didn't need me to complain.

Not only did I never say, "No," I always went with a smile on my face and said, "Yes, sir." I did whatever I could to help him. That was my job and to do it in any way I could to fully support him. I was convinced that they had to assassinate the president to save the world, and felt a part of this grand effort. I functioned the best I could, as a very good soldier.

Actually, part of my job was attending school an average of two to three days a week and try to act, as much as I could, like a typical twelve-year-old boy and do what twelve-year-old boys are supposed to do. But then I would sit in class, look around at the others, and think to myself, "*These children live in one world and I live in another. They play children's games and live in a world of Disneyland, and I live in this secret world with men who are planning to assassinate the most powerful man in the world, and they're going to succeed.*"

But under the circumstances, it wasn't that easy for me to act like a normal twelve-year-old boy. Yes, my interest in girls at this age was something that would appear 'normal' and would consume most of my free time away from U.S. Sonics. That part was easy because I really did love interacting with girls, experiencing their newfound interest in sex, which suddenly seemed to fascinate nearly all of them. Besides, for the most part, girls at the age of twelve are more mature and sophisticated than boys. I could talk to them about things that interested me and they would usually understand and why I was interested.

At U.S. Sonics, there was only one place I couldn't go freely, General Born's office. He was the only person there who seemed bothered by my presence. He knew why I was there, but I knew that he felt I was learning way too much and that worried him.

I would sometimes sit in on the meetings that the CIA men had either at or away from U.S. Sonics, and as before, they would sometimes ask my opinion on a social issue. All of their full meetings took place away from U.S. Sonics; those at U.S. Sonics were limited to two or three men. I only knew them by their faces and personalities, but I liked them. They were different, more sophisticated and to the point. Where Born always seemed nervous, they seemed confident and relaxed. If he were at U.S. Sonics when they came, no one had to tell me not to come into a meeting. I knew my place with all the different men and how to treat them individually.

I think one dynamic that might have been in play was that all these people knew I was going to learn a great deal about the assassination by just being around them. So, their approach was to not keep so much from me that I might become curious and seek answers in my own way; that could be worse than just letting me in on enough to satisfy my curiosity. But, at the same time, keeping from me what was necessary.

It felt like they wanted me to feel like one of them, equal, a necessary part of the project. When one feels this way, an exclusive part of something, one naturally feels a stronger allegiance to the group. This was just simple psychology and it worked well on this twelve-year-old. Besides, I think that most of them trusted me emphatically and believed I wouldn't talk, no matter what the circumstance. They knew that I clearly understood that this wasn't a game and that people's lives were on the line.

The one major thing they did keep from me successfully, was the fact that they were going to kill Lee Oswald immediately following the assassination. They knew he and I had spent a lot of time talking in the past months because of my interest in the U.S.S.R, and I had developed a special relationship with him. They knew I wouldn't willingly agree with that.

15

SUMMER 1963

Shannon Rose Hill Cemetery

The summer of 1963 was one of the best for me in many ways. It was also the most stressful, even though it was much quieter than it had been during the previous eight months. By now I was well-aware they were completely serious and well on their way to killing President Kennedy. I was also very aware of the danger for my father and his people, so constantly worried. Especially when I wouldn't see him for a couple of days.

The initial Dallas part of the assassination planning was nearly complete. Oswald was tucked neatly away in New Orleans; when they finally received word of the expected date of President Kennedy's arrival in Dallas they would move him back and finish the few remaining details. They knew they would be able to influence the parade route to some degree using Dallas officials they could control, if this became necessary.

Orris' trips were much longer; instead of two or three days, he would be gone four or five. So, I got a reprieve from going to Dallas and had time to explore Meadowbrook and the surrounding area on my bike. I was twelve years old now and felt old enough to strike out on my own.

There was an electric power plant about three or four miles east of our home. One Sunday morning, I decided to take a long walk along some railroad tracks that led directly to it. I had never really walked any distance along railroad tracks before, and this was an adventure thinking of all the history that went with railroads.

Finally, I could see the electric plant in the distance to the east, but to the north I could see a cemetery. This cemetery had caught my attention several months earlier, when we had driven past it and every time since. I couldn't understand why I was so taken by it, so now I decided to check it out.

Walking up to the big black iron gates inviting me in, I read its name, Shannon Rose Hill Cemetery. In comparison to other cemeteries I had seen, it wasn't big. Even though I knew I had never been here before, I was still strangely drawn to it, as though I had been. It felt as though I knew someone buried here and that I needed to go in and visit whoever it was.

Cemeteries had never frightened me. It just awed me to think of spending all eternity in a place like this after being alive just a few years; it just didn't quite add up. As I ventured deeper in, the feeling that I knew someone here became stronger and stronger, and I started reading the headstones to see if I might locate someone familiar. After wandering around about thirty minutes reading names of the deceased, I ended up on the top of the hill where, sure enough as tribute to its name, roses were blooming brightly in the morning sun. I sat there for a good hour, enjoying the morning and the sweet smell and beauty of the roses.

I finally reached the conclusion that I didn't recognize any names after all. Ironically, it would eventually turn out that my grandparents and Lee Harvey Oswald would be buried here. My father would anonymously pay for Oswald's burial, regarding him as a national hero.

A Partial Reprieve; the Club

Although Orris' increased absences changed my visits to Dallas, when he was in town, I still went there every day with him, without question. Going to U.S. Sonics was now such a common-place event, he no longer had to tell me to accompany him. I was always ready to go before him and at the car waiting. But I was getting pretty tired of the place. I had explored just about every inch of it, and everything in the neighborhood. Because it was zoned an industrial area, there wasn't really much close by I could find in the way of commercial retail businesses.

There was only that ominous electric maze of transformers across the street from the company. I would be haunted by my distorted memory of this monster electric sub-station with flashbacks for many years afterwards. And then when I would revisit and actually see the electric labyrinth and the live Oak trees, I immediately remembered the nightmares that had plagued me and realized why they had occurred. This was what I saw while sitting on the steps in front of U.S. Sonics for hours and hours, worrying about my father, the murder he was involved in, and what might happen to him as a result. And seeing the electric tangle muddled behind the huge Live Oak had somehow seemed to make those feelings worse and more ominous.

But his absences gave me a partial reprieve so I could spend time like a normal twelve-year old. At our club, I would swim in the morning, play golf for about two hours in the afternoon, then go back to the pool. Any of my sibs there would have left; I didn't mind swimming alone, it was my real passion, and time to concentrate on something else, like a pretty girl.

While in the pool, I would keep my eye on the parking lot for my father's car. The water was always cold, and he would come get me out. I would grab my things, run to the car, and get in still wet. The car would be cold, the air conditioner on. I remember all these sensations, cold, hot, and cold again. Barefoot on hot concrete. And the distinct smell of Orris when I kissed him on the cheek. Then as my wet bottom hit the seat, I changed from that innocent boy, Frank Sinatra or Dean Martin playing on the radio, and me sitting next to this man in a Neiman Marcus suit, wearing gold cufflinks, and a Marlboro between his lips.

The girls I had been with in the pool, would witness this rather unusual routine and ask me who this man was and why I would be so excited, and in a hurry to leave so quickly.

I was at the pool one day in July with sister Carolyn. We hadn't seen our father in nearly two weeks, the longest time that summer without him. I happened to look over to the parking lot just as his car pulled in. I couldn't mistake that canary yellow Ford Galaxy 500 for someone else's.

I had been very worried about him and hadn't even talked with him on the phone, which was unusual. I had no idea where he was and neither did my mother. And I knew how dangerous the situation was for him, that he could be killed at any time. Now to know he was alright was such a relief. I yelled to Carolyn that Daddy was in the parking lot. We both jumped out and called to Stephen, lying on a towel on the nearby grass. Together, we headed for the entrance and ran up to kiss him. He could tell how much we had missed him and how much we loved him. I know he was excited to see us as well. We all got in the car to go home, where he received the same kind of reaction from my mother and other siblings.

After watching men teeing off from the first hole, I felt challenged to learn to play golf. My father didn't play; that he didn't, seemed a little strange because many of his military officer friends did. Occasionally, he even made fun of them, saying it was a boring, simple game. Initially, it was pretty much a disaster for me; the first try I only lost about ten balls to the water and woods. But I wasn't defeated; nothing had ever defeated me.

I made one friend through golf. But in many ways, he didn't really count. I went to his house several times, as well as seeing him at the swimming pool on a regular basis. It was a cold relationship and I kept him at arm's length. But I couldn't help but be intrigued. He was quite a bit different from other boys, more worldly and sophisticated, being from Italy the United States for only a few years. But because my father had spent time there and was involved with all these Italian Mafia people, I was interested in this boy's Italian heritage and Italian culture in general. I wanted to learn why Italians seemed to be so different from the American norm, so I could perhaps better understand how and why Orris' Mafia men were such a secret and integral part of the President's assassination.

One of the activities I began to enjoy was fishing alone on a nearby lake, the solitude. It seemed as though no one had fished this lake before, which was strange since you could see it from a heavily travelled road. It became a sanctuary, another escape for me. A place where I could have the inner debate that I needed about everything going on in my life. Usually, I would bring my brother Stephen. He was pretty good company, and I enjoyed his friendship, but he didn't have the love for fishing I did. He would carry a big tackle box for me. I would catch maybe twenty bass on any given day and end up keeping six or seven to bring home. I would clean them, and my mother was always happy to cook them; bass are not only some of the prettiest fresh-water fish, they are one of the best tasting.

The Girls and the Nights

But meeting with girls was the best thing I could do to get my mind off the assassination. Sometimes, I would totally forget about it for fifteen minutes or so, when I was with a girl that I really liked; but then it would suddenly come back to me. It was driving me crazy, but I didn't know this at the time. I wasn't sure what crazy was then, and besides, weren't we all supposed to be a little crazy?

At twelve years of age, I was going through puberty, but was probably more mature and relaxed with girls than most boys my age. I was well developed physically from football, swimming, track, and just about any sport. I was told I was handsome, and it seemed I was attractive to twelve-year-old girls and had no problem forming relationships with them. In fact, many sought me out, rather than me having to go find them.

I become very close to six or seven of these delightful creatures, besides my Suzy. But there were social consequences because of the Kennedy assassination. Being as sensitive as twelve-year-old girls are, they seemed to know there was something on my mind bothering me, but which I refused to talk about. They were especially curious why I would disappear to Dallas with my father as often as I did. After all, it was summer when most children led a life of leisure and play.

If a girl wanted us to meet me at the pool tomorrow and I agreed, but the next three days in a row I didn't show, she would naturally want to know what had happened and where I'd been. Of course, I couldn't tell her that I'd been hanging out in Dallas with the men planning to murder the President in the fall. I had to lie, something I hated doing and was terrible at, making up things that usually didn't sound very good or realistic. I'm sure they usually knew I was lying.

I remember one girl where the situation was a little different. She was a beautiful blonde who lived about a half a block away from the pool. I would see her sometimes when I was coming and going from it, but she would never come swimming. I couldn't figure a way to meet her, other than just go down to her house and knock on the door. One day, my Italian friend asked to meet him on the golf course that night. He, his girlfriend, and another girl, but he wouldn't tell me who. He knew I really wanted to meet this blonde and when I showed up that night, to my great surprise, here she was, sitting in one of the warm sand traps, looking up at me with a big smile on her face. What a great surprise!

We spent most of the night having a good time. I think this was the first time in months that for the whole time, I only thought about the Kennedy assassination once or twice. Her name was Sarah. When I asked her why she never came to the pool, she explained her father was a strict Baptist, who didn't believe in recreational swimming. Her mother had died years earlier, so he had raised her alone. According to her, he was a tyrant and overly strict, and she was very afraid of him. Thankfully, she could get away with this all-night venture because he worked at night.

There was an old movie theater, Meadowbrook Theater, on Lancaster Ave. few miles from our house. I would regularly meet girlfriends there on a weekend night that summer. On Saturday, they would have Rock 'n' Roll bands play after the main picture. I had never seen that kind of band, and one night I decided to stay after the movie to see what it was all about. A guy imitating Buddy Holly was giving a pretty impressive performance, and the girls went crazy over him and this wild new music.

I didn't quite know what to think of it though. It was an addicting sound but seemed a little decadent; almost a religious thing reminding me of being baptized by a black preacher, while the congregation gyrated and sang praises to the Lord. And here in the Bible Belt, the bastion of the Baptist Church, many parents would forbid dancing at all, actually considering this music the true work of Satan. I couldn't help thinking, "*What's going to happen to our society because of this new music?*" Personally ambivalent about religion because of my rebellious streak, I nevertheless bore the Church's teachings.

Although I had been venturing into the night alone for several years, I began to spend a lot more time out after dark now, experiencing beautiful things about it I hadn't known before. I was fascinated and had no fear of it, a whole other world. I loved the stars and moon a few hours before the sun would first begin to lighten the eastern horizon. My father was so engrossed in the assassination and my mother so bewildered by it all, I was more or less left on my own when not with him. I was a child prone to exploring the world around me and did a good job of drawing my own boundaries. I wasn't a mischievous child, and never got into trouble as a result of my late night exploring. And my mother didn't seem to worry about me as I never got into any kind of trouble, and she knew I needed this time away by myself in order to deal with what I had to.

Part of the night's lure were the locusts, much more plentiful in our area of Fort Worth because of the older, larger, and more abundant trees. And our backyard with its own forty Oak trees, was a breeding ground for these strange creatures; they seemed very content and happy there. Although sometimes it would make me crazy, I actually loved the sound they made; I would sleep out on our screened-in back porch, so I could listen to them all night long. It was a high-pitched screeching sound with a cadence that started slowly and quietly, then increased in tempo and volume. It was all you could hear, except for the Mocking Birds, which seemed to be competing with them; themselves, louder than usual, but in the distance. Locusts come in cycles, something like every seven years and this was one of those years.

They would calm and cease their beautiful sounds about two or three in the morning, leaving the Mocking Birds with their beautiful lovely impersonations of other birds, the only sound. The quiet was so beautiful and beyond description. I was alone in the night and the Kennedy assassination was a million miles away in Dallas. It was another good escape for me; I would be sad sometimes, thinking about what I had heard that day at U.S. Sonics or wherever, but the nighttime with the locusts was a private time that no one could steal from me.

The Magic Bullet

One Saturday in mid-July, I was at U.S. Sonics with Orris, the only two people there. I was bored as hell as usual now, and decided to go into the 'White Room' that was no longer being used, to try to find something there to do. Going through the airlock chamber leading into it, I found a fifty-five-gallon, blue steel drum, filled to the brim with what looked like water. I knew this didn't belong here. Next to the drum stood a stepladder about four feet high.

I walked around the drum several times, trying to figure out why it was here, what it was for. This 'White Room' had cost over two hundred thousand dollars and they just didn't leave such things in it unless there was a special purpose. After pondering all the possibilities produced no suitable answer, I decided to go ask Orris.

He was on the phone, so I had to wait anxiously for him to get off. When he finally hung up, I asked if he knew about this barrel and knew why it was there. "Yes, we fired a rifle into that barrel last night, the rifle there in the corner."

I turned around and picked up this old rifle, a type I had never seen. My father always kept his rifles in perfect condition. While this was worn, and I could tell some rust had been removed, and it had been buffed. It was a bolt action with a mounted scope, the wood stock old and rough. The chamber was clean and well oiled. Someone had obviously taken time to put it back into the best condition possible. Whose was this? Only later would I learn that it was Lee Oswald's Mannlicher-Carcano.

I asked my father why they had fired it into that barrel. We had dug bullets out of the ground or an old tree before, just out of curiosity to see what had happened to it on impact, but never a barrel of water. And, of course, I knew that every rifle has a distinctive 'rifling', the arrangement of spiral grooves on the inside of the barrel.

He smiled with this look of satisfaction, looking pleased with my awareness of everything around me and my undying curiosity. He explained, "We wanted to retrieve some bullets from the rifle and this is a good way to do that, firing it into a barrel of water." Well, of course, that made me even more curious. I asked him why in the White Room? It could have been done anywhere. He answered that they needed it to be done somewhere soundproof; they didn't want to draw attention to themselves.

Of course, I asked the inevitable question, "Well, whose rifle is it?" He looked at me, paused a few seconds as though trying to make up his mind, and then simply said, "It's Lee's."

He then opened his desk drawer and took out a white envelope, pouring out eight bullets onto it, one of which he handed to me. It was longer than the 30.06 bullets I had seen before, and slightly distorted and curved into a banana shape, I guess from hitting the water at an angle. And on the tip, scuffed on one side, probably where it had hit the side of the barrel. On inspection, they all looked basically the same with nearly identical damage.

Later, I would find out that one of these bullets would be the so-called 'Magic Bullet', found on a gurney at Parkland Hospital that supposedly fell out of Governor Connally's leg wound, but placed there by Jeff Miller.

International Planning; Whether to Alert Russia

Whether the assassination was successful or not, there would obviously be repercussions, nationally and abroad. So, the planners, primarily the CIA, felt it necessary to alert and discuss it with certain individuals and organizations in the international community. Firstly, they would need to reassure friendly nations, reinforce basic diplomatic relations.

But, what about the unfriendly Russia. Since the Cuban Missile Crisis, the assassination planners had continued concern that the Russians were always ready to take advantage of any American civil disruption. And in the climate of the Cold War, they felt there was no way they could trust the Russians. Now, chaos resulting from the assassination could result in a first strike, nuclear attack.

To prevent this, there seemed to be no choice but to let the Russian military leaders know that something major would take place in November and not to try to take advantage of the situation. The Americans would be fully ready, during this event, to retaliate immediately if they attempted to do anything aggressive toward the United States.

This was something of a paradox in that Kennedy had been trying to thaw relations with the U.S.S.R., while the stated reason for his assassination was anything but.

But there was one other concern about the Russians. That prior to the assassination itself, they could possibly find out about the plan anyway. It was, after all, a high point in the Cold War and both countries had many spies and informants in one another's military, government, and intelligence agencies. So, they would have several options, which could be very detrimental.

One, they could let Kennedy know about it and who was behind it. Two, because the Russians were likely to believe that once Kennedy were assassinated, the U.S. military leaders would decide to attack Russia with a first strike sneak attack—what LeMay called a 'Sunday Punch' --- and so, make their own sneak attack. Or just if they found out about the full scale, long-range implications of the assassination, which would be detrimental to their interests, they might decide to do so.

Of course, this led to the problem as to how to put the military forces at the state of readiness, necessary to counter any resultant Russian moves, without alerting Kennedy's staff or anyone else of influence. The solution was to have the Joint Chiefs order so-called training maneuvers to take place. They would start right before Kennedy left for Texas and would continue afterward. And through their intelligence, the Russians would detect the preparation and occurrence of these maneuvers and not be concerned.

Once the assassination took place, the military would automatically go to a higher level of alert. What was important was t the Joint Chiefs already be prepared to do this and for anything the Russians might do militarily, in reaction.

As can be seen, when all the various factors are brought into perspective, the range and magnitude of the Kennedy assassination were huge. But for the instigators, the ultimate message to the Russians would be that the Joint Chiefs were in charge now. There would be no more weakness.

There were two possible negative outcomes, if Russia were forewarned. First, the potential of a nuclear exchange right after the assassination and the ensuing chaos before the nation and its military could be adequately mobilized. But just as debilitating for America would be the likely result if Russia or, for that matter another entity, decided to warn Kennedy about the ensuing assassination and the names of those individuals and organizations involved: the Joint Chiefs, Lyndon Johnson; the CIA, J. Edgar Hoover, and so many more.

What would Kennedy do? How could he deal with such a large group within the government? And what would the Joint Chiefs and the CIA participants do? They would have no alternative than to forcibly take control of the government, which would likely lead to a civil war, some factions going with Kennedy and others with the conservatives. And, again, Russia might possibly attempt to take advantage of this chaos and launch a limited or full nuclear strike on the U.S.

And, so, to attempt to prevent these possible or similar scenarios, certain trusted international assets had to be briefed on the possibilities and how to counter them. I know that such meetings took place in the Mexican cities of Mexico City, Monterey, and Matamoros, as well as in the U.S. at Padre Island, Texas.

Meeting Sam Giancana

As I have stated, I had never given my father a problem when he had asked me to go with him in the past year. No matter what I had planned, he came first. I felt a responsibility to him and besides, I loved him and no matter if there were issues about the Kennedy thing bothering me, I got to spend time with him between phone calls and meetings. I also felt as though I had a responsibility to the assassination players who had trusted me with this very secret project; that made me feel like a part of them, even if I were just a diversion.

On the last two Sundays in August and the first Sunday of September, I went with my father to downtown Dallas. This was a little unusual, but not unheard of for him to ask my company on a Sunday. On the first trip, we arrived about eleven in the morning and parked in an outside lot, beside the tallest bank building downtown, a new building surrounded by not so tall buildings dating from the early twentieth century period.

Dallas was completely deserted because of the Texas Blue Laws, made to restrict all unnecessary business on Sundays. So, it was like a ghost town. Even though we were on one of the usually busiest streets, I would see no cars come down the street that day. The temperature was at least one hundred three and worse here, with all the cement. The buildings were blocking even the slightest breeze that might have been.

When we arrived, Orris clearly emphasized, "Don't get out of the car, under any circumstances, Bruce." This was unusual because he normally took me inside with him and certainly, rarely told me to stay in the car. But I accepted this without complaining. I watched him cross the street, walk very cautiously about half a long block, and then enter an old, nameless, nondescript, three-story building. I was relieved because I could at least clearly see the entrance.

After about an hour in the boiling car, I finally opened the door for more air. The windows were down, but that was hardly enough; I was about to pass out, it was so hot. Besides I wanted to walk down the street where he had gone, to see what I could see. I was becoming worried because he had been gone so long. But as instructed, I didn't venture out of the car, even though I was tempted to at least sit on the curb, where there might be a small breeze. So, I just sat there with the door wide open, until I finally gave in and got out to sit down on the hot curb in front of the car. Of course, it wasn't any cooler there, only eerie feeling.

I knew my father was visiting with Sam Giancana, because I had asked him on the way over. For two and a half hours, I stared at the door he entered, waiting for him to emerge and worrying about the situation, feelings that just got worse as time wore on. Finally, just about when I was ready to pass out from heat exhaustion, he did come out.

He walked back to our car, maybe with a little more bounce to his step, but still looking around cautiously. He got in without saying a word, started it, and finally turned on the air conditioner. On the drive home, he was absorbed in his thoughts, so unusually there was no talk about his meeting. And of course, there was no acknowledgement or apology for my 'near-death' experience with the heat.

On the next Sunday, we visited the same location, at the same time of day. I t was a complete repeat of the previous time. I was left in the car while my father entered the same door in the same building. Again, it was so deserted in the middle of the day, it was terribly eerie, like the Twilight Zone, without a single car coming down this road running through the middle of Dallas. And just as before, it was too hot for anyone to sit in a car in the sun, even hotter by a few degrees, so that I'm sure the heat might have been causing a little bit of heat stroke by the time Orris finally returned. Again, after over two hours.

When he did come back, he was quiet, just as on the previous Sunday. I could tell he was deep in thought about whatever they had discussed. At least this time, we went to a restaurant and got a late lunch. But, by the time we returned home, there still had been no conversation about his meeting. It appeared to me that the event he and the others were planning was taking on a life of its own; becoming more of a reality. He was becoming preoccupied with it and seemed a little more worried, compared to his usual pleasant, content demeanor, joking in his own satirical manner. I was becoming more than a little worried about him.

On the next Sunday, my father said the same thing to me about accompanying him to Dallas. I thought, "*Oh no. I'm going to have to sit in that hot as hell car again in downtown Dallas for hours.*" But I didn't complain. Not a word about nearly dying. And for what!

We went to the same parking lot, parked in the same place, and I expected the same situation to prevail. But no, to my great surprise, he looked over at me and said, "I want you to come in with me today, Bruce." Something must have changed his mind. Whatever the reason, these few words were a great relief.

When we arrived, he got out and locked the car -- those days most people didn't lock their cars -- and crossed the street. Again, it was so very hot and so strange because of the almost overbearing silence of the street. As we walked down the street to the same non-descript building, I sensed he was more relaxed than previously, but his eyes were still canvassing the street up and down. And I was almost giddy, happy to be out of that car and going into a cool building.

The door turned out to be rather unusual; aluminum frame with glass painted black inside so you couldn't see through, and without any name or number. Orris pushed it open to a small, very warm foyer with an identical door, but with a quarter-sized hole scratched in the paint. When he knocked, an eye appeared in this 'peep-hole' to observe us. I heard keys rattle and then this last door was unlocked and quickly opened by, of all people, Jack Ruby's Mr. Senator.

Senator stepped to the side, greeted Orris by name, and motioning us to enter, also letting in some welcome cool air. After relocking the door, he, nodded to me, and pointed to a large room to his left. The room was dark, so my eyes had to struggle after coming in from the bright sunlight. There were six small round tables, each with two chairs, and spaced comfortably apart, so that you could talk quietly and not be heard easily at the others.

Then I made out a strange man sitting at one of the tables, wearing a little felt fedora and dark sunglasses, even though the room was so dark. He was not a big man, but not small either, rather stocky, and about sixty. I had always been greeted well by Orris' men in the last nine months, pleasantly surprised at everyone's acceptance of me prior to today. But he practically jumped, when he saw me. His mouth fell slightly open as he quickly stood up, staring at me. It was apparent that he was completely taken by surprise at my being here, and then his expression turned into disdain. He shrugged his shoulders and raised his hands toward me in a typical Italian way, as if to say, "What is this!"

As I approached closer, I was unmoved by his actions, prepared because I had replayed in my head the scenario of something like this happening. I was unflappable after ten months doing this with my father, attending what seemed like hundreds of meetings, and hearing everything there was to know about killing Kennedy, or nearly everything. Besides, my friend, George Senator, was here; I had been around him many times now, and he always made it clear that he liked me and my presence.

In response, Giancana moved over to a second table, and shook his head in an obvious gesture meaning, "I'm not sitting with him." Understanding what was happening, my father motioned me to sit at the first table and then shook hands with Giancana. Before they sat, Giancana looked back toward me, as though he still didn't quite know what to make of me. Orris leaned over close to his ear, telling him why I was there with him, quietly explaining that I was alright and for him not to be concerned. Finally, the man's face softened a little and he looked right at me, nodding his head in acceptance as if saying, "Oh, now I understand."

All this over, Orris and Giancana sat side by side at their table with heads together, talking quietly. Senator had moved to my table, standing there waiting for Giancana to get settled with my being there. Then in his usual comforting way, he asked what I would like to drink. I replied, "A Coke would be good." He smiled and went over to the two men to stand wordless, until they gave their orders.

I was soon captivated by a huge, beautiful salt-water aquarium in the middle of the room. I had one in my bedroom and loved them. This one was as nice as they get, about one hundred-fifty gallons, well-kept, and stocked with just the right number and variety of beautiful, very colorful tropical fish and plants. The water was crystal clear. It was brightly lit and at this time of day, it was the main source of light for the room, glowing with a warmth that distracted from the rest of the décor, simple, stark, and cold; nothing on the walls. The hum of the pump and bubbling from the aquarium were the only sounds in the room. I was completely content to just sit and watch it.

Senator came back with the drinks from a back room, where there was a bar and small kitchen. He would have to repeat this several times. But when not acting as manservant, he was like a mannequin, standing at the back of the foyer, from where he could closely watch the whole room, the front door, as well as the back of the building.

The two men were talking intently, but nearly whispering, and occasionally I could make out a word or two. I heard the names Kennedy, Marcello, Ruby, Civello, and Oswald, among others. I finally needed to use the bathroom, but didn't want to interrupt them, so I just got up to find it myself. As soon as I stood, Senator anticipating what I needed, quietly pointed it out.

The meeting lasted for over two hours. Finally, they stood abruptly, shook hands, and said goodbye. As if on cue, Senator moved to unlock the door. My father looked back to Giancana, who was still standing and wearing his hat and sunglasses, and nodded to him. The man responded the same and surprisingly looked over and nodded goodbye to me as well.

As we left, Senator shook Orris' hand, and said, "Goodbye Mr. Bell, have a good afternoon." He nodded goodbye to me as I passed him out the door, before closing and locking it behind us.

My father waited until this inner door was locked, before opening the outside one into the blinding light and scorching Texas sun. The sudden temperature change was startling. Orris was relaxed with the unusual slight smile he did when content and pleased with what he had done. It seemed as though a large weight had been lifted from his shoulders. Same milestone in the planning had been accomplished.

He then made a sarcastic joke about the man's strangeness, to which we both laughed. This was typical of him, to find humor at such things. He frequently had something funny to say to keep people as relaxed as possible, even in the Kennedy murder meetings. Giancana was obviously one strange cat, an eccentric man with probably no idea how strange he really was. My father turned to me, "Bruce, that was Sam Giancana for you, from Chicago. I hope he didn't upset you too much by when we first arrived."

Having been in that room with him, I knew Sam Giancana hated President Kennedy with extreme passion. What I didn't know was in less than three months, a young American President would have his brains blown out right down the street from where this meeting had been.

More Disturbed Than Anyone Knew

Several times during the summer, I wanted to go to my father and ask him if this had all been a bad dream, never real, and that he wasn't really involved in planning to murder Kenned. I desperately wanted to hear from him that U.S. Sonics was only what it had originally been; a business cleaning rocket engine parts.

There had been several ways I managed to escape the Kennedy assassination. But now, the night was usually the only way I could accomplish this. When my father was home, I would stay out as late as possible after the sun went down, then go home, eat a late dinner, and as soon as everyone else went to bed, go back outside again.

Because I wouldn't be able to sleep for hours for the never-ending ruminating about the upcoming assassination and what could go wrong. That Kennedy's wife and children would be left without a husband or father. Even if he were this terrible person that my father had portrayed, he was all that his wife and children had, so they would be terribly distraught when he died.

My walks in the middle of the night were miles long. I would go to the Golf Course and lay in the sand traps, holding the heat all night long from the hot summer sun. Sometimes I would take Stephen with me. I wasn't supposed to talk to anyone, not even my family, about the assassination; so of course, I didn't, and he knew nothing about it or what I was dealing with.

Other times, I would meet a few friends there to run through the sprinklers in the dark, a great relief from the heat. But if the night were cool, we would revert to the warmth of the sand traps where I often I found myself with my Italian friend and two girls. They would be talking about their fathers and the work they, while I could think only about my father, his conspiracy associates, and what I was living through. It would be totally unbelievable if I had wanted to tell them.

I was living two lives: one, as a boy of twelve and doing what boys do at twelve, and another involving men planning the assassination of the President of the United States. The contrast was amazing, mind-boggling. But even though it was bothering me so much, I accepted the strange life I was leading. What else could I do! I loved my father very much and if this was what he wanted, I would do it, without questioning him. But I was beginning to question him privately in my mind.

By August, I was beginning to feel so different, it was startling. Was it just that I was getting older, or because of the assassination. I had been a happy child, but now there were so many things bothering me, I was terribly confused, not happy at all; even though I did a pretty good job of faking it. But thinking about it, I realized this change had started after General Born's speech in November. But I hadn't been seriously bothered until now; I was being taken to U.S. Sonics much more often, as many as four days in a row when Orris was in town.

I felt guilty because at times, I found myself wishing Orris would go out of town, when he was out so much already. I still liked being around him, but he was changing quickly and not for the better. His over exposure to the Mafia was impacting him.

At the same time, I was feeling a real part of the Kennedy murder thing. Especial that such a powerful group of men would trust me this much, part of this very secret activity. How could I feel any different? I had been convinced they were about to kill someone on the same scale as the Devil. I was completely brainwashed. The constant ridicule and criticism of the Kennedy brothers had done to me what they wanted to do to everyone. I had come to hate the very word 'Kennedy.'

The beautiful pictures of a loving president with his children and wife on television contradicted all that I was hearing at U.S. Sonics, but I was convincingly told this was just the press trying to subvert the truth and attention of the public away from the real truth. So, I believed what my father and his men were saying. I had no choice.

But I felt alone as a child in it all and bothered, part of me beginning to not like it. They were going to kill someone and as a child, that frightened me. And there had never been anything before I couldn't talk to my friends about or even my brothers and sisters.

I knew I was the only child in the country experiencing this. And no one had asked my permission to be involved. I might have been my father's son, but I wasn't a rag doll. I had a brain of my own. If I had made a decision to kill the President, I would surely ask my father if he wanted to be involved, before I just made him part of it, whether he liked it or not.

More difficult, I was now beginning to see what my role had really been. Not a contributing part of their special group, but to a decoy to help disguise their activities. Although I was expected to show a certain amount of enthusiasm as they did, to voice support, I was only a utilitarian piece of this complex planning. Not that different from what I was beginning to realize Lee Harvey Oswald was, someone to use. And something I didn't realize at the time, someone to then dispose of and forget about, when it was all over and done.

But surely there had to be more to my involvement than what was on the surface. I couldn't understand what that reason was, but I knew there had to be. I earnestly hoped there was.

I couldn't say what I really wanted to now; that I had come to believe there had to be another way, other than killing this man. I had changed and this was obvious to me, but they were too engrossed and blind to see anything other than murder.

By mid-August, I was seriously feeling the stress. There was no longer any question as to the complete reality and inevitability of the assassination. In the spring, I had told myself that it was some kind of a dream. This really can't be happening with my father and me. He wouldn't really kill the president. I was in denial and had been trying to create every possible excuse or reason as to why this couldn't be true.

But that hadn't worked, no matter how hard I tried, I would be exposed to the reality again and again when a new player or information was introduced. It got so bad that at one point I found myself thinking of putting a gun to my head, seeing no alternative to this nightmare.

I really feel that if it wasn't for the girls I was involved with now, I probably would have taken my own life. They were able to take my mind off everything. Regardless, summer would soon be over and I would be going to the seventh grade, a big deal to me, and most importantly, I wouldn't have to go to U.S. Sonics so often.

16

FALL, 1963

Seventh Grade, But No Football

Just a few days after meeting Giancana, I started school at Meadowbrook Junior High. I was to enter the seventh grade, something I had looked forward to for a long time. It was a milestone for me, as it is with most children, a time when I no longer went to the same school as six-year-olds. I would now be one of the youngest, instead of the eldest, which was alright with me.

There was a secret reason I wanted to start school. I wouldn't be going to U.S. Sonics as often and I wouldn't be exposed to the assassination to the same degree. Little did I know the future would be a million times worse than what had already taken place, my hopes dashed on the pillars in Dealey Plaza.

But when the first weekend from school came, I found myself back at U.S. Sonics by nine Saturday morning, and again on Sunday. And

225

two days the following week, I was taken out of school to go to there. On the first, we had lunch with several men and, as usual, I sat there pretending not to listen or comprehend anything being said, something that had become very easy by now. The next, things were quat at the company. But after lunch, Charles Lundquist arrived from L.A., and we all went to his hotel, the Western Hills Inn, where I got my standard swimming in their beautiful pool, while the two men talked. And so, the routine was maintained

But maybe a bigger disappointment of September was to be football. I had been looking forward to playing for years because this would be the first time in a school-sponsored program. I had played in a privately organized league every fall since I was eight years old.

The brother of the school head coach was the man playing 'Hoss', Dan Blocker, on the popular television series 'Bonanza.' In fact, he looked just like his brother; the family was from Fort Worth and the brothers had grown up in the Texas football environment. Coach Blocker learned that I wanted to play football when I met him on the first day of school. He listened to me describe my experience and quickly concluded I might be just who he was looking for, a good running back or half-back, positions not that easy to come by. He gave me forms my parents needed to sign, and said he was looking forward to me being on the team.

But that night when I gave the forms to my mother, she unexpectedly told me I was going to have to talk with my father about it. This was very strange as she usually performed such duties as this, not him. I asked her what was wrong, but she only repeated that she couldn't make the decision. What was the problem? He had wanted me to play league football in the first place. And he knew how much I had been looking forward to playing this fall.

I knew it didn't have anything to do with my getting hurt. He had always encouraged me to play rough sports and my mother had never objected. They had supported me completely. In fact, it was my father who got me started playing football when I was eight. He had surprised me one fall by bringing home a new football helmet, football pads, cleats, along with a new football and said he wanted me to play. I hadn't even asked for this equipment.

So, why were they now being hesitant about football? Could it have something to do with the assassination? But what could my playing football have to do with their interest in killing Kennedy?

When my father got home that night, I immediately approached him to sign the forms. He hesitated, then said he hated to deny this, but it was because he still needed me to accompany him, and didn't want my coaches to become curious why I was missing practice and games. It would just be better all-around, if I didn't play this year. He would make it up to me, if I could understand how important it was for me to go with him.

Even though terribly disappointed, I accepted it and didn't give him a hard time, but tried to let it go the best I could. But I suspected one other reason he didn't want me to play football, was wanting me to not get that close to Coach Blocker; if I did, I might say something about the Kennedy assassination if the subject came up before, or even after.

When I didn't bring the forms back or report for practice, the coach came to my class to ask why. I could only answer I had changed my mind. He could tell I was disappointed and didn't seem to buy it. Of course, he asked me why and I told him part of the truth, my father didn't want me to play this year, and left it at that.

However, he continued to pry as to the real reason. He asked if I wanted him to talk to my father and I said, "No." It was clear that he was confused. After all, nearly every boy, especially those who had already played, was eager to play. And just a few days earlier, I had expressed a lot of enthusiasm. He apparently even talked with a few of my old coaches to learn my father was always very supportive. When he asked again if I was sure I didn't want him to talk with my father, and I replied I was sure, he obviously concluded the problem had something to do with my parents, not me. Still, he pursued the issue further, coming to my classroom a few days later when I was in Dallas.

My Teacher

The following day, my teacher also asked me why I was giving up football. Again, I explained it was my parents' wish. I didn't think the coach or my teacher was being overly nosey. They just knew how disappointed I was.

For some reason, she then posed a proposition, "Since you are not going to play football, Bruce, would you like to stay after school and help me grade papers and do other things I need help with?" It was common for teachers then to ask a student to help out after school. I knew my father would not want me to do this, for the same reason he didn't want me to play football, but after a few seconds thought, I impulsively answered, "Yes, I would like to do that." Being with her would make up for not being able to play football, but it was still very hard to let that go completely, and I found myself occasionally going to the practice field to watch from a distance.

My reaction to help her was also largely because I liked her very much. She was only about twenty and seemed to have a personality suited to my own. And besides, she was very pretty. This was her first year as a teacher, and because she was so young and I so old for my age, I nearly saw her as a peer, instead of someone I was supposed to be subordinate to.

So, I did help her when I actually attended. Being alone with her was a total opposite from being at U.S. Sonics with my father. We developed a private relationship different from any other I had had with someone her age. She was so nice to me, I couldn't help but fall in love with her. Even though I was twelve years old, in 1963 a relationship with a young teacher was more common and even accepted by many as normal. But even so, perhaps ours was too close. Regardless, I didn't want to lose this private time I had with her, especially since it took me away from the Kennedy assassination, another needed diversion.

This was obviously a situation I had to hide from my parents. To become this close to anyone outside of family could create serious problems, because this person could become concerned about my unusual activities, or I might inadvertently say something I shouldn't. So, I didn't tell them. "*They will never find out*", I thought.

Eventually my sporadic appearance at school constituted itself one of the 'unusual activities' Orris wanted me to avoid. And, sure enough, in the last week of September, alone after school one day, my teacher queried me about this. "Bruce, why have you been missing all of this school? Don't try and tell me you've been sick, you're strong as a bull." To cover my absences, my mother had been writing notes saying I had been ill. But it was the same note every time and, in reality, I was as healthy as a horse, if not a bull -- I wasn't sick one day during this time. So, it became ridiculous for me to bring such note.

My teacher didn't believe it, and I knew she didn't. Another situation I hadn't been prepared for because in the sixth grade, my teachers hadn't seemed to care when I was absent, hadn't said a word. When she asked me this question, I hesitated, so she knew something was wrong. I had spent a great deal of time with her by now, so she knew me quite well. Knew I wasn't telling her the truth. And I always was a terrible liar, anyway.

Nevertheless, I answered, "No, I was really sick." Sick and tired of going to Dallas was what I was sick of. So this wasn't a complete lie, allowing me to pull it off pretty well, without giving away too much.

Exasperated, she finally said, "OK, if you don't want to tell me the truth, I'll let it go at that." She had tolerated my answer for now, but I could tell she was becoming suspicious and very curious that something was going on behind the scene; what was I really doing when I didn't come to school?

Now, there was someone who was seriously questioning me and my unusual behavior. Someone who could sense something was wrong. And my seventh-grade homeroom teacher wasn't someone I could just avoid, because I spent all day with her, except for physical education and shop class, after which I would return to her room and stay after school, alone with her.

The relationship I had with her made me feel somewhat different from the other children. But I obviously felt different too because of the secret life I was leading, something they would never be able to imagine. A terrible, horrible secret I had to live with every day. Plus, I had so much more knowledge than most children about the politics of the world and how everything actually worked. So, I thought of myself as much older, living more in an adult's world, whereas they were naive children, still living in a child's world, playing children's games. The game I was now playing wasn't a children's game.

I had always been a very social child, both at school and out. But now I began to withdraw from this social world into myself. I no longer enjoyed being around children my own age the way I had before. I no longer felt like I fit into their lives. Besides, I didn't have a lot of time for social interaction.

I was putting off vibes I wasn't aware of, and that was something my teacher and others were noticing. I guess you can't be part of a clandestine plot to kill the President of the United States, be aware of all the secret goings on behind the scene, and still seem perfectly normal to others. Not when you are twelve years old, anyway. You just don't have these deceptive arts down, yet. But I was doing my best.

Oswald in Mexico

In mid-September, my father told us he was planning on going to Mexico City for ten days. He would usually go to Mexico City and Monterey at least three or four times a year, sometimes with my mother. I didn't know why he used to go there, but it wasn't on aerospace business. This time, he would be leaving in a few days and seemed unusually excited. In fact, he had seemed in a very good mood for the past two or three weeks since our visits with Sam Giancana.

Lee Oswald was still in New Orleans where for the past month he had been getting more and more concerned about what was going to happen to him after the assassination. A number of times, they had discussed a plan that would work for him, but he was becoming more and more concerned. In fact, they were beginning to worry he was getting 'cold feet.'

So, now they had to further convince him he would be well taken care of, when in fact, they fully intended to kill him and place the blame of the assassination completely on him. It was time to take care of the problem before he became any more upset. Lee had become by far too important to their overall plan to allow him to become any more paranoid. A trip to Mexico City would help.

Orris was a man raised around horses and knew that to put a bridle on a difficult horse, you used a little sugar to get it to come to you. He was a man who preferred this approach to life and its problems; applying his sugar theory to all his business dealings, he found it nearly always worked. So, rather than just telling Oswald arrangements had been made for his escape, Orris decided to get him to Mexico City to see these supposed arrangements for himself. The sugar would be the good time they could show him in Mexico City. For a change, everything would be for Lee and anything he wanted would be his.

So, in late September, Orris and Jeff Miller flew down to Mexico City to prepare for Lee's visit. Lee would take a bus from New Orleans to the Texas border, then change to a Mexican bus to Mexico City. He would check into a cheap hotel as a cover, which would serve later as documentation of his stay. Orris and Jeff would already be settled in a very expensive hotel, the same one Orris usually stayed in, and where Lee would actually spend most of his time with the two men and the designated CIA man, while working on finalizing their plan.

Lee had been reassured he would be treated like a hero in both Cuba and Russia for being implicated by the U.S. Government as the one who assassinated President Kennedy. The plan to get there, as outlined to Oswald, was that immediately following the assassination, he would be flown to Mexico City on a private plane. Using a Cuban visa, he would then board a commercial plane to Cuba, and then to Russia, where Marina and their two daughters would meet him to live the rest of their lives. This all seemed plausible to Lee, a plan that he liked. To further satisfy Oswald, Orris also told him that secret arrangements had been made with Cuba to accept and give him political asylum if necessary.

It was now time to take the first steps, get Lee a visa for Cuba, Russia, or both. Cuba seemed like the better option because he could get one there to Russia later, if not now. So, to satisfy both Oswald that the plan was real, as well as any post-assassination investigation, he would now go to both the Cuban and Russian Embassies several times. He would purposely create disturbances there so he would be unquestionably remembered by the embassy employees. The scenario of these actions—causing disturbances, obtaining a Cuban visa, and discussing relocating to Russia—would turn out to be one of the strongest single pieces of evidence to establish Oswald's Communist identity and his role as Kennedy's assassin.

After doing all this, it was now time to make Lee feel as though he were someone special to the assassination planners, and in reality, he was. Besides, for all three men a little vacation was well-deserved after ten months of continuous work setting everything up. Orris would try and make this trip as pleasant as possible by showing Lee a good time. Orris had come to like him but knew something that he didn't. He didn't have very much longer to live.

Orris was very familiar with Mexico City and always enjoyed. The only truly international city in Mexico and not just a vacation destination for the jet set, like Acapulco and a few others. So, he would take Lee to some of the better restaurants, the bullfights, and anywhere else Lee wanted. Here, in Mexico City, they could feel free to do whatever they wanted. In a population of millions, no one would remember three Americans doing the tourist thing in two months.

The high point of the trip would be a bullfight at the best arena. After that, the three would join the main bullfighter for dinner at one of the best restaurants. Orris was a fight *aficionado* and knew a great deal about it, as well as a number of world-class fighters and toreadors. (This particular bullfighter has come forward, talking about having dinner with Lee Oswald and two other men in Mexico City in September 1963).

So, Orris had accomplished his goal. Lee was now back in line and ready to go forward with the next phase of the assassination planning. After the trip, he returned to Dallas permanently, bringing back several gifts for Marina from the bullfight, well- documented in the Warren Commission Report.

Orris, himself, arrived back home on about the third of October, a bright, warm Saturday morning. He seemed very excited as he took us all out to his car, opening the trunk to show us the gifts he had brought back. This was unusual for him, something special. Occasionally, he would bring back gifts from trips for my mother or sisters and sometimes, for my brothers and me; but gifts for all of us was rare. It was something of a ceremony as he passed them out in the driveway to all seven of us. He had expensive dresses and jewelry for my mother and sisters and handmade cowboy boots for my brothers and me.

But besides these gifts, he gave me an unusual one, two very colorful pairs of the picks placed in the bull's neck by the bullfighter during a ceremonial, but very dangerous process before the actual fight. These picks were bloodied from the fight they had attended in Mexico City, and I thought were representative of the soon to happen killing of Kennedy. The danger to the fighter when he placed these picks in the bull's neck, seemed similar to the danger Orris was experiencing in the planning of the assassination.

As for Oswald, he now attempted to find work at Padgett Printing. a different firm from where he had worked previously. He was refused the job because of a bad job report from the previous employer, Bob Stovall, who said Lee was a troublemaker and Communist. Having Stovall give this bad report was part of the ongoing set up of Lee, further marking him as a Communist and a nut. The plan all along was to have Lee hired at the Dallas School Book Depository.

Ruth Paine and Marina Oswald

When I met Michael Paine with my father in 1962, I had heard Ruth's name. The two had since separated amicably. But I first started hearing her associated with the assassination in March, even before she became Marina Oswald's handler, taking over from the DeMohrenschildts when they left.

Orris had foreseen an obvious problem, what to do with Marina and the baby, while working with Lee. For one thing, they needed someone who spoke Russian; but it would practically be easier to find a dog that spoke Spanish, than a suitable woman who spoke Russian and could be trusted inside the assassination.

There couldn't have been a more perfect individual available in the Dallas/Fort Worth area than Ruth. He knew he would have to talk her into taking part in the assassination as Marina and baby June's caretaker. But there was another problem. Lee was having difficulties keeping up with both living and assassination-related expenses. And just giving him money was out of the question, in keeping with the need to maintain his independent image.

To further complicate matters, Lee and Marina began fighting, probably because of the severe stress they were under. The planners were very concerned that this could ruin everything. Lee, and therefore Marina, were integral to the project.

So in February, Ruth had been introduced to the Oswald by the DeMohrenschildts as a potential solution for both problems. Ruth was fronted as a kind and helpful Quaker woman, coming to their aid by providing food and other basic needs for Marina and baby June. Then in early April, Marina and June moved in with Ruth. Meanwhile, Lee rented a room in Dallas, but stored belongings at Ruth's home.

Lee and Marina continued to spend time together and, in fact, she would follow him to New Orleans after he moved there in April. In September, Ruth visited her sister, Sylvia Hyde Hoke, who lived in Virginia, close to CIA headquarters in Langley, where both she and her husband worked. On her way home, Ruth drove directly to New Orleans to take Marina back to Dallas when Lee made his Mexico City trip.

I saw Ruth with Marina on several occasions. Orris took me to Ruth's house in Irving at least twice. The small wood frame house was only about eleven to twelve hundred square feet. I got the impression she had moved from a larger house, bringing everything with her because it was cluttered with furniture. The little tables and hutches were somewhat mismatched, of simple design, not cheap, but hardly expensive and not fashionable at all. Neat and clean, not worn. The backyard was fairly large for a small house with well-watered Saint Augustine grass and several small trees.

When I first met her, I did not like her because she seemed very evil. I knew all too well that the role she was playing with Marina and Lee was false. In reality, she no more cared about them than a cat cares about a bird it has just caught and is about to devour. I thought of her as a very good CIA soldier, who enjoyed her role in the conspiracy. I think that Marina couldn't help but feel this; she was a sensitive woman and her body language conveyed that.

On the first visit with my father in the spring, we stayed about forty-five minutes. Marina, June, and I were in the living room, while Orris and Ruth went into the kitchen to talk privately. Marina still didn't seem able to speak any English, so we sat there somewhat uncomfortably and watched June play on the floor.

As always, I was taken by Marina's beauty; she reminded me of a younger version of my own mother. Blonde hair, blue eyes, and the same facial features. I felt sorry for her, an innocent in the middle of all this hate and deception. And surely, she had to sense something very strange and evil was in the works; I wouldn't be surprised if Lee hadn't shared the story with her. This caused me to feel closer to her than she realized.

I saw Ruth twice during the summer, late June and early August, when Marina was in New Orleans with Lee. On each of these visits lasting about thirty minutes, I was sent out to the back yard. Something unusual because Orris had long since stopped hiding anything from me. I began to conjecture that something sexual was going on.

I didn't see Ruth again until October, surprised to also see Marina had returned from New Orleans, just as had Lee. It was good to see her again because I had thought about her several times during the summer, wondering if I would ever see her again. After about fifteen minutes and iced tea in the kitchen, Orris suggested Marina and I go outside in the backyard with the baby, while he talked with Ruth alone. I thought he wasn't concerned about my hearing their discussion, but what Marina would hear. But even though she had learned some English by this time, and she had said, "hello," when we first arrived, her English surely didn't seem as good as my father thought it might be; I don't believe she would have been able to understand him, if we had stayed in the house.

I assume the topic of their conversation had to do with Lee's role in the assassination. Perhaps Orris, knowing how attached I had become to him, was still trying to protect me from knowing what his role was to be, certainly the eventual fatal outcome. I doubt Ruth knew about Lee's planned demise either. She was to be utilized to point him to a job at the Dallas School Book Depository and was obviously more involved with the assassination plot than just as Marina's caretaker.

Marina and I were out at the picnic table with June at our feet for probably thirty minutes. I was amazed at how much June had changed since I had first met her; she was now walking. I had seen her probably ten times altogether in the past year and was comfortable with her. I liked her and the fact she was from Russia was still fascinating. I wanted to ask her more questions, but it was too difficult to get across to her what I was trying to say without anyone to translate for us. Last time she had been pregnant, but not now; she must have just had her new baby which must have been asleep in the house.

It was hot for October, but in Dallas, it can get hot in October. Ruth came out to ask us inside for iced tea. She then sat down to translated for us, while we asked Marina questions about her life in America, in Russia and the comparison, as well about her new baby. I actually did most of the questioning, not my father. By the way he was talking to her, it became apparent he had been around her enough to the point she was comfortable with him.

We were at the house for about two hours and then went back to U.S. Sonics. I didn't see Ruth's children that day or Michael and, in fact, didn't even know at the time, they had any children.

Backup Plans, Miami, and Los Angeles

The planners felt it was essential to kill Kennedy before the next presidential election in November 1964. There were backup plans in Miami and Los Angeles if for some reason, it couldn't happen in Dallas. Dallas was always the primary desired site, but there had always been concerns, even after Johnson's manipulation of Kennedy, that plans might have to be changed. President Kennedy could be unpredictable, as he had proven in the past few years. And even though it could lead to political problems in the upcoming election, he could possibly avoid Dallas and go to other large cities in Texas to achieve his political goals.

Miami was their preferred alternative option because Santo Trafficante had the necessary influence and control in Florida for an assassination and the following investigation. Even living in Tampa Bay, he still controlled the Mafia in Miami and Florida, in general. And, importantly, if they couldn't get Kennedy to Dallas in the fall of 1963, they were sure they could get him to Miami. They knew absolutely he would go there during the presidential campaign, sometime between late 1963 and the end of summer 1964. In fact, he would probably make at least two trips there.

The plan for these two other cities was essentially the same as that for Dallas. Move Oswald and the three practiced shooters and carry out a similar scenario. Blame the entire event on Oswald and then, of course, kill him as soon as possible.

So, during the summer, before the effort to get Kennedy to Dallas had been assured, work on the alternate plans continued. Orris made a number of trips to Miami and Tampa Bay to see Trafficante and the men helping him there. Similarly, Lundquist and Orris would meet frequently about plans for Los Angeles.

And when they found out that Vice President Lyndon Johnson had accomplished his effort to get Kennedy to Texas, they didn't scrap their alternate plans. Anything could happen to stop the Dallas plans. Even on the planned day of the assassination. They waited until the president was dead, before they terminated Miami and Los Angeles' plans.

The Dallas Parade Route

As early as March, I had heard my father and the Dallas planners talking about shooting President Kennedy while he was in a parade. Other than that, I wasn't made aware of where the actual attempt would be made, until afterward. I did know from the media, he was to arrive first in Fort Worth where he would make public appearances, spend the night, and then fly from Carswell Air Force Base to Dallas Love Field.

The planners would do everything they could to anticipate the parade route before getting the final word in mid-November. If necessary, they would then attempt to influence it through their people in Dallas and Washington. The one thing they knew, he was expected to give a speech at the Dallas Trade Mart.

Looking at past parade routes through downtown Dallas, even some that had involved presidents, gave them a good idea of where this parade would most likely travel. The traditional 'parade route' for politicians for many decades had been along Main St. and through Dealey Plaza. This had been the route that Forrest Sorrels, the Secret Service agent in Dallas, was likely to propose; he had participated in a 1936 visit by President Franklin D. Roosevelt using that same route.

But there was a logical reason the parade route should be changed. First, the traditional route had proceeded west to east, but Kennedy's drive from the airport to the Trade Mart would be east to west and would require entering the North Stemmons Expressway, which could only be done from Elm St.

Second, as the planners themselves traversed this route, they started looking at buildings and settings that could be used. They needed a place to put Lee Oswald and three shooters in various positions that could be coordinated into the overall shooting scenario. They immediately concluded that Dealey Plaza had to have been designed and built with the Kennedy assassination in mind. It was obvious, they couldn't have asked for anything better than this.

The first advantage of this location was the Dallas School Book Depository, a block north of Main St., would provide the perfect and easy position in which to place Oswald. They had no concern about the probability of making the killing shot from here, because it would only be a decoy shot and a way to pin the assassination on Oswald. And with the building that housed the Depository being owned by D.H. Byrd, a close associate of the Texas Oil Group, Ruth Paine would have no problem in getting Oswald hired there. Coincidentally, on the day of the assassination, Byrd would be on an African safari.

Walking the Plaza, looking for the best locations for the three actual shooters, the planers decided to locate two of them behind the picket fence on the grassy knoll on the north side of Elm St. and the third on top of the Dal-Tex building on the northeast corner of Elm and North Houston Streets, across from the Depository. The elevated location on the grassy knoll was perfect because it was concealed and could provide an easy quick escape route. And, obviously important, it was a site that would make the shooting of President Kennedy easy for the two experienced riflemen. They simply could not miss.

But, in order to utilize Dealey Plaza, other changes in the parade route were needed. Commonly it went directly through the center of the Plaza on Commerce Street, a distance from the Book Depository, the grassy knoll, and the Dal-Tex Building. Instead, the planners needed the parade to make a right turn off of Main Street onto Houston St., as it got to the east side of the Plaza, and then make another turn left on the north side onto Elm. This would make the parade pass directly in front of the Book Depository and then the grassy knoll. This route would now give the President maximum exposure to the expected crowds and while slowed down, to the actual shooters.

In addition, some Secret Service presidential parade protocols needed change. Making these two turns would slow the limousine below the desired speed the Service would normally allow, and for a longer period of time, both of which were actually desired. Other problems with the normal Secret Service parade protocols would be overcome as well.

And as anticipated, when Sorrels finally announced the parade route, it was indeed the traditional route, but included the necessary modifications that the assassins needed.

But there were other issues needing to be addressed. For instance, they needed to find locations for the multitude of support people. They needed to manipulate such things as the parade vehicle layout, the presidential limousine driver, blocking parking areas so they wouldn't be used. And they would have to do all these things without going too far and giving away their real motives to the wrong people. The CIA people were instrumental in solving many of these problems.

But the biggest problem was developing a foolproof escape route for the actual shooters from the picket fence behind the grassy knoll. A clean, quick, and secure escape. And to leave no evidence that it wasn't Oswald's shot that had killed the President or that he had acted alone. No actual shooter could be killed or apprehended; so a waiting automobile in the parking lot just a few feet away on the west side of the Depository, would be easy to arrange.

Fulminate of Mercury-Tipped Bullet

I first started hearing Orris talk about a 'fulminate of mercury-tipped bullet' in early October. He was talking with Jeff Miller, General Born, Lundquist, Lyon, and others. After hearing the term for about a week, I asked him what it was.

He explained very clearly what it was and how this exploding bullet is made. He told me a small hole, about one eighth of an inch in diameter, is drilled into the nose of a 30.06 bullet, about three-fourths of the length of the bullet deep. The hole is filled with fulminated mercury, stopped with a brass plug, and then sealed with hot plastic or wax. Any good gunsmith could make such a bullet, provided he has the fulminated mercury. It's that easy.

Orris said this bullet would explode when it hit its intended target and break into tiny pieces, resulting in severe damage. I knew they intended to use this bullet to shoot President Kennedy and when I later heard that Kennedy's head 'seemed to explode', I knew it was the 'fulminate of mercury- tipped bullet' that had done the job.

Was Kennedy Aware?

Kennedy was warned by his staff of threats against his life if he were to go to Dallas. And Billy Graham unsuccessfully sought to meet him to warn he had a "foreboding" of tragedy befalling the President during such a trip. One could speculate whether his foreboding was because of his close alliance and association with the Texas Oil Barons.

And there was another omen. On the warm October 5 morning, his meeting of the National Security Council in the Rose Garden was interrupted by daughter Caroline. She just had to recite his favorite poem by Alan Seeger, written prior to his World Ward I death, which began, "I shall have a rendezvous with Death," and ends, "And I go my pledged word and true. I shall not fail that rendezvous." After she finished, the National Security advisors, most of whom were opposed to his attempts to bring peace with Russia, were stunned to silence. Kennedy reiterated his pledge. If God had a place for him, he was prepared for whatever destiny awaited.

But there were other possible warnings. Two from his clandestine affairs. One from Mary Pinchot Meyer, ex-wife of Cord Meyer who headed the CIA's International Division responsible for covert "removal" of governments and assassinations, and so undoubtedly knew of Kennedy's assassination; we can only speculate whether in one of their bitter fights about her affair, he informed her. Mary was assassinated eleven months after JFK. Toward the end of his life, Cord was asked if he knew who killed her. He replied. "The same sons of bitches that killed Joon F. Kennedy;" the implication being her murder was because of her knowledge.

The second "affair" was the well-k own one with Judith Campbell Exner, simultaneously involved with Sam Giancana.

The Italian Restaurant and My Evolving

It was obvious that Orris' involvement with the Mafia had steadily increased during the past year. One beautiful, warm late October afternoon, after returning the day before from Southern California where he had been with Chuck Lundquist and Johnny Roselli, he came home unusually early. He announced he was taking the entire family to dinner at a very good Italian restaurant. This was unusual for him. Obviously, he had eaten there before and more than likely knew the owner, who I'm sure was Italian.

I immediately knew he was up to something the second he mentioned 'Italian Restaurant.' And he seemed strange this evening, not himself. His expression wasn't normal, but I had seen it before. It looked as if the devil were lurking somewhere in his deviant mind. He was up to something not normal, just to amuse himself at the expense of his naive family. Granted, there would be no harm to his family, they wouldn't even know what was going on, only Orris and I would. It is strange that a man so deviant could have a family that was so innocent and appeared on the surface to be so normal.

My brothers, sisters, and mother were excited by this unexpected announcement. There had been little attention paid to the family since October of 1962. Our father had been far too busy with the planning of the assassination. All eight of us loaded into one automobile to head off to dinner at a restaurant unknown to the family. Fifteen minutes later, we were pulling into the parking lot of this 'Italian Restaurant' on Lancaster Blvd.

I recognized it immediately; being right across the street from the Meadowbrook Theater, I had frequented it myself with friends, usually various girlfriends after a movie. Twice, a girlfriend's parents had come to pick her up and invited me to dinner there. It had the setting and feel of an Italian villa. The first time, it seemed as strange on the inside as on the outside. I was always captured by some strange aura emanating from it. The light dim, with candles glowing everywhere. Wine bottles covered in straw hanging from the walls. The waitresses dressed in traditional Italian garb.

During these dinners, my mind couldn't help but wander to my father's involvement with the Italian Mafia in the assassination. I had been saturated with Italian names: Joseph Civello, Carlos Marcello, Santo Trafficante, Johnny Roselli, Sam Giancana, and these were but a few. So, when I was there, my mind would be occupied with visions of Italian architecture and Italian looking men being with my father. It felt very strange to sit with a normal American family in an Italian restaurant, knowing not only my father's involvement in the upcoming assassination, but also his involvement with the Italian Mafia in it.

Now, my first thought was, *"Oh no, now he's going to ruin this place for me."* By this point, my feelings about the assassination and everything about it had begun to change. The excitement of being the only child in the world with this dark secret, and to be directly involved with its glamour and the close association with these powerful men, had begun to wane. Not only had it begun to wane, I was now beginning to believe that maybe they were all demented and insane.

No longer did I feel like an extremely privileged child. Rather, I felt forlorn, used, and lost. Lost in a nightmare out of control which severely frightened me. Frightened about what could happen to my father. Frightened about what could happen to my mother. Frightened about what could happen to my sisters and brothers. Frightened about what could happen to America. And frightened about what could happen to me.

On top of all this, it bothered me that it was murder, murder of the President of the United States, a man with a family, who would probably feel the same pain, sorrow, and fear as me. I had always been taught that murder was wrong. Despite all I had heard that was wrong with Kennedy and his bringing danger to the nation and the world, I believed in my heart that there had to be another way. There had to be a way of removing this danger, besides killing this man.

And besides, I didn't like the Italian Mafia. They were purveyors of all that was evil and wrong. Everything I had heard about them had been bad. I knew what prostitution was. I knew gambling could ruin people's lives. I knew the Mafia employed 'Hit Men.' If my father and his associates were so concerned about the welfare of the people in the world, why were they so involved and concerned with the Mafia and its future in America. It was obviously not similarly concerned about the safety of the people.

When we arrived at the restaurant, my mother and siblings were excited and quickly got out of the car. On the other hand, I was slow to get out, and stayed back with my father to have a word about why he was taking us to this particular restaurant. It all seemed strange, unnecessary, and maybe even risky. I'm certain, now, my thoughts at the time were overly cautious, but I had thought the plan was to keep my siblings in the dark about the assassination and the Mafia's involvement as much as possible.

He was grinning at his family's enthusiasm to get into the restaurant in a hurry and asked him, "What's with this?"

"What do you mean?"

"You know what I mean, this Italian restaurant. What are you doing by bringing them here?"

"Nothing, it's just an Italian restaurant."

"You've been involved with the Italian Mafia all year long and there is more to this than just an Italian restaurant. I can tell by that look on your face."

He looked at me, shocked that I would say this to him, here in this parking lot, but barely suppressing a grin on his face, now that he knew I understood what this Italian game of his was. "Bruce, I'll do what I want to do, I have my reasons. Let's catch up with them; the Maître d' knows we're coming."

I let it go at that, but it was clear to me that he wasn't acting like himself any longer. He was getting some demented, self-serving pleasure out of taking his innocent family to this Italian restaurant. He was leading a covert life with the CIA, the Mafia, and a number of other treacherous groups, in the planning to murder the president. And this now was his way of amusing himself. To feel he could bring his family this close to the life he was leading daily and which they didn't even know. They had no idea what his bringing us to this restaurant was about, what it really meant to him.

Inside, the Maître d' knew my father and treated us importantly. I kept looking at my father to see what he was up to. I could still see clearly, in that expression on his face, that he was up to something. He had this way of being the only one who knew what was going on and I could always tell when he was doing this because I knew him so well. He would have this half-grin, half-smirk on his face; a look that was unmistakable, like a Cheshire cat about to eat the canary. I knew he was thinking, "*This secret world I am so involved in with the Mafia is so different from this one with these little children. It amuses me that I can do this, lead these entirely separate lives.*" This was all just a game to him, bringing his family to this Italian restaurant and I was beginning to get to him.

Regardless, we had a very good dinner as far as the food went. My brothers and sisters seemed to enjoy themselves. But this event added one more piece to the confusing puzzle I was trying to put together with only the pieces they provided me. I was smart enough to know that the game had to be getting very dangerous. I wasn't afraid for myself, as much as for my father and family. He was not only in potential physical danger, but maybe more imminent, in psychological danger.

The Rifle Rack

Now being in the seventh grade, I had the choice of two elective courses. Wanting to make something for my father and something for my mother, I took a wood shop class, as one of my electives. I decided first to make a rifle rack out of mahogany for my father. I was able to get a set of plans from my shop teacher, a three-rifle rack, as nice as I could make it with my very limited woodworking experience. I was very excited about this project because my father always kept his rifles in a bedroom closet. This rack would give him an option to have three of them out where he could see them.

It took me about five weeks to finish, and I was able to take it home the second week of October, shortly after he returned home from Mexico City. Shop class was in the morning, so since I was going to bring the rack home that afternoon, I took it back to my homeroom. I set it against the wall behind my teacher's desk since it was too big to put under my own. When I stayed after school that day, she asked me why I had chosen a gun rack to make. I told her it was a surprise for my father who was a deer hunter and didn't have a gun rack for his rifles.

I hadn't even told my mother I was making this rack, and I was so proud of it, I showed it to her when I got home. But her reaction was strange. She looked at it for a moment, not seeming to know what to say, a little confused. I asked her what was wrong. She hesitated, before replying, "Nothing,"

She was looking at it in a way that said she couldn't quite believe that I was holding such a thing in my hands and for my father. I asked her again what was wrong, and she answered, "Nothing, nothing is wrong," she was just surprised that it was a rifle rack. I thought maybe she knew something I didn't about his desire to keep his rifles in the closet, or something else I didn't know about his rifles. And she just didn't want to disappoint me, now that I had made my father this gift.

When I asked her if he were coming home tonight, she confirmed it would be before it was too late. When he did get home a few hours later, I immediately went to him in his bedroom, rifle rack in my hands. My mother hadn't had a chance to say anything to him about it yet. He looked at me as I came through the door and then down at the rack in my hands. Immediately, a look of confusion appeared on his face.

I walked over to him and held it out to him, "Daddy, I made this for you." He looked at it for several seconds as though he couldn't believe what he was seeing. He didn't move to take it from me, but actually took a step back, looking down at it in my hands. I looked up at his face full of disbelief and confusion about something I couldn't grasp at all.

I could only ask, "What's wrong? Don't you like it?" Here I had only wanted to surprise my parents; the first thing I had ever made out of wood, and I was very proud of it. He glanced over at my mother standing there with us, and I could clearly see a look now, telling me there was something wrong. I asked him again, but with more feeling, what was wrong. They both just stood there, as if frozen, looking back and forth at each other, and at the gun rack extended from my hands.

He suddenly realized by the disappointed look on my face that his response was making me believe he didn't like it. At last, he reached out and took it from me, but as though it were hot. I looked at it to see if I could determine what he was seeing, something wrong with it

I hadn't noticed. But it looked fine to me, "*I did a good job making it. It's only q rifle rack, after all.*"

He looked over at my mother again as if trying to confirm something with her, finally gathered his composure, smiled, and said, "Thank you, Bruce." He seemed to understand that there was no hidden meaning, malice, or otherwise, on my part. I had made the gun rack from love for him. He laid it down on his bed, reached out to hug me a long one, and then put his hands on the sides of my head to give me that kiss on the cheek he did when really wanting to express his love.

But his reaction to the rack still seemed very strange. It seemed, as though he were feeling something I didn't understand. Odd in a way, because I had gotten to know him very well in the past eleven months. We no longer needed to say much to each other to know what the other was thinking. I could read him, as he could me. But we weren't communicating at all that day.

For six months now, I had known my father would shoot the President with a 30.06 rifle, a little over a month from the time I gave him the rifle rack. But, in no way, had I made the rack for him with any thought in mind of that. I made it because he was a hunter, mainly a deer hunter, and I thought he needed a better place to put his rifles other than in his closet.

Now looking back at my making the rifle rack just a few months before the assassination, I think it may have been a subliminal reaction. A subliminal worry, or maybe an attempt, on my part to cry out to him to put the Remington semi-auto rifle away and replace it with his deer hunting rifles. Not to do this treacherous deed.

17

THE LAST MONTH BEFORE THE ASSASSINATION

Activity at U.S. Sonics

In the last month before the assassination, things got even quieter. They had decided not to take any unnecessary chances of exposure, so moved all their meetings there elsewhere. Everyone was tense, though trying not to show it. Reality was upon them, but they were also confident.

I accompanied Orris to Dallas only six or seven times. Lee Oswald visited U.S. Sonics a few times, and we spent more time together during those few visits than before, because it was of the quiet. Orris, Nesbitt, and General Born would still be on the telephones constantly, talking with people all over the country. Nesbitt seemed more involved, and my father and I met with him twice at the Dallas Athletic Club, where he was a member. They would actually get on a handball court to talk;

it was strange and amusing to see my father, who didn't play the game, out there trying to play.

We also met there with several others, influential in one way or another. After they finished at the Club, we would all go to lunch for a couple of hours at a good restaurant nearby. Otherwise, lunch might be with anyone from Lee Oswald to Jack Ruby to Joe Civello or with someone I would only see that once and never see or hear of again.

Nesbitt, my father, and I would go back to U.S. Sonics late in the afternoon. They would make phone calls for two or three hours; often until it was fairly late. Then, occasionally, my father and I would meet someone for dinner. If General Born or Lundquist were in town, it would usually be with them. Nesbitt or my Godfather, Jeff Miller would sometimes join us.

Of course, during this time, the assassination was the only thing on anyone's mind and the only thing being discussed. It seemed there was always another problem, or possibility of one, to be dealt with. Always someone who needed reassurance in one way or another.

As planned, a few weeks before the assassination, the military went on special maneuvers at several strategic locations around the world. SAC's secret alert status would last several weeks after, with the ruse of a possible problem with the U.S.S.R. which was informed these were routine.

The Dallas Police Uniform

I usually arrived home from school later than my brothers and sisters because of my staying to work with my teacher. About three weeks before the assassination, I came home one day to what seemed like an abnormally quiet house. And when I called out to see if anyone was here, no one answered. This seemed strange, so I walked back through the house to see if I could find anyone.

My parents' bedroom door was partially open and when I looked in, my mother was sitting on her bed, sewing. Looking closer, I saw she was sewing cuffs onto a pair of pants which had a distinct stripe running down the side of the legs, like a military uniform. I had never seen her sew anything not belonging to our family.

Before saying anything, I glanced over at the closet door handle, where a police uniform jacket was hanging. When I went to have a closer look at the jacket, it turned out to have a Dallas Police insignia patch on the shoulder, making it part of a dress Dallas Police uniform, obviously matching the pants, she was sewing.

I was trying to figure out what this uniform was doing in their bedroom and why she was sewing the pants. My mother was now watching me very closely, so I asked her the question she knew was coming, "Who does this Dallas Police uniform belong to, and why are you sewing the pant cuffs?"

She stopped sewing and looked at me as if she didn't know quite what to say. I asked further, "Daddy isn't going to join the Dallas Police, is he?" I knew this was ridiculous, my father would never join the police, but it seemed like a question I had to ask. She looked right at me and said simply, "Ask your father," and went back to sewing, as though she didn't want to answer any more questions about this mysterious uniform.

I went out to play in the neighborhood until it was getting dark. But the uniform kept coming back in my mind. It couldn't be for Halloween; that had already passed.

When I finally went back home, my father's car was in the driveway. Energized, I went in and straight back to his bedroom. I needed an answer to this perplexing question.

And sure enough, my father was standing, wearing the uniform pants, and just slipping on the jacket. Even more puzzled, I asked him straight out, "Why are you putting on that Dallas Police uniform, Daddy?"

He looked over at me and thought for a second, seeming to be searching for the right answer. It never came, he could only answer, "Never mind, Bruce." Regrettably, I knew this answer. I had heard it many times before. It meant, don't ask him again.

So, I kept my mouth shut and watched him as he looked in the mirror to check the fit. To my eye, it seemed to fit him very well, and he seemed satisfied. Dissatisfied, I finally turned around and left the room. It was apparent I wasn't going to get any more out of either of them. I assumed the answer was my father wasn't going to join the Dallas Police.

I think the main reason he reacted the way he did was because my mother was there with us. He didn't want her to learn how much I knew about the assassination, especially that he was going to be a shooter. I was even forbidden from talking about the assassination with my mother.

He would wear this Dallas Police uniform on the day of the assassination, as would the other two shooters, Charles Lyon and Tom Lawrence. He also would wear a regular Dallas Police uniform, when he went to talk with Lee Oswald at the Dallas Police Station, after Lee was arrested

Jack Ruby Before the Assassination

I saw Ruby with my father twice in October, and everything seemed normal between them, or as normal as things could possibly be under such strange circumstances. The next time was early November, less than three weeks before the assassination was to take place. I had answered a number of phone calls at home over the past year from men I knew were involved, but none were like those from Ruby now.

Every day I did attend school, I would usually get home around five thirty. If the phone rang shortly after, it normally would be one of my girlfriends. I had several now, so I always eagerly answered, almost like a ritual.

The first time Ruby called, I was sitting at my father's desk, the late afternoon sun shining across it, and the house was quiet. A man politely asked, "Is Orris there?"

I didn't recognize his voice because he sounded so strange and excited. I just answered, "No, he's not home yet."

He then identified himself, "This is Jack Ruby, Bruce. Have your father call me as soon as he comes in. Do you expect him home soon?"

I was surprised that he not only remembered my name, but obviously recognized my voice. "I'm not sure when he will be home, Mr. Ruby."

"Do you know where I can find him?"

"Have you tried U.S. Sonics yet?"

"Of course, but he wasn't there. Tell him to call as soon as he gets home. Do you have a writing pat there, Bruce?

"Yes, I'll write it down right now."

"Don't forget. Tell Orris, as soon as he gets home, to call me."

"OK, I will."

He then hung up, leaving me rather bewildered. *"He's obviously coming unglued. I know he's involved in the assassination, but why is he so upset?"*

When Orris came in about nine that evening, I told him about Ruby's call. "He sounded pretty excited and to make sure you called him as soon as you come in. Right away!"

A little more than a week later, Ruby called again at the same time and with the same questions. But this time, I recognized his voice, and he sounded worse, more desperate, more excited, nearly out of breath. I could only give him the same answers and assurance I would tell my father to call. This time Orris didn't arrive before I went to bed, but I left him a note.

The calls were repeated twice, closer to the date of the assassination, the last about four days before, but with even more urgency. I always remembered to tell my father. After this, I never saw or heard from Ruby again. Apparently, he called nearly everyone he knew in the few weeks prior to the assassination, as his phone records indicated and documented in the Warren Report.

I believe he called out of hysteria, thinking he might very well be dead in just a few days. He had been given an order by Sam Giancana to kill Oswald, if Oswald had managed to avoid being shot by the others, as planned. If Ruby didn't carry out this order, then he himself would be executed by the Mafia. And Ruby of course, knew this. He had no choice.

Anticipating the Investigation

Anticipating the inevitable investigation and how to control it was almost as important as the planning of the assassination itself. The planners believed they would be able to control it, but they weren't going to take any chances. Their biggest concern was to keep the actual instigators unknown, to save the men in Washington, who in fact, were the real assassins. Implicating the CIA, Joint Chiefs of Staff, LeMay, Dulles, and politicians such as Johnson, would be an obvious disaster, not only for them, but for the country and potentially, the whole world.

One of the most important tasks was to get any investigations out of the hands of the Dallas and State of Texas authorities, as quickly as possible. They could be serious threats, if they uncovered the truth, and not as easily controlled as federal authorities. So steps were taken, well in advance of the assassination. I recall them talking in October and November about what Lyndon Johnson should do immediately to control the cover-up. Chief Justice Warren was mentioned and a formal committee anticipated which they would need to impede by restricting funding.

Their approach had begun with their long campaign by painting Oswald as the obvious assassin, the lone nut, communist conspirator, acting alone, but on behalf of Cuba or the USSR, with no obvious ties to the planners. This had been the most complex part of the planning, but I think they went way too far and made it a lot more complex than it had to be. So complex and perfect, an intelligent observer could easily see it as a cover-up and not reality.

If this cover-up wasn't completely working, or if Oswald hadn't already been killed, the use of Jack Ruby to assassinate him would be the beginning of intentionally blaming the assassination on the Mafia. If the post-assassination investigation couldn't be stopped at Jack Ruby, as it was in reality, then Carlos Marcello, Santo Trafficante, Sam Giancana, and, potentially, the entire American Mafia would have to go down, thrown to the public.

The next layer essentially focused on Orris and U.S. Sonics. They didn't believe the investigation would go that far, but if it did, they wanted to make sure it did not go any further. So, the CIA told Orris at the very beginning, to use only people he knew personally in the actual Dallas on-site planning, and as participants. They would try to stop it there by saying that yes, Orris was completely responsible, along with the Mafia and a radical group of extremists, nearly all from the Dallas/Fort Worth area.

The major problem with that plan was General Charles Born and his connections to LeMay and the hierarchies in the Pentagon and Washington. This was something largely unavoidable. Born had already been firmly associated with Orris and U.S. Sonics, before it was decided to use them, but in the end, if it came to it, Orris Bell would really be the ultimate 'fall guy.'

Of course, what actually occurred were the deaths of hundreds of individuals within the first few years. People, like journalist, Dorothy Kilgallen.

I Consider Betrayal

I don't think my father ever expected that one day I might disagree with what they had planned and that I might become a danger to them, now or in the future. I might develop a mind of my own. Surely as his son, I would share the same political beliefs and the same moral and ethical values.

At the beginning of the planning, in early November 1962, I had been convinced that Kennedy was as bad as I was told he was by my father and his people. But as the planning evolved, I thought there was a possibility something might happen to stop the assassination or the planning, because it all seemed so impossible. However, after Born's speech, I was fully convinced it was going to take place, but then from time to time, I would oscillate on this. But then, with Lyndon Johnson's maneuvering to bring Kennedy to Dallas, I knew there was now no turning back, and late November 1963 was when it would take place.

At the same time, I wasn't sure there wasn't another way to deal with the Kennedy problem. And I felt if I didn't do something now, in early November 1963 to stop it, it would happen. Surely, no one else I knew would.

My own feelings about Kennedy now, so shortly before the assassination, were mixed. I didn't believe he was nearly as bad as my father had told me and I didn't necessarily believe there would be a nuclear war, if he wasn't killed. I had read enough about his administration that I had formed my own opinion. If anything, Kennedy was his own worst enemy by trying to do so much more than what was possible and making enemies of people he should have known better than to do so; Allen Dulles for one, General Curtis LeMay for another.

So, I felt I should at least look at trying to do something to stop the assassination, because if I didn't, Kennedy was more than likely a dead man. But obviously, if I were to take some action, there would be tremendous consequences. My first concern was my father and family; if I exposed the plans, my parents would be arrested, and we children would be scattered. I also thought about the families of the other men whom I knew personally, who were involved. What would happen to them if I went to the authorities?

After working through this for a couple of days, I began to consider how I could go about actually exposing the assassination plans. The Dallas and Fort Worth police departments were out of the question because I knew for a fact I couldn't trust them; members of both were involved. I also knew that people within the FBI and, of course, both federal and local CIA agents, were participating in the assassination in one way or another.

I did consider telling my seventh-grade teacher who was already suspicious of something going on. But I felt the planners and their associates would more than likely control her and the local school officials. I also worried she could even be killed if she didn't handle it correctly, and there was no way for her to do that. So, she wasn't the way to go.

Finally, I reached the conclusion the only local agency I could possibly trust would be the Fort Worth FBI office, and I wasn't that sure about them. But in the end, I would have to give them a try.

I looked in the phonebook for the address. How would I get there? I could walk the four-and-a-half or maybe five miles, but that would take forever for a twelve-year-old, even with a bicycle.

I thought about somehow getting my mother to take me downtown on some other pretense and then going to the office on my own. I gave up on that idea though, because it just seemed too complicated.

I finally reached the conclusion that the bus on Lancaster Ave., about three-quarters of a mile from our house, was the best way to get there. The only problem, I had never ridden a bus and wasn't sure how I could determine I was getting the right one.

And another concern. Ever since the summer had ended, it felt as if I were being watched rather closely, except for when I was in school. I was expected not to be gone from home for very long, or too far away either. My father was concerned that the house might possibly be under surveillance and had told me to keep an eye on our street for any suspicious cars parked close, or men who didn't seem to belong there.

These weren't just passing thoughts. I had become serious about trying to expose the Kennedy assassination plot. I was really dedicated to doing this, if there was actually a way I could; of course, I couldn't be certain I would be successful. And it wouldn't do anyone any good for me to get caught and fail and it probably would cost me my life.

In the end, after about a week or so thinking long and hard about it, I reluctantly gave up. The Fort Worth FBI office would definitely be under control of the assassins, at least to some degree. Also, it came down to the disastrous effects it would have on my family.

And maybe I could be wrong. If I were to successfully stop the Kennedy assassination, maybe what I had been told by my father and his associates could happen. The entire world could be destroyed by hydrogen bombs or something similarly catastrophic. So, I gave up and was even more depressed and confused than when I had started.

18

LEAD UP TO THE ASSASSINATION

Dealing with the Inevitable

In early November, when I had found out that Kennedy was definitely coming to Texas and the Fort Worth/Dallas area, I asked my father if this was where they were going to kill him. From everything I had heard, this was going to be it, but I still wanted confirmation. He looked at me with sad eyes and told me he couldn't talk about this now. That was confirmation. I could tell by that look in his eyes and the tone in his voice.

Maybe some of that sadness was because he was aware I knew enough about the assassination plot, I shouldn't even need to ask such a question; after all by this time, I could accurately predict many of their moves before they made them. But maybe his sadness was an acknowledgement it was his fault, having exposed me to so much, that I knew so much, too much.

In the last month, he had changed his attitude toward me and stopped discussing things with me as easily as before. He had become secretive, so I was suddenly left guessing as to what their final plans were. Maybe, they felt they were done with me as a cover, and they really didn't give a damn what I thought or felt. They had used me just like Oswald, deceived me and now had thrown me away,

But I did know they were going to kill Kennedy when he came to Texas later this month, and do it when his parade went through Dealey Plaza. I don't believe that my father actually relished the thought of having to assassinate President Kennedy. Rather, it was something he felt had to take place, not for personal gain or out of some type of revenge on the Kennedys, but primarily for his country and the security and safety of its citizens. Most of those directly involved on-site in the assassination believed similarly, without thought of personal gain. They had been completely brainwashed; they had brainwashed themselves! A number however did stand to gain, both financially and politically.

But in reality, in the back of their minds, they knew their hate for this man was because of what he represented to them; Liberalism, Socialism.

Now, despite my father's non-answer, I knew for certain the imminent assassination would be occurring here, and my ambivalence waned for some reason. Sort of like Patty Hearst, the Stockholm Syndrome. Over the next few weeks, I prepared myself as best I could. I tried to lay aside my concerns about why this was happening and any negative consequences. Instead of worrying about Orris and his people, I tried to tell myself that nothing would go wrong, even though I knew in my heart many things could happen to cause the assassination attempt to blow up in their faces. And that scared the hell out of me.

Most of all of course, I was worried for Orris himself. About eight months ago, I had realized he would unquestionably be one of the triggermen. But even though I had come to accept this, I didn't know he was going to be the primary shooter. I had considered it a possibility, knowing him as well as I did; he would consider it his personal responsibility that Kennedy was killed, and on that day, he would place himself in the primary position. And now the time had come. He had taken the job last year when he could have said, "No," and found someone else to do it. But Orris, being who he was, had no choice in this; he had to say, "Yes," he would do this. It wasn't in him to pass this on to someone else who might fail.

As the day grew closer and I learned the exact day of President Kennedy's visit, I became more and more excited about this inevitable event. Or maybe I was becoming more anxious. There was no longer any reason to obsess about it. There was nothing I could do about it.

But because Kennedy was to visit Fort Worth first, the possibility of it being the site instead of Dallas, lingered in the back of my mind. I had heard them discuss the option of Fort Worth as a possible location if for some reason, Kennedy decided not to proceed from there to Dallas. That would have been a logical last minute, second choice for the assassination, mainly because of the influence and control they also had there, in reality greater than in Dallas. In fact, I knew that the first in-roads had been made to prepare for this possible alternative.

So, knowing the planners could surprise me, I prepared myself for the Fort Worth possibility. I didn't want to be caught unprepared for a shock like that.

The Morning of November 20th

On the morning of November 29, two days before the assassination, my mother and father got up long before the sun; early for both of them. I had guessed correctly he would get up early and try to leave before we had a chance to say goodbye; and showing no signs of what he was about to do. But I awoke early myself because I could barely sleep, and when I went for breakfast, I found them talking quietly, nearly whispering as they ate.

I could clearly feel the tension. I was so in tune with both of them that I could feel even subtle changes in their moods, let alone this morning. Everything about them said it was finally going to happen. Their eyes when looking at each other, and the way they moved, their body language, an obvious sadness. It was evident.

It also seemed they wanted to be alone with each other, and when they went in the bedroom and closed the door, I knew all the preparation was over. Nothing could stop things from moving to the next step now; the final step. I kept repeating to myself, "*It is going to happen. There is no question now*". I knew they were saying goodbye to each other, with a real possibility they might never see one another again after this morning. Although she and I had never discussed the assassination plan or his role in it, I knew my mother was aware of it all.

It was having difficulty too thinking he might be killed, leaving this large family father-less or worse, and this could all happen in the next few days. She had never "worked"; her "job" being to take care of the household, her children and husband. What would happen to us if something happened to him? I wanted to scream at him not to go, "Don't do it. It's not worth it. Don't do this to yourself and us."

The night before, he had told the family he would be leaving on an important trip and might be gone for some time. It had felt rather ominous and vague, but I knew what he was referring to, even though I didn't think my siblings did, except Stephanie and Debbie. I had never discussed the assassination planning with anyone in the family. But in September, after the visit with Sam Giancana. I had said to Stephanie, "Do you know what Daddy and General Born are planning to do to President Kennedy?"

"Yes!" she had replied without hesitating, mad because I would even ask her. And if Stephanie knew, so did Debbie, neither kept anything from the other. Like twins, so close. They could understand each other so well, and nearly always responded the same way emotionally. It was like dealing with one person. I knew they were both suspicious and somewhat jealous of my over-involvement with our father, my many trips to Dallas, and what that was all about. And they certainly knew about his relationships with some unsavory Mafia individuals.

When the two girls came for breakfast, I could see by their reaction to my parents, they knew what I did, the assassination was going to happen now that President Kennedy was soon to be in the Dallas/Fort Worth area. It was clearly understood between us without discussion. We knew how dangerous this was; we might not ever see our father again. This 'trip' he was taking, wasn't just another of his many.

Last night, he had implied that he would not be returning for some time, but I didn't think it would be for more than a few days, let alone six months. If I had only known that, I would have made a point to say goodbye in the appropriate way. And it would have been better for me if we had been able to sit down together to talk about it in the way we had so often done over the past year.

My anxiety had been building, while our parents were in the bedroom. My worry for my father and the rest of us, was increasing by the minute. If the wrong people found out before the assassination was to take place, he and his associates would be arrested or worse. Or if they found out afterwards. My father seemed likely the first to die in a shoot-out with the authorities. He would not allow himself to be arrested to face prosecution, but would do whatever necessary to prevent being apprehended. As would all the primary assassination planners, even if it meant death.

The three of us children stood in the living room, too uncomfortable to sit down. Stephanie and Debbie huddled together, looking about to cry, but I knew they didn't want me to try comfort them. After about twenty minutes, our parents emerged from their room to start out the door for Orris' car. It was obvious he didn't plan to say goodbye to us. When we saw he was about to leave, we quickly followed them outside.

This unusually abrupt departure only intensified the negative aura we were experiencing. My sisters were in such a state of mind by this time, I thought they were going to start crying any second, or even scream at him not to go. I felt terribly sorry for them; I could sense their confusion, hurt, and feelings of hopelessness of stopping him from doing what he was going to.

We caught up with tour parents just as they were going through the door. Outside, they stopped and turned around to finally face us. The sun had just come up, and we were standing in it shining directly in our eyes. My sisters were now crying, trying to fight back tears in front of our father. Our mother stepped to the side, realizing there was no way that he was leaving without first saying goodbye in a way we needed. I don't think he wanted to address us before he left, feeling that might be worse for all of us, including him, if it became too emotional.

Rather, he was trying to stay completely focused and keep the necessary composure, for what lie ahead.

But now he realized he had no choice, he had to make the goodbyes we needed. I stepped back a little as I always had, to let him deal with my sisters first. He took Debbie in his arms, hugged her hard for a long time, whispered something that we couldn't hear in her ear, and then kissed her on the cheeks, while holding her head gently in his hands. He finally let her go and repeated this with Stephanie. Debbie stood there, still fighting back tears now running down her cheeks. Trying to show him she was brave and could keep her composure and not be hysterical.

He then turned to me. I could see how terribly sad he was, even hurt he was having to do this to us and himself. He took me in his arms and hugged me the same way he had my sisters. Whispered in my ear not to worry, he would be alright. He loved me. Then he did the usual, took my head gently in his hands, looked me in my eyes, and kissed me on the cheeks. That smell and feel of his cheek felt against mine. No other man smelled this way and no other man ever put his cheek against mine and kissed me in the way he did.

Then he repeated the same type of instruction regarding the project's secrecy I had heard so often, "Bruce, you go to school and act as though nothing is going to happen on Friday, like it's just a regular school day. If anyone contacts you before you get home, and asks you anything about the assassination of President Kennedy, you deny you know anything about it. Do you understand what I'm telling you? Don't say one word or admit to anyone you have ever heard me or anyone I've been involved with, talk about it." After I nodded my acknowledgement, we stepped back and rather solemnly said goodbye.

Sensing our parents wanted to say goodbye to each other alone now, we children went back inside, but not without looking back to watch them as they walked to the car, holding hands like two kids in love, not wanting to say goodbye yet. They knew we were watching them, but they didn't seem to care. They were in their own world now. They stopped, faced each other, and embraced for a long time as my father whispered in her ear. Then a long kiss and their goodbye.

It was Debbie who turned first, no longer able to keep her composure. She ran into the house, leaving Stephanie to glance at me with a very strange, hurt look on her face, as though again this was somehow my fault. Before running to catch up with her sister.

I looked back at my parents just in time to see them finally let go of each other. My mother stood back intently watching Orris at this almost tragic moment. In what felt almost like slow motion, he opened the car door, got in, closed it, started the engine, and turned to look over his shoulder to slowly back down the driveway, stopped in the street to put it in drive, hesitated to look at her through the windshield, returning her waved.

After he drove away, she turned to come back into the house. When I held the door open for her, she stopped and reached out for me. She was crying quietly, just like my sisters had been, trying not to cry out loud. We hugged for what seemed like an eternity with her head on my shoulder. Kissing her on the cheek, I could taste the salt of her tears.

Once we were in the house, she went straight to her bedroom, and I went to make sure my sisters were okay. I found them in their room, with Stephanie crying now like a child, sitting on the floor in a fetal position, elbows on her knees and her face buried in her hands, back against the wall. Debbie was standing on her tiptoes to look out a high window, hoping to get one final glimpse of our father before he turned the street corner. Although he waw undoubtedly long gone, she continued looking, as if she could still see him. Realizing how terrible this was for them, that they wanted privacy, I backed out of the room, closing the door behind. Their lives would never be the same again and all because of our father's involvement in the Kennedy assassination and his dedication to a group of insane military leaders. But for now, they were as alright as they could be.

I went back down the hall, not knowing what to do with myself. My mother's door was still open and I looked in to see if she were okay. She was lying on her bed, face buried in a pillow, crying. It was rare to see her crying like this. She usually could keep her composure, no matter what the situation, unless it was really bad. I had developed a different attitude toward her since her to suicide attempt in 1960. For the longest time, I was continuously watching for any possible signs she might try again. Thankfully she never did, so I had reached a point I felt she had fully recovered and wouldn't attempt it again. But I still had to make sure she was alright when she was in the state of mind she was now.

My younger brothers and sisters started coming down the hall, one by one. They had slept through our father's departure and knew nothing about any of this. They were much too young to be able to understand what had been going on, even if they had known. I rounded them up, got their breakfast, and went to tell Stephanie they were up, and I was going to leave for school. She was sitting in the same position, but no longer crying and nodded to let me know she heard me, without raising her head from her hands.

Orris, along with the other actual assassination participants, spent the nights of the 20th and 21st in Dallas at an undisclosed location. They were too important to the assassination to risk any one of them not being available on the slated day. Each had a primary role and trained for that position. And any one of them would be difficult, if not impossible, to replace at the last minute.

My Day, November 20th

Walking to school, the sun was very bright that morning and it hurt my eyes, so I walked in the shade of the large old trees lining the street, treasuring the sensation of changing from warm to cool to warm again. The Blue Jays were out, calling to each other with their unusual caw that I loved. It seemed like a normal day in most ways, but none were now.

I couldn't help obsessing about the President bring killed in the next several days. He was to arrive in Fort Worth tomorrow, on the 21st, where he would spend the night and then proceed to Dallas on the 22nd, a Friday. He was scheduled to go to Austin later that day.

But I was confused. I thought Orris would have explained to me what to expect now and after the assassination, but he hadn't. He had sort of closed med out, so I was on my own to figure out where, when and what was actually going to happen.

It felt prescient that Orris had left us this morning and kept mentioning Friday. I was still betting on Dallas as the location, rather than Fort Worth, simply because that was where they put in by far the most effort in their planning. And I had overheard their discussions about the parade route, meaning the attempt on the President would most likely be during the parade.

By the time I got to school, I felt less confused, and had pretty good control of myself. I could get through today okay without being too worried. After all, my father and his people knew what they were doing and would be successful and safe. But at the same time, in my heart I dreaded it would not be. And in fact, as terrible as it had been for the past year, what was going to happen soon would be much worse.

Somehow the day went by amazingly fast, although I kept looking at the clock, wanting for it to be over. By the time I left school after helping my teacher, I felt pretty good for some unknown reason.

Our November 21

The next day started very much like any other in the past three months. My sisters and mother had regained their composure. No talk of anything abnormal breakfast, everybody was quiet, probably to be expected under the circumstances. I left for school thinking today would go by as quickly as yesterday.

But I hadn't anticipated my teacher remarking that President Kennedy would be coming to Fort Worth later this day. She asked if any of us would be going to see him. A few raised their hands. Her doing this was disturbing, even though in my head, I thought it shouldn't be. The rest of the day passed quickly, but I became more and more worried. Then I kept thinking my father might be home when I got there later today, even though I knew the odds were terribly against this. When I finally got to leave, after staying with my teacher, I hurried home, anyway.

In fact, I ran the last block. But then resumed my now habitual routine of "scout," and moved to the opposite side of our street, so I could better see our driveway. I had done this many times before in the past year; run down our street, cross over to the other side, and look in anticipation to see if his yellow Ford were in the carport; or a car that shouldn't be. I was well-aware that my father and his fellow planners were fearful that somehow someone might become suspicious of his involvement in the assassination planning, and be watching me, my mother, my brothers and sisters, as well as our house.

Of course, I wasn't surprised now that it wasn't. Just wishful thinking, he would be home safe. Inside, when I stopped to listen, still in scout mode, it was very still, except for a faint sound coming from the kitchen, my mother preparing dinner. It seemed she must have gotten her composure back and was going about her usual daily life. Something to.my surprise, the other children had gone to school that day, but none were home yet.

So, I had the opportunity now to discuss the situation and the assassination with her, but sidestepped it, confused about how much she was aware of my involvement. It seemed we were supposed to act as if neither knew about the assassination or its planning. Besides, I didn't want to bother her now with my issues.

After dinner, we all huddled around the television to learn about the President's Fort Worth visit, just like every other Fort Worth family. I was curious if anything had changed or anything unusual had happened. No, everything s going as planned. He was to arrive at Carswell Air Force Base later that evening and stay at the Texas Hotel downtown. After a breakfast speech, there would be a short flight to Dallas, where there would be a parade from Love Field Airport through downtown Dallas and on to the Apparel Mart pavilion to give a speech.

All this reinforced what I knew and what I had figured out. But the worry, the anxiety, were getting to me so much, I was no longer one hundred per dent sure of anything. Especially after Orris/ recent silence.

Later that night, acutely aware of my father's absence, I watched the news again to make sure Kennedy was actually going to be in Dallas tomorrow. I continued to worry I might possibly never see my father again, as so many things could go wrong. I kept hoping he would call, but he never did.

I went to bed thinking the President was sleeping just a few miles from where I would be sleeping myself. This could be his last night alive. But the more I thought about it, the more I began reconsidering the possibility of trying to stop this terrible thing. I should just get out of bed, walk to downtown Fort Worth, find a secret service man at the Texas Hotel, and tell him all about the assassination planned in Dallas tomorrow.

At least, I was naively thinking, tomorrow it was all going to be over. For the past year, I had to deal with the constant stress of the planning, but after tomorrow, I could go back to school and forget about it all. I struggled with this for an hour before finally falling asleep, the lousy savior that I am.

In reality, I would never go back to my school again. I would never see the girlfriends I had in my school again. I would never see my teacher again. I would never even go back to the seventh grade again. My father had arranged all this change for me and intentionally not told me, because he knew I would seriously object.

That night I had a strange dream so much like reality that when I awoke on the morning of the 22nd, I wasn't sure it hadn't been real. In it, the President flew onto Austin from the Fort Worth Carswell Air Force Base and never set foot in Dallas. His visit to Austin was uneventful, as in Fort Worth. It appeared the President had survived his Texas visit and all would be well.

And then I woke up.

November 21ˢᵗ Elsewhere

In the 1950s, there was an illegal gambling and cat house in North Fort Worth called the 'Four Duces', located on Jacksboro Highway and owned by W. C. 'Pappy' Kirkwood, the father of Pat Kirkwood, owner of the Fort Worth club, 'The Cellar', located downtown Fort Worth. The 'Four Duces' was famous and one my father would visit occasionally. Patrons were limited to an exclusive Texas group, their friends and associates, so a regular place to find Lyndon Johnson, Clint Murchison, Sid Richardson, Carlos Marcello, and a number of other Texas politicians, Mafia figures, and wealthy oil men in their fifties, sixties. Gambling, drinking, and partaking in some of the best North Texas whores were common fare.

On the eve of the assassination, secret service agents assigned to protect the President, were there until the wee hours of the morning, drinking heavily, some would describe, getting drunk. As arranged by Orris.

At the same time, Clint Murchison hosted a well-documented party at his Dallas mansion for members of the power elite "8F Group," so named because it held meetings in Suite 8F of Houston's Lamar Hotel. Ostensibly to give a final "Go" or "No Go". A number of Kennedy's greatest enemies were present, businessmen, senators and congressmen as well as Howard Hunt, Hoover and Nixon. Also included was Johnson's guest, Madeline Brown who wrote the book "*Teas in the Morning*" about her long love affair with him.

When years later, Robert Groden, the present-day assassination expert introduced me to Madeline, she told us Lyndon arrived well after midnight and immediately went into a back room with other men. Emerging thirty minutes later, he appeared anxious, even red-faced, and came directly over to whisper in her ear, "As of tomorrow, those

Kennedy bastards will never insult me again." Then he was out the door to that party at the "Cellar Door." (To be fair, Madeline's story has been dismissed by some investigators.)

19

NOVEMBER 22ND

My Morning

I got up early to again look for Orris' car in the driveway, had he returned after I had gone to bed. Of course, it wasn't there. It was looking worse and worse for any chance of seeing him again before the assassination, or even talking to him on the phone. I was sure now they were going to do it today in Dallas. I wasn't happy, but excited. It had finally come. Today was the day, and tomorrow I could go back to my normal life. It would all finally be over.

I knew I was the only boy in the world who knew what was going to happen today. A day that would alter history permanently and take its designated place along with other infamous days in history, the assassinations of Abraham Lincoln and way back, Julius Caesar. It seemed strange I had to get up, go to school, and act, as though nothing were going to happen. But that is what I was supposed to do.

My father had specifically said that on Friday I was to act normal, no matter what took place.

I knew he was going to be one of the three actual shooters, but I didn't want to think about my father going to shoot and kill someone. Killing anyone was terrible to me, even if that person was going to get us all killed by allowing a nuclear war with the U.S.S.R.

I went into the dining room for breakfast and my two eldest sisters were already seated across from my usual place. They had changed again overnight, and I felt it. Tired, worried and so touchy, you couldn't even look at them without their almost shouting, "What?" Hatred in their eyes, as if it were all my fault. For some reason I couldn't understand, they seemed to blame whatever was going on these last few days on me, as if I could have had any influence over our father.

But this was the way the two of them became when terribly upset about something. They were very judgmental and convoluted in their approach to everything and everybody that had anything to do with what was upsetting them. There wasn't any reasoning with them when in this state of mind. They were like elephants, never forgetting anything. And when under this pall, as they w ere now, they would blame that person for anything that might have happened years ago, something that anyone else would have forgotten long ago.

On the other hand, the situation now was different, maybe more understandable and forgivable, so I couldn't help but feel terribly sorry for them. Our father was in grave danger and as young teenagers to have him apparently put himself and maybe even his family in such a situation, was beyond their ability to comprehend or accept. And perhaps, they were more correct than they even knew. Maybe there was no excuse for what was about to happen. If someone was going to kill the President, it shouldn't be a married man with six children huddled in a house in Fort Worth, scared to death, and knowing that any minute they could learn their father was dead. That just isn't supposed to happen in America.

When our mother came into the dining room, even though I could tell she was trying to hide her concern, she looked extremely worried. She was truly the best mother we could possibly ever have had. Completely giving in every respect; so loving, warm, and kind, with such a wonderful heart. And now she was having to endure so much, pretending that everything was okay, making sure we had breakfast, and got ready for school. It was all just too crazy.

I tried my best to ignore my sisters' distress, there was nothing in the world, I could do about it. I ate breakfast quickly, said goodbye, and started my walk to school. I was early and planned on taking my time, so I could think about what was going to happen today. But distract myself some by experiencing the Nature that I love, beautiful and much more interesting than anything man could ever make himself.

Fort Worth could be very beautiful this time of year, far enough south that a warm autumn could almost feel like spring. And that's how it felt this morning, after a little rain earlier had made the air clear and clean, with that beautiful remnant smell of the cool fall rain. Because of this warm autumn, many bugs were still active, especially locusts in the trees and butterflies in the air. I loved bugs of all kinds. Moths probably my favorite, so mysterious and beautiful, with unusual pastel colors. I hate pesticides of any type, because I see man unbalancing nature by indiscriminately killing these creatures.

The sounds and sight of these bugs, along with the birds chirping and the dogs barking, all mesmerized me, putting me in a special state of mind. It allowed me to isolate my thoughts, better and clearer, in a type of meditation followed by a flurry of logical thought. Being able to achieve this state of mind had become second nature, maybe because it was a coping mechanism.

I knew my father and his fellow planners wanted everything to appear normal, especially today. And for all appearance, it did seem like a normal day. Traffic seemed normal, no unusual vehicles.

I reached school in about twenty minutes, but it hadn't been long enough. There was no longer any question about today's event. I knew the men involved; when they made up their minds to do something, there wasn't very much that could stop them. It didn't make any difference if they were building a rocket that could fly into outer space, re-enter the atmosphere halfway around the earth and strike its target precisely, or an airplane that could fly at three times the speed of sound and circumnavigate the earth by refueling in the air.

These men had already done these things and much more. Assassination couldn't be more difficult than the tasks they had already accomplished. My father had been chosen for this job by military leaders, generals, who knew who had the capability and who didn't. Failure wasn't an option on this day for him and his men, so I don't know what I was so worried about.

As I entered through the front school doors, little did I know I would never enter through them again. To me, entering and leaving symbolized the change I experienced that day. I was entering a somewhat happy, naive child, in spite of what my father and his people had put me through. And I would leave, an adult having endured a special rite of passage, a terrible rite of passage.

Until today, it had all been something of a very exciting game. Yes, all along I had known they actually intended to assassinate the president. But I didn't really know what to expect as a result of that action, let alone the degree. For me personally, the American people, or the world politically, economically, socially, and culturally. Indeed, the basic security of the world.

During the assassination planning, my father and his associates knew I was a happy child when I was with them. And so, they also knew how this catastrophic event would affect me. They had to.. They were very intelligent, aware of nearly everything in their surroundings. They could not have just thought of me as some kind of a fixture that came with his father, acting as though he could care less about what they were talking about, some kind of a mannequin. They had to know how this was going to affect me. Did it matter?

Life was very different then. The early 1960s was the end of a long run of innocence in America. It would never be the same after today. It wouldn't just be the Kennedy assassination that would start the ball rolling. The Vietnam war, the racial riots, the Nixon problem, drugs, the sexual revolution, the government killing innocent children on college campuses, and much more, would contribute to the end of this innocence.

The Set-Up for the Assassination

CIA people had been tracking Kennedy from the time he woke up in Fort Worth and would continue right down to the seconds before the first shot was fired. There were probably nearly as many CIA men in Dealey Plaza as there were private citizens, and many of these so-called private citizens were actually CIA men in disguise. Many were hiding in plain sight, but most were hiding behind something, such as the picket fence or the School Book Depository, in the bushes, or in and behind a railroad car. They were wearing Dallas Police uniforms or expensive suits, flashing false Secret Service badges.

The CIA operatives who would actually control the assassination had been in place for most of the morning, looking for anything unusual that could affect the plans. There were a number of issues which could cause the assassination to be aborted, and the final decision by these operatives to go or not, would come down to the wire, just seconds before the shots were to be fired.

The CIA was tracking the three primary shooters, the situation on the sixth floor in the Depository, a second team of assassins on the west side of the train bridge overpass, and the general situation in Dealey Plaza itself. Those in the Plaza were tied through radio communication to another group who would track the progress of Kennedy's limousine as it progressed from Love Field Airport and on through downtown Dallas en route to the Plaza. This group was also tied by radio into their superiors in Washington, who could also order the assassination be aborted, down to the last second, for whatever reason deemed necessary.

One hour before Kennedy's limousine would arrive in the Plaza, the actual shooters, Orris, Lyon and Tom Lawrence, moved into staging areas close to their designated positions. Several CIA operatives were with Orris and Lyon for control of civilians, in case the need arose. The control CIA operative then contacted the shooters' aides by radio to ensure they were ready.

Approximately two minutes before, the control operative got the 'all go' from his Washington connection. Twenty seconds before, he gave all the shooters visual and radio, "Go." As the limousine turned onto Elm St., all three primary shooters were tracking President Kennedy with their rifle scopes.

The plan was to shoot and kill him without killing anyone else, especially Jacqueline Kennedy. Everyone was to take extra care not to kill her. To assassinate a president who was terribly unpopular with all conservatives, as well as some liberal backers, was one thing, but to kill the very popular and beloved mother of two young children, who were also loved and adored, was something else altogether. A greater public outcry would surely follow if the Kennedys' two children were left parentless. And possibly a more extensive post-assassination investigation.

But if they didn't kill him with their first round of fire, they would have no choice but to saturate the limousine with bullets, killing everyone in it. The President could not survive once the shooting had started. If by some unforeseen circumstance he were to survive, all the men involved would be discovered and prosecuted.

The Umbrella Man

In case of a breakdown in radio communication, visual markers were also used for the shooters and their aides. One CIA operative who signaled some of these came to be known as the Umbrella Man in the President Kennedy assassination lore. This man had visual sight of, and radio contact with his coordinator, who fed him information right up to the last second.

He actually had several essential functions. First, to signal the actual firing at the president. If he was to open and hold his umbrella high, it would mean 'Green', to fire. If it were closed and held down, it would mean 'Red', to stand down. It was simple, but effective.

The second function was also simple. The arrival of the President's limousine to where he was standing signaled the firing of both the decoys from the Depository and those of the three actual shooters. It was essential that all of the shots take place as close together as possible, so as to make it look as if there were only one shooter, Lee Harvey Oswald.

The Second Team, the Three Tramps

During the summer and fall, I had heard Orris, Born, and others talk in a hushed up, quiet way about a 'second team' of assassins. This mysterious 'backup tea\m' would use a heavier weapon of some sort if Orris' team failed to accomplish a "confirmed kill." If they had to use their weapon, Oswald would still be blamed as the primary assassin; the team would be tied to him through some plausible, pre-arranged story.

I don't believe I met any of these men, they ever came to U.S. Sonics while I was there, or knew it was the primary planning location. At any rate, they were not part of the local Dallas group tied to Orris. Rather, they were other Texans on the scene, ready to take action, and could be killed along with Oswald if necessary.

On that fateful date, the team was located right to the west of the train overpass on Elm St., on the same side as Orris and Lyon. When Kennedy's head exploded and he was obviously dead, it was told to stand down, "Don't fire."

I believe without question, the second team was the three so-called 'Bums' found hiding in a railroad car. And I believe they were probably supposed to vacate the scene by car or van, but for some reason they couldn't get to it. Either they ran out of timed, or in the confusing aftermath of the assassination they got confused and had to take refuge in the boxcar.

When apprehended, they were briefly questioned. No one even took the time to get their real names before they were released and be gone into the night, never to be heard from again. Thanks to the magic of Nesbitt, McCord, and perhaps, J. Edgar Hoover.

White Supremacist Joseph Milteer

I remember Joseph Milteer's name first being spoken in association with the assassination at U.S. Sonics in May. Then I saw him there in July. I knew he was from Miami, because my father went to visit him there in June, when he went to see Santos Trafficante in Tampa.

He seemed quite different from the U.S. Sonics people and void of their sophistication. I didn't like him when around him; he radiated an evilness you could feel when he looked at you. But he clearly hated Kennedy passionately too, and continually professed it. I also knew he was a White Supremacist with strong connection to the KKK and other radical White Supremacist organizations.

But I never could clearly understand his role in the assassination, unlike most of the others involved. It might have had something to do with Miami being a backup location, in which case he might help control any investigation.

Regardless, Milteer was in Dealey Plaza on the day of the assassination, as documented by a photo I've seen of him there. I believe he was there as an observer and played no direct role in the assassination himself. He was close enough to Orris, he would have been told its location and invited to observe; he did seem to be trusted and respected.

The Actual Shooting of the President

All three shooters were wearing Dallas Police uniforms, their aides, wearing suits with false Secret Service badges. There was a clearly designated sequence of firing, pre-planned and repeatedly practiced at the Palo Pinto Ranch. From where they would fire, they didn't need to be exceptional marksmen. Rather, they needed nerve and confidence much more.

The three actual shooters waited to hear a first shot from the Depository before immediately firing themselves. But because it was a little late, they were thrown off some, forced to wait an aggravating few seconds.

Their positioning was purposeful. The first of the fatal shots was to be fired by Lawrence positioned in the Dal-Tex Building, a seven-story office building located across the street from the Depository. The bullet's trajectory fired from this position duplicated that of Lee Oswald's shots, both from behind the limousine. Tom was to fire when he had a clear and direct shot at the president's head, when the limousine was directly in front of the picket fence, the greatest opportune point. His first shot, a little high, missed the President's head, hitting a piece of steel above the limousine's windshield, deflecting into the air. His fired his second shot, at Kennedy's upper back, but pulled it high and to the right. This shot missed again, rather struck Texas Governor Connally in the back, exiting his chest, hitting his wrist, and deflecting to the inside of his left thigh.

(As further evidence of Johnson's prior knowledge and Connally's importance to the oil cabal, Johnson had attempted to have him moved from Kennedy's limo to his.)

The other actual shots were to come from Lyon and Orris, behind the picket fence and in front of the President. Lyon was supposed to aim at the President's upper chest, a shot which would have been fatal in itself, but he inadvertently pulled it a little high, the bullet striking Kennedy in the throat, exiting slightly to the right side of the upper back. This shot, nevertheless, probably would have killed the President in itself, destroying Kennedy's throat and causing him to suffocate.

Then Orris, waiting until the limousine reached a point directly in front of him, fired his first and only shot, one of those fulminate of mercury-tipped exploding bullets I had known about. This hit Kennedy in the right side of the skull, above the temple and a little above and in front of the right ear. It exploded, blowing approximately thirty-five percent of his brain mass into the air, killing him instantly.

Thus, the mission was accomplished, a mission that cost several million dollars to plan and several million, as payoff to as many as forty to fifty individuals. Of course, if the three shooters were not successful, they had backup plans to be executed by others.

Orris would, later, go to his childhood farm in East Texas to retrieve a pine tree to plant at his house in Bedford. Being the religious man he was, he performed his duty to God; it says in the Bible, "To plant a tree for a slain enemy."

Immediate Aftermath

As soon as the shooting had started, a reign of confusion enveloped the area. People on the grass-covered knoll were lying on their bellies, cowering from flying bullets. Orris and Charles Lyon, along with their CIA operative, had arrived in the Plaza in a white van disguised as being from a "Bug Extermination Company." It took but seconds to fire their deadly shots, throw their rifles into it, and then themselves. Norris Lawrence was the driver, waiting with the engine running. They cleared the scene before anyone realized what had actually taken place.

They left the same way they had come, driving in front of the Depository, left onto Houston Street, and onto a designated downtown Dallas location from where the post-assassination events were to be run.

Tom Lawrence, assisted by his CIA aide, hid his rifle at a designated spot in the Dal-Tex Building, where it could not be found. He reached a waiting car, just outside the Building to make his exit to the same location. He was nearly hysterical by the time he got there, breaking down over the pressure of the assassination.

Knowing ahead of time, the dead President would be taken to nearby Parkland Hospital, Jeff Miller was there waiting for Kennedy's limousine carrying both the President and Connally. There the severely injured Texas Governor was placed on a rolling gurney. After he was moved to an operating room, the bloodied gurney was left behind, allowing Miller to place the false bullet on it, the bullet that had been fired from Oswald's rifle at U.S. Sonics into the fifty-five-gallon steel drum. This bullet was later found and became the infamous 'Magic Bullet', believed supposedly to have fallen out of the Governor's leg.

The Decoy Shot

The plan for the shots from the Depository had Oswald coming up to the sixth floor from the cafeteria to take his place twenty minutes before the presidential limousine approached the Depository. Roscoe White and a CIA assistant would ensure he would make the appropriate shot when the Plaza operative gave the signal to "go." The assassination planners knew he couldn't hit the president from the sixth-floor window without a lot of luck, but that didn't matter. The first shot was intentionally supposed to be fired well over the head of those in the presidential limousine, so as not to accidentally strike Mrs. Kennedy.

As Kennedy's limousine was approaching Dealey Plaza, White's assistant urgently communicated to his CIA operative that Oswald had not come to the sixth floor. It turned out Oswald got cold feet and stayed downstairs in the second floor cafeteria pretending to quietly eat lunch, knowing that White would take his place. A neutral Dallas Police officer entering the building immediately following the shooting, saw him there.

Indeed, the operative told White to follow the alternative plan. To stand in at the window, using Oswald's Italian Mannlicher-Carcano rifle -- it was this confusion that made that shot a little late, impacting the real shooter's mission. White was then to wipe the rifle clean of all unintended fingerprints and hide it on the sixth floor at a designated location.

Lee knew Roscoe well and had been told Roscoe, wearing his Dallas Police uniform, would help him escape the building and escort him out to safety. But after Lee fired, Roscoe was supposed to shoot him in the chest several times with his police revolver, while Lee was still holding the rifle in his hands; clean proof that Oswald was the assassin. Police Officer White had courageously shot him.

However, Lee foiled that plan too. After the assassination, before White could reach him, Oswald left the Depository and found his own way to his boarding house as though nothing unusual had taken place. There, he retrieved his revolver and some other personal possessions and papers he thought he would need for the escape to Mexico City and Cubs that Orris had promised. Expecting he would rendezvous with someone who was to drive him to the airport, he headed for the Texas Theatre.

What choice did he really have at this point? He needed to get out of Dallas, and he probably thought his contact would have no idea what had happened at the Depository. And what difference did it make now anyway? His main function was to pose as the assassin, and that he had done. At this point, he probably knew nothing of his planned murder, although he was somewhat paranoid and might have suspected something.

J.D. Tippit Succumbs to the Pressure

Because White had been unable to kill Oswald at the Depository, the second planned effort now went into effect with police officer J.D. Tippit. Tippit knew the planned walking route that Lee was supposed to take to the theater and was already in that neighborhood, in case he was needed. So notified, and knowing the route Oswald would take, he began looking for him with the aim of shooting him.

What the public has been told is that Tippit located Oswald, and when he got out of his car, drew his revolver and started shooting. Lee already had his revolver in his hand and began firing back, winning the 'shoot-out.'

What actually took place was something very different, as I learned seven months later when I asked my father why Oswald had been shooting at Tippit. Apparently, Tippit collapsed emotionally under the pressure of the day and reneged in his designated role to kill Oswald. (Remember that the two were friends.) He broke down and foolishly told the assassination planners over his secure radio, he had changed his mind, was not going to kill Oswald. Instead, he was going to try to locate Lee to warn him before he got to the theater, he was going to be killed by the very people he was working for, the CIA.

The planners attempted to talk Tippit out of doing this, but to no avail. He had "lost it ", and was completely irrational, obviously not realizing that he was in fact, committing suicide himself by telling the planners this. They would now have to kill him and do it quickly, before he could reach Oswald.

The CIA was working from a pre-designated location in Southwest Dallas, close to Oswald's boarding house. They had contingency plans for nearly every possible scenario that could go wrong for each of the players. Well aware of the extreme pressure that would be on these men.

Ironically, Roscoe White was already in the area with the intention of assisting Tippit in locating and killing Oswald. But now that the situation had changed, the planners met White to brief him on the situation and his new assignment.

White looked somewhat like Lee, only a little taller. They changed him out of his police uniform and into clothes similar to those Oswald was wearing. Monitoring Tippit's location, they drove White a block near. He then walked the block over to meet Tippit. At first glance, as the planners hoped, Tippit mistook White for Oswald, drove up to him, and exited his police car, intending to do his warning of "Oswald." White was ready, quickly shooting and killing him. As he ran from the murder scene, witnesses saw and later identified him as Lee Oswald, because of the similar clothing, size, and looks.

Oswald's Final Days

In the meantime, Lee had continued on to the Texas Theatre, knowing nothing about any of this. When he arrived, the Dallas Police who were part of the plot, were already waiting behind the theater as planned. They were to kill him if he resisted their "arrest." But if he did not resist, they would have no alternative than to actually arrest him. The planners knew there would be many witnesses at the theater watching the movie, so the situation had to be dealt with legally to some degree.

When the police rushed into the theater, Lee realized immediately he had to give up or be killed. So, he threw down his revolver, thrust his hands into the air, stood up, and yelled loudly, "I'm unarmed! Don't shoot! I'm unarmed! Don't shoot!" Yelling until he was knocked to the floor by an officer. They couldn't shoot him in the theater because there were at least twenty witnesses, who could clearly see Lee's arms in the air and that he was unarmed. Instead, after he was handcuffed, dragged from the theater and beat up, he was taken to the downtown Dallas police headquarters location.

Orris donned a regular Dallas Police uniform and went into the Station to talk to Oswald to calm him down and try to prevent him from revealing anything about the assassination. They would get him off. They would get him the best attorneys in the U.S. He hadn't even fired a shot at the president, so he could hardly be convicted of the assassination. Of course, Lee was very skeptical of anything being said to him by Orris.

In fact, he did have another contact with the outside world. Marina and his mother visited him in the early afternoon the next day, after which, he attempted to call an attorney in New York. And after seeing his brother Robert in the mid-afternoon, he made two phone calls to Ruth Paine. He was also visited, in the early evening by the president of the Dallas Bar Association.

But, in the end, what choice did he really have, other than to go along with Orris' advice? So, Lee kept his mouth shut, truthfully insisting over and over again, he hadn't shot anyone. He didn't know anything about the assassination of President Kennedy, which wasn't quite true. In the end, he went to his grave being faithful to the CIA and his duty to them. Perhaps, he was actually the only honorable man out of all the assassination players, including the CIA. As in the military, you are not supposed to ask questions, just do your duty.

It was one of Orris' responsibilities to ensure Oswald be killed following the assassination, and as soon as possible. Lee had now survived the first three attempts, more by cruel fate. Now the fourth plan needed to be implemented, shifting his assassination to the Mafia's Jack Ruby, whose role I had never known, but had been making those frantic phone calls.

This was an almost foolproof plan. And like it or not, Ruby couldn't disobey Giancana's order; he had no option. The Mafia would hunt him down and kill him. Nowhere to hide, they would find him wherever he went.

School That Morning

Shortly after I arrived at school, the morning bell rang for homeroom. Kids were running in different directions to their rooms, so they wouldn't be too late. As I ran for my own class, I noticed something different about the others, especially the girls. Dresses more formal, starched and neatly ironed. As if they were going to Sunday School. All because the President of the United States was visiting the Dallas/Fort Worth area, the Baptist bastion. This sign of respect for his visit was what made Texas what it was in 1963. Even though many in this area might have wanted to murder him, there were still plenty of Democrats who respected the position of the President and actually loved this one.

Otherwise, it seemed like a normal Friday at school. Fridays always seemed a little more cheerful, everyone anticipating the coming weekend and talking about what they had planned. Following my usual routine, I went to my locker and then reached my homeroom just as the principal was starting his daily morning announcements over the intercom. After smiling at my teacher, I headed for my seat near the front of the class, a location I liked because I could see and hear just about everything going on.

I noticed the girl who always sat next to me on the left was, like the others, in her Sunday best, starched and prim as she could be, and very pretty as usual. I told her she looked beautiful in her light pink dress. Although very shy, she was my favorite in homeroom and I would talk with her everyday about whatever. The principal mentioned that the President was in town, and he appreciated that many children were dressed appropriately for the event.

My pretty, young teacher seemed in a good mood and asked if anyone had gone to see the President when he flew into Fort Worth yesterday at Carswell Air Force Base. A few raised their hands and she asked how their experience was. As a moderate Democrat who wouldn't have it any other way, she obviously liked President Kennedy very much, maybe even loved him. Several times before she had expressed that he was the long-needed answer to the nation's social and international problems.

I looked around at my classmates who had no idea what was about to happen today. I didn't know what their reactions would be, let alone that of the public or the police. One thing I did know, I was sure they would cancel school when the word reached us.

The morning passed quickly, perhaps too quickly. At first, I couldn't keep my eyes off the clock, next to the intercom speaker. I had listened closely at breakfast when the television announcer commented that the President's parade in downtown Dallas was going to start as twelve o'clock. That time was fast approaching.

I tried to get into what the teacher was saying and did for a few minutes, but not for long. I couldn't help thinking again that a great deal was going to change not only for the world, but for me as well.

Then minutes before they were going to shoot the President twenty miles from where I sat, it hit me that my own father was at this moment getting ready to do it. What was he thinking, what was he going through himself? His life was about to change forever too.

The clock informed me that the parade should have started by now, it was twelve ten. My teacher was talking about something I wasn't paying no attention to. That wasn't usual, but today I was a million miles away. Picking up on it, she asked me a question about the Math lesson. I didn't even hear the question, let alone have any idea what she had been talking about.

After I confessed that, she asked me what was wrong. I could only apologize that I had been preoccupied about something altogether different. She just gave me a concerned look and a reprimand, "Pay attention, Bruce. You might miss something important."

It was now twelve forty and getting close to lunchtime at one. I desperately wanted to hear about the assassination before that. I wanted to be here in my homeroom class where I felt more secure. I kept watching the clock as the seconds ticked, the minutes peeled away. It was like a race in my mind. I was no longer listening to my teacher at all. I wasn't even in Fort Worth at school. I was in Dallas and in that parade as it moved through the downtown.

The next ten minutes seemed to go by like ten seconds. At then, the intercom speaker abruptly erupted, startling us all with a blaring loud male voice, much louder than normal. The announcer sounded hysterical, yelling so loudly it was difficult to understand at first. And then I heard him crystal clearly. It was the principal yelling, "The President has been shot! The President has been shot in Dallas! The President is dead! President Kennedy has been shot in Dallas during the parade, and is thought to be dead! He is on his way to Parkland Hospital now, but there doesn't seem to be any hope."

The intercom then switched to a Dallas radio station, where the announcer was making the same statement, the President had been shot and was now presumed dead. My eyes glanced from the speaker box to the clock, it was twelve fifty-eight.

I was instantly ecstatic. My body reflexed and I leapt out of my seat high into the air, my feet completely off the floor, while my arms and hands flew up over my head. It felt as though I was suspended in the air, floating above the room. When my feet hit the floor solidly, I yelled out, "They did it, they did it!" They had succeeded. It was finally done. It was finally over, and the President was dead!

Obviously, this was an instant, spontaneous reaction over which I had absolutely no control. I was happy that President Kennedy was dead, but also that the whole thing was over and life for me and my family could now return to how it had been before our involvement in this terrible deed.

Just after I landed, I heard something strange. That girl next to me was crying like a young child, weeping softly. As my response had been one of instant elation, hers had been fear and sorrow.

Then my eyes returned to the clock and my teacher, standing directly under it. Tears were falling down her cheeks, and she had the strangest contorted look of utter loss, confusion, and shock, all at the same time. I was confused and amazed that she was crying and that her reaction, too, was instantaneous.

But then I realized she was staring directly at me, only a few feet away and her expression had changed to just plain distorted, sad confusion. She stood looking at me for several seconds, which seemed like a very long time. I was sure she was thinking, "*This isn't the Bruce I know. He's happy someone is dead. He's happy the President is dead. This can't be Bruce.*"

When she finally seemed to get over her initial shock at my unexpected reaction, her expression changed to one of slight anger. She turned her head at an unusual angle slightly to the side, and actually yelled, "Bruce, sit down!" She had never raised her voice to me before. We were good friends. Why was she yelling at me? I hadn't done anything wrong. But as my eyes met hers, I realized immediately that my uncontrollable reaction of glee had been a major mistake. I sat down.

She glanced around the room and instructed, "Everybody just stay calm. I'm going out in the hall to find out what we are going to do, and I'll be right back." She was still sniffling with tears on her cheeks, trying very hard to control herself. She turned suddenly and left the room, closing the door behind her, obviously needing to go out to regain her composure. And get some direction as to what to do now with these shocked and nearly hysterical children. And decide what to do with me.

The Reaction at School

After my teacher left, I heard a strange noise off to my right and behind. I turned around to see three boys openly crying. This confused me. It was one thing for my shy girl and my teacher to cry. They were the weaker and the more emotional sex. But another thing for boys to be crying. As a matter of fact, why was everyone crying? Didn't they know we were all safe now this terribly evil man was dead? Our country was once again safe from his insane tyranny. Could they all be this confused and taken in by his lies?

I focused on that girl next to me. I knew her well, so she must be really hurt and upset to be reacting this way. Feeling sorry for her, I could only say, "It's alright. It will be alright. Don't worry, it will be alright." She raised her head, looked me in the eyes, and could only reply "OK". She tried to smile and repeated, "OK".

I wanted to tell her that, as a matter of fact, it was going to be much better now that Kennedy was dead. I knew she wouldn't understand that, but I wanted to try once again to make her feel better, so I repeated my attempt to comfort her. "Don't be so sad, everything will be alright. Don't worry about this, it will be alright in a few days." But, as if she couldn't understand a word I had said, she looked at me in her usual very shy manner, before again repeating, "OK.".

I still couldn't stifle my sense of relief. They had succeeded. Kennedy was finally dead, and life could go back to normal now. I repeated to myself my earlier rationalization. I would be able to go to school all week long, without having to lie about being sick. My life with my father could go back to the way it was before. We could be together as father and son again, without me playing the role of partner in the assassination with him and his people. It was over. It was finally over. All the planning, all the waiting, all the stress was finally over. Or so I thought. Little did I know that it had only now really begun and would last my entire lifetime.

Sitting there listening to these kids sniffling and trying to get their composure back, was hard. I looked around the classroom again. Thankfully, they seemed to be getting better control of themselves. Still sniffling, but not t crying out loud. I was confused and amazed they had reacted the way they did, but I knew my life was very different from theirs. I had been raised by men who knew and understood the truth and hadn't been deceived by Kennedy and his lies. But still, their parents must have known something wasn't right with this man, Kennedy, and should have expressed their doubt to them.

I began worrying about my big mistake, reacting the way I had in front of my teacher and my classmates. What was going to happen now? Would it just be forgotten, or would there be a problem? Although it had only been a few minutes, it seemed she was out in the hallway too long.

But then she came back into the room quietly, no longer crying and seeming to have some control over herself now. She said to the class in a good strong voice, "We are going to let school out now and I want you to go out to the front. They are going to be bringing the buses around for you to go home on. Look for your parents before you board your bus though, many of your parents have called and said they were coming to pick up their children right away. Now, I want all of you to go and do just what I have told you, orderly and quickly. Don't stay in the halls long. Go outside to the front and wait there for your parents. If they don't come soon, get on your normal bus. Now, go."

But she then looked right down at me and said in a hard voice, "Bruce, you stay here. I want to talk with you."

Of course, I knew why she was going to keep me here after the others left. She was going to ask why I jumped out of my seat and acted the way I did. Why I seemed happy about Kennedy's assassination. I could tell she wasn't mad, only confused and worried. Worse, she looked as though perhaps she had finally, in some strange way, found the connection to my mysterious activity in the past three months. I thought to myself, "*Oh, this is it. I've blown it. What am I going to say to her?*"

She knew me so well, she could nearly read me like a book, and she would certainly know when I lied to her. We were more than just close., nearly crossing the line several times. Of course, I hadn't provoked it; she had incited this by intentionally placing her breast against my cheek when I was sitting down and grading papers.

The other kids left the classroom quickly and quietly. They had stopped crying, but were still very solemn and seemed a little confused why this was even happening. After the door was closed by the last student, I was left alone with the teacher who addressed me with a degree of sympathy, "Bruce, will you come up here, please?"

I was still sitting in my seat with her staring at me like a Cheshire cat, a look on her face that clearly seemed to say she was going to finally get the answers she had been seeking for the past three months, as strange as they might be.

Obediently, I got up and moved to stand beside her. She sat down in a chair beside her desk. It was obvious she was still slightly unstable by what had taken place, and now that the other students were gone, she needed to try to catch her breath. She was quiet for a few moments, obviously in thought about everything that had happened in the last few minutes. Then as I expected, she asked the dreaded question, "Bruce, why did you respond like that? Why did you jump out of your chair? Why were you happy that the President was killed?"

I looked back into her sad, beautiful blue eyes and realized what I said to her might make a difference in whether she would just drop it or pursue more information. My brain was quickly trying to decide how to respond. All I could think was, "*Don't tell her the truth. Don't tell her the truth. I'm not supposed to tell anyone the truth about this, no matter what.*"

I came up rather lamely, and simply replied the best I could, "I don't know, I don't know why I reacted that way." And left it at that. She knew I was no moron, just the opposite. She might feel I was confused and upset like everyone else. But still, she might feel my reaction was so opposite of what it should have been, that she would know there was something wrong and it might have something to do with President Kennedy. Would this work? But I had no alternative.

However, she must have concluded I was lying, I really knew why I had reacted the way I did. She could see the deception in my face, in my eyes. But I had to stand my ground and figure out what to say or do later.

At the same time, she was determined and, not letting go continued, "Bruce, don't tell me that. I know you know why you are happy that the President is dead. So, tell me. Tell me why you are happy about it."

I replied again, "I don't know."

Sighing, she simply said, "OK, if you don't want to tell me now, when you come back to school, we are going to have to talk about this again. Now, go home. Go straight home and don't stop anywhere. Do you understand me? I don't want you to stop anywhere. I want you to go straight home."

Relieved, I replied, "Yes, I will."

She reached out and gave me a hug. I walked out into the hall thinking about my next meeting with her and what I would tell her. In reality, she would never have the opportunity to question me, for the simple reason we would never see each other again.

All the hours we had spent together alone after school, quietly talking about many different things, and yet she had no idea I knew all along that the President was going to die when he came to Dallas/ Fort Worth. How could she have ever possibly imagined that this quiet, polite twelve-year-old boy was so involved in the Kennedy assassination?

On the Streets

She knew I walked to and from school, so had a pretty good idea no one would pick me up today. She was right, no one did come; my mother had gone to pick up my siblings, probably feeling I could take care of myself, and would already have left anyway by the time she got there after picking up the others at their schools, which were a long distance from mine.

I left the room and walked down the hall. There were only a few kids still at their lockers, hurriedly trying to find whatever they needed before leaving. I was surprised that most were gone so quickly. Normally after school, it would take twenty to thirty minutes for everyone to leave. Everyone would usually stand around to talk in small groups and then slowly drift away.

In contrast, I was in no hurry. I wanted to take my time to figure out what was going to happen now. What had happened in my classroom had caught me by such surprise. I was very confused by everybody else's reactions. This was not what I had expected, but now I realized I didn't really know what I had expected.

But today the halls were quiet, except for the muffled noise of the buses that were beginning to arrive at the front of the school from their parking lot, a block or so away. I could hear their diesel engines were being revved higher than normal in an effort to warm them.

When I opened the door and stepped out onto the elevated landing, I couldn't believe what I saw. It was chaos, utter chaos. Even though it had only been such a short time since Kennedy had been shot, here were what seemed like over half the children's parents. Kids were standing all around in small groups, hugging their mothers, everyone crying.

Confounding it all was a complete traffic jam, parents just abandoned their vehicles in the middle of the street as they went to find their loved ones. Leaving them running, jammed together, facing all different direction, doors left open. I had never seen anything like this and was deeply moved. Surely, I could never have imagined anything like it. It was like having stepped out of the deserted school into the twilight zone.

The buses were sitting there, idling, with drivers in place, but very few children on board. Normally, they would be full, but kids were refusing to board them. Those not already with their mothers, were looking up and down the street for their cars, standing alone, crying in a worse state of confusion than before. It was a tragic scene.

After watching for a few minutes, I had to stop for a while longer to take it all in before heading home. I needed to try understand why these people were all so hysterical about this man being killed. After all, he wasn't their own father.

Not wanting to stay here on the school steps, I looked around for a vantage point, from which, to watch. Across the street was a big white Catholic Church and its steps seemed like a good place. So, I started it, wading through the mass of children and parents. I sat down on the fourth step to watch and yet, not be too close.

No one seemed to be in any hurry to leave; tightly hugging and crying with heads bowed down, as though engaged in some type of prayer together. As I sat alone on the steps, completely isolated from it all, unable to share any of their emotions, no loss nor sadness nor despair. At the same time, terribly concerned for them; without question, they had been trust into an abyss so suddenly and deeply, they did not know where to turn or how to regain their composure.

Incongruously, the sun was out, and the day continued beautiful and warm. While all hell was going on right in front of me. Maybe, I shouldn't refer to it as hell. Hysterical chaos is probably more appropriate and besides, I was sitting on the steps of a Catholic Church. John Kennedy was a Catholic, the first Catholic president and probably the last, or at least the last for some time.

As they continued standing together in what appeared to be embraces in slow motion, they seemed lost, not knowing what to do next, what direction to turn to. So, they weren't going to do anything other than stand there, cry, and hold each other. That at least seemed to provide some security, when only minutes before, it had been completely shattered. Now, to even loosen their embrace with each other for even a moment, would be too much to bear.

More parents were arriving to add to the confusion. And children who hadn't found their parents yet, wandered lost and aimlessly searching, crying among those embracing, looking for someone, who would hold them and give them some comfort, some relief from the sudden shock.

I was quickly coming to a realization I had not contemplated in the past year. Here was a reality taking place right in front of me that I could not ignore. Completely unexpected, I wasn't sure how to deal with it. That there were many, many Americans who without question loved this man, John Kennedy. Whether they loved him as a man or as the President, it didn't seem to matter right now. They felt a terrible loss at his sudden death, so deeply disturbed, would they ever fully recover. And it upset me to see and have to acknowledge that.

And the fact of the matter was I had taken a direct part in creating this tragedy. I might not have pulled the trigger, but I had willingly helped the men who did. Could they have been wrong in their interest in killing this man? How could they have been right, if all of these people were reacting this way? This had to be going on all over the nation. Meadowbrook in Fort Worth was no different from any other middle-class community in America. Millions of people must be crying right now, all over the country.

They never told me that maybe they were a minority in feeling the way they did about this man. It was too confusing, I had to talk with my father about it. He had to explain why these people were so saddened by Kennedy's death, if he were truly such a terrible person. All of the people here couldn't be wrong. It must be Orris and his friends who were wrong.

Finally, as fast as it had come together, the crowd seemed to react as if on cue. Everyone released their hold on each other, wiped the tears from their face, and started toward their vehicles. Children whose parents hadn't shown up yet, were leaving with other parents and friends, rather than being left alone. The buses, barely half-full, began to leave as well.

Only two girls were left in the schoolyard, both looking down the lane for their parents to come and retrieve them. They looked very lonely, and I felt sorry for them and wondered how long they would wait there alone, before someone noticed and helped them. Soon however, their parents arrived, and they departed in the same way as all the others, in tears and hugs. Leaving the school showing no sign this calamity had ever taken place only a few minutes before.

All was quiet now, as I still sat on the church steps wondering why this had all happened, in the first place. To my surprise, I hadn't seen even one teacher leave the school or out in front helping with this disaster. When I looked over to the teachers' parking lot, it was full; apparently, no one had left. Strange they were all still here in this otherwise abandoned, quiet school. Where were they, what were they doing? They too must have been in shock trying to gain some sense of security with each other.

It was my teacher I was really looking for. It bothered me for some reason, I hadn't seen her leave. I would have felt she was now safe herself, once away from the school.

No Choice, I Have to Go Home

I sat there for another twenty minutes thinking, thinking. What was going to happen next and how would I deal with it. Somehow it felt like I had been raped, my childhood stolen from me. But regardless of my feelings and no matter how much I wished I could avoid it, it was time to start my walk home.

I just had to do it. I knew what it was going to be like there and had no desire to subject myself to the torture. Debbie and Stephanie would sit in front of the television and continue to glare at me for causing everything. Stuart, Stephen, and Carolyn would be confused and would not really understand what this was all about or why.

My mother would try her best to calm them and keep her children safe and steady too, when inside she would be terrified and concerned that any minute she would hear her husband was dead. She might need me for something. And was there any word from my father.

I did take my time walking home, though. I needed to do quite a lot more thinking about everything. Meadowbrook seemed deserted. Like a Sunday. It was still the middle of the day, not much more than an hour since John Kennedy had been assassinated, but I saw hardly more than two or three cars come down the street. Meadowbrook Drive wasn't a freeway, but it was one of the main streets through this large neighborhood. Always with some degree of traffic, especially at this time of day.

My old elementary school looked completely deserted. Even the houses seemed quieter. No one coming or going, the doors all shut with no noise whatsoever, emanating from them. I didn't even see or hear any birds. No dogs barking in the distance. It was as though even the animals had been affected by this strange aura that was permeating everything. Quiet, quiet, that was it. It was way too quiet.

I got to Suzie's home and stopped in front, remembering our times together. Should I see if she were home; probably not such a good idea right now. What if she were crying like everyone else. That would be nearly as bad as being at home. So, I resumed my slow walk realizing I was trying to find anything I could do to keep from actually getting there.

That wasn't right. They probably needed me at home to help them feel safe or at least, as safe as they could be right now. So, I increased my pace and didn't stop again until I reached my street and stopped for a few seconds to look down to my house. More than ever, I was concerned there might be police cars or some unrecognized vehicle. All looked still though, nothing out of the ordinary, no unusual activity, a relief. Best was my mother's car; at least she was home and hopefully, safe.

I paused in front of the house, preparing for what I might encounter. I really didn't want to go inside. I didn't want to deal with it, no matter what it was. Would anyone besides my mother be there. She would have gone to pick the other kids up when this first happened, like the other parents, but maybe not.

Until this moment, the situation had not seemed really personal. I was isolated from the reality affecting everyone else. I could resist experiencing the emotions the others had experienced at my school. It had been purely an analytical experience for me. But once I entered the door, it would change. Suddenly, I would be thrust into an emotional environment unable to ignore. I would become emotionally involved.

My two older sisters knew what had occurred as far as our father being involved, but not the details and extent of his involvement. My mother obviously knew much more. So, the four of us would share the same feelings, very different from what millions of other Americans were experiencing. We would know the truth of what had just taken place in Dallas.

The Reaction at Home

I climbed the stairs to our front porch, hesitated at the front door to listen, but couldn't hear anything. I turned the doorknob slowly and when I opened the door a little, there were faint sounds from the television in the living room. They were home. After hesitating another minute, I walked down the hall and into that room.

My beautiful mother was standing behind the couch where my brothers and sisters were seated. Her blue eyes met mine and said it all. Filled with guilt and fear. I was certain she saw the same reflected in mine.

I looked down at my brothers and sisters. All five huddled together like little frightened rabbits in front of the TV, watching a live broadcast from Dallas of the unfolding events. When they turned to me as I stood in the entrance, Stephanie and Debbie looked more shocked, scared, and frightened than I expected. But again with that complete disgust they had developed for my being personally guilty of this calamity suddenly destroying their comfortable lives. The other three children just looked terribly confused and worried by something they couldn't comprehend.

On the television, a man was standing in front of Parkland Hospital reiterating that President Kennedy was pronounced dead at one p.m. Dallas time. Governor John Connally was in surgery, his condition and prognosis, whether he was expected to survive or not, unknown. Strange because I had never heard talk about shooting the Governor. Must be a mistake, making me worried even more, imagining a possible bad shootout between the assassins and the Secret Service, the Governor caught in the middle.

They kept flashing various shots from the hospital; men shoving one another. Something about a physical fight between the Secret Service and the Dallas Police over Kennedy's body; it seemed the police didn't want to give the body to the Secret Service over a Dallas jurisdiction issue. Shots of a bloodied Jackie Kennedy entering the hospital and flashes of Dealey Plaza that I recognized from being there many times. A crazy collage of film clips with no real continuity.

I looked back at my mother and as we stared into each other's eyes, she seemed to know how I felt. I felt certain I knew how she felt. It seemed like a lifetime we had lived over the last year. That this was real, not a horrible, surrealistic nightmare was difficult to grasp. And the guilt that we both felt was nearly unbearable. Finally, I looked back down at my siblings, and she turned to go into the kitchen.

Suddenly another announcer broke in, "We just have word that a Dallas Police officer has been shot in Southwest Dallas and he is thought to be dead." I instantly pictured my mother sitting on the corner of her bed, sewing the pants cuffs of a Dallas Police uniform less than a month earlier. This could be our father. We all leaned closer and held our breath. Finally after a long five minutes, the announcer returned, "It has been determined that the man's name is Tippit, Dallas Police Officer J. D. Tippit,, and the police are looking for the man who did this."

This struck me hard. I knew this man and had seen him at least five or six times over the past eight months. He had something to do with the assassination, but I never knew what his role was. And now, he has been shot dead. What the hell is going on over there in Dallas? If Tippit has been killed, then my father and the others are in even more danger. This doesn't sound good, not good at all. Clearly something had gone terribly wrong.

It didn't make any difference how well everything had been planned, including attempts to anticipate specific problems. They still had to make allowance for the unforeseen. This was a complex operation, in spite of all the efforts to keep it as simple as possible. There were so many variables what with so many different agencies and individuals dedicated to keeping the president alive. And in the event of an attempted assassination, dedicated to the capture or killing of those involved. But to counterbalance this, there were a number of people employed in key positions in those same agencies, working on the inside on behalf of the assassination and the escape of the assassins.

One of those unforeseen problems or mistakes had just happened. I should find my mother to tell her about this; she would recognize his name. This would be the first time we had been alone together since the assassination. She was alone in the kitchen trying to make herself seem busy at nothing in particular.

As I entered, I immediately saw the severe concern and stress on her face. She was trying her best to mask how she actually felt; an effort I could easily see through. It was disheartening to see the expression of dire helplessness and utter distress, mingled with fear. She let herself go for just a short moment, but I'm sure she knew I had seen what she was experiencing. I was her only child who she would dare let see this side of her, this weaker female side.

I don't think her retreat into the kitchen was intentionally ignoring what was going on in Dallas. Preparing dinner now was just her being an unbelievably courageous person, probably feeling it better not to glue herself to the television set watching the drama unfolding just twenty miles away, when she had no control over anything happening. She wasn't one prone to hysteria. Instead, solid as a rock in a time of impending disaster, and this is how she was now. And going about her usual daily affairs, as though this weren't even happening, might be better for her children. As though nothing going on could change her own personal life forever. At any moment, she could hear her husband had been killed or arrested as an accomplice to be hung by the neck.

It was only the two of us in the house, who could share these feelings of opaque uncertainty concerning the real danger my father was in. Of course, I assumed she knew what the basic plan was for after the assassination, while I knew very little; they had intentionally kept this very secret and only disclosed it to those who needed to know their individual role.

I gave her a hug and we stood together a few moments to give each other some solace and a moment of rest from the isolation we were both feeling. After we broke from our embrace, I told her about Dallas Police Officer J. D. Tippit being killed. Although I didn't want to burden her any further, she only would want to know about any important new events as soon as she could. Maybe, I was wrong though, possibly she didn't want to be bothered with these types of things, things which might only lead to greater frustration. I didn't know just how to help her now, or even if I could.

She and I went back into the living room. Was there any new information about Tippit's death that could help me better understand what was actually going on. The newsman was only saying the police were now canvasing the neighborhood where Tippit had been killed, questioning the witnesses they had. It was not known at this time whether there was any association with President Kennedy's assassination. Of course, there was no question in my mind about that. It couldn't be a coincidence. I had seen him too many times at U.S. Sonics and overheard him talking with the planners. Somehow this was related to the assassination, but how?

My apprehension concerning all of this was driving me to want to leave and never come back, this was too much. Short of that, it was time to take a break from everything and go outside, where I could try to figure out what was really happening. There just wasn't enough information right now, to make heads or tails of it.

June Lawrence Arrives

Just as I reached for the knob, the door flew open, banging against the foyer wall, and in came June Lawrence, hysterical, crying, and screaming, "They did it! I can't believe they did it! I can't believe they killed the president! I can't believe they killed the president!" Obviously, the reality had been too much for her. I knew she was aware they were going to kill President Kennedy. Yet surprisingly, here she was, out of her mind. I couldn't believe she wasn't more prepared for this; although I had seen her many times in the past year, I hadn't seen any sign of stress.

What did she expect? Why hadn't they kept her better informed? Maybe, it was they simply didn't trust her to know more than she did. But no, June and Norris were like part of our family and were fully trusted.

This was the last thing we needed. For her to be here in this state of mind, acting this way. I followed her down the hall to the living room, still screaming. I looked over at my family to measure their reaction; I could see the shock on everyone's face, mouths open in amazement at this display of uncontrollable emotion. Their expression said it all, "This can't get any worse. What's going on?" Even though we children all knew her practically as well as we knew our own mother, we barely recognized the person now in front of us.

June went straight to our mother, still standing behind the couch where I had left her just seconds earlier. Our mother reached out and put her arms around her, immediately leading her down the hall toward her bedroom to do everything she could to help June get control of herself.

My siblings continued staring at me in disbelief. I was beginning to feel very sorry for them and their confusion over everything. It was in no way their fault. It was our father's doing, his lack of concern for his own family. He should have prepared everyone better for this day, including June Lawrence. When someone they knew and respected as much as they did June, acted in such a manner, they didn't know what to expect next or how to deal with it.

She had succeeded in scaring the hell out of them, and they just sat there, looking at me like scared little rabbits who couldn't find a hole to hide in. It would be better for them if I were to sit with them for a while, rather than go outside to try to get my own mind together. If I sat with them, acting calmly, maybe it would rub off on them.

More News

It wasn't five minutes after I sat down, before the TV announcer was relaying new information surrounding Tippit's death. A person matching the description of the man who had shot and killed him had been seen entering the Texas Theatre, a short distance from the murder scene. Employees had stated this man had been acting erratic, not even purchasing a ticket when he entered, just running in. Police had surrounded the theater, and even though he was armed with a handgun, he was arrested without shots being fired.

Then shortly following this announcement came the most shocking bulletin. The man, who had been arrested and was now being accused of killing Tippit, was named Lee Harvey Oswald. Lee Oswald! What in hell was going on over in Dallas? How could it be that I knew both of these men and that both were involved in the President's assassination? It had to be wrong that Lee had killed Tippit. It didn't make a bit of sense. Oswald would only kill Tippit for one reason, if Tippit had been trying to kill him. But why would that be?

Over the last month, Orris had become more secretive concerning what he wanted to disclose to me. Maybe this was one of the things he was keeping from me, or maybe not. Regardless. there was no use trying to make sense of any of this, and besides, this wasn't what was really bothering me.

I was more concerned about my father because something had obviously gone seriously wrong. I began expecting to hear his name announced at any minute. Until now, I had felt more than likely he was okay. But at this point, all I could think was, *"Please don't let me hear my father has been killed."*

This had been the worst day of my life so far and it wasn't getting any better, it was getting worse. It had been terrible enough at school to see all of those children and their parents so disturbed. Then, now to see my brothers and sisters in the state they were in. And my mother, her condition was heartbreaking. And I had no idea what the result of June Lawrence's breakdown would be; surely, she shouldn't be driving a vehicle in such a state.

It wasn't another ten minutes before the announcer was saying it was believed there was some definite connection between Lee Oswald and the President's assassination. Oswald worked at the Dallas County School Book Depository, located on Dealey Plaza and where the fatal shots had been fired. They were implying that it was Oswald, who had shot the president. I knew that wasn't true because he wasn't to be an actual shooter; I knew who the three actual shooters were.

This had now gone too far for me. Once things reach a certain point, I just sort of shut down and become kind of numb to it all. If I don't do that, I feel like I could just come unraveled. And I had just about reached that point. When I had gotten up this morning, I was a little confused as to what was going to actually take place today, but that was just a little confused. But I felt I knew enough to get through the day without being too surprised by very much. Then it had been a beautiful day on the way to school and I had all but forgotten t they were even planning to kill Kennedy today. Now it was totally different. Now it was a complete tragedy. How could things change so much in such a short amount of time, in just a few hours?

My mother and June finally came out from the back and June was no longer screaming hysterically. Instead, she looked to be in total shock, completely unresponsive, staring off into space. It was easy to tell by looking at her face and eyes she had suffered a complete collapse. Not only exhausted, little more than a bowl of jelly, completely lost. She was still intermittently sniffling and crying softly, as she stood at the edge of the living room, clutching my mother's hand.

Suddenly she spoke abruptly, "I have to go. Goodbye. I have to go." Then turned quickly, started for the front door, and was out. My reaction was slow because I was so surprised. I took off to try and stop her, concerned she would have an accident as she was so out of it. But she was in her car and left before I had a chance to stop her. There was nothing else I could do, other than to watch her car speed away. As fast as she had come, she was now gone to where, I had no idea.

My mother had followed us outside and looked over at me with an expression that could only say, "We have to let her go and recover on her own. There's nothing else we can do for her now."

She turned and walked quietly back into the house and into the kitchen. I felt terribly sorry for her because I knew how much she loved June and to see June like this was heartbreaking. The whole damn thing was heartbreaking.

Back in front of the television screen, our heads turned in unison to see the inside of the Dallas School Book Depository. A man in a suit was holding up a rifle, claiming it had been recovered from the sixth floor. They were sure this was the weapon used to kill Kennedy and it was being checked for fingerprints. When they panned in for a close look at it, I immediately recognized it as the one I had seen and even held in my father's office. He had told me this Italian-made Mannlicher-Carcano belonged to Oswald. And I remembered it had been used to fire bullets into that barrel of water in the White Room. Now the Dallas Police had this rifle and Lee Oswald.

But I knew the police had it all wrong. When my father had gone to that rifle range with Lee, he had been dissatisfied with his performance, and didn't think he had what it took. This man I had gotten to know so well, this quiet man, couldn't possibly have pulled the trigger on either President Kennedy or officer Tippit. I might not have gotten all the facts about the assassination, but I knew I had this part correct.

But what I was concerned about now were the actual shooters, of which, my own father was one. What was going on with them right now? Were they in serious danger of being caught or even killed because of the situation involving Tippit and Oswald?

This was so exhausting and even, outlandish. I needed a break from the craziness and the television for at least awhile. I wanted to just leave and go fishing. To stay in this house with these gloomy people waiting for the sky to fall, was just too much. I suggested to our mother my sisters and brothers also needed to get away from it all. My older sisters overheard and, in their usual defensive manner, retorted that I should mind my own business and leave them alone. I could do whatever I wanted, and they would do what they wanted. They were going to continue watching the TV, and that was that.

The three youngest ones were neutral and didn't respond, they really didn't know what was going on anyway. June's reaction had frightened and confused the hell out of them and our own reaction to her had made it worse. They were beginning to pick up on all our abnormal vibes and it was having a negative effect on them. They certainly didn't deserve this, they were innocent children.

My older sisters suspected enough about our father's involvement to know he was in severe danger right now. But I knew they had never heard of Tippit and questioned whether they knew who Lee Oswald was. They certainly knew nothing about Lee and his family visiting at our house. Their concern now was just that these shootings must be related to their father. Maybe, it was even worse for them than for me, being they only knew a little. So, I was in no position to object to their desire to sit here and watch the television, out of their sheer concern for their father. They were both very intelligent, strong-willed, young women, raised by their mother to be this way, and I obviously had little or no control over them.

So now, I had no other choice other than to let it go and get away from it for a little while. I went outside and sat down in the front yard, trying not to think about it. I couldn't help but notice how quiet it still was outside. No movement, no cars, no people coming and going. And I still couldn't hear any dogs barking. Where were everyone? They must all be locked in their houses, glued to their television sets, too. I could understand my interest, but not theirs. How could they all just stop living because this man had died? People die every day. Sure, he was the President of the United States, but he wasn't their father, their brother, or even, their cousin. Their lives were going to go on. Nothing would really change for them personally. I was exhausted by trying to understand.

After about thirty minutes outside, I went back in to see if anything new had taken place. My siblings were still right there in the living room and probably hadn't even moved. A film clip of Lee Oswald in the Dallas jail was now being shown. This was the first time I had actually seen him since his arrest, and he looked as if he had been beaten up, with cuts and bruises on his face. He was saying in response to the questions the press was yelling at him, he hadn't killed anyone, he was 'a patsy.' A patsy!

I had never known what Lee's role was, first thinking it be as a driver or some such utilitarian position. But they had spent a great deal of time with him, more time than with any other individual I knew of. So, I had surmised it was a very important position. I had heard them in private refer to him as the 'fall guy'. To me, 'fall guy' and 'patsy' were basically the same thing. A 'fall guy' an individual who knew he was in that role; 'a patsy' someone who didn't know he was to be the 'fall guy.' This had to be it. They had set him up to go down for the assassination all along. And maybe they never intended for him to leave the country and go to Cuba and Russia as they had promised. Instead, they probably intended to have him killed.

If Tippit had tried to do this and Lee responded and won the gunfight, then everything made sense. Would they really go this far and intentionally have Tippit kill Oswald? Of course, they would. They had just assassinated the President of the United States. Lee Oswald was nothing to them really, just 'a patsy' as he has just proclaimed.

It all made sense now. They had not only deceived him, they also had deceived and used me, intentionally letting me and even encouraging me to get close to him. Which I had. They must have been very careful not to discuss this in front of me.

If this was right, then probably my father was safe and would be okay. These killings now had nothing to do with his safety. I was tempted to pose my theory to my mother.

But first, I watched the television for about twenty minutes, while the announcers kept going over and over the whole day's events in short sequences. News about bullets being found at Parkland Hospital on a gurney. The Governor of Texas, John Connally, being shot in the same limousine as President Kennedy. Vice President Lyndon Johnson being sworn in as President, Jackie at his side. (Apparently the day before the assassination, U.S. National Security Advisor McGeorge Bundy prepared a memo annulling Kennedy's prior one to halt the Vietnam conflict. I would later be told that Johnson was threatened that if he didn't sign this, he would be subject to the same fate as Kennedy.)

Thankfully, nothing about my father, a great relief. Nothing about anyone else either. Maybe it was basically over, maybe there wouldn't be any others discovered. I hated to see Lee in jail like this, but better he be alive and better him than Orris. Now, if only this didn't lead to my father's arrest, it would be okay.

I found my mother sitting on her bed, just sitting there thinking. I sat down beside her and told her, "There is no word about Daddy or anyone else on the television, other than Tippit and Oswald. Maybe all the others will be alright."

She didn't respond, other than to just nod her head in acknowledgment. Finally, she looked at me seriously and said, "Bruce, don't worry about this. Your father will be alright. He knows what he's doing. What you're seeing on television might seem strange, but it is part of their plan. Don't worry about it so much, they will be okay."

She then confirmed my theory about Lee Oswald. That he was supposed to be killed by Tippit. If that failed, he was supposed to be arrested, and then killed. I looked at her in shock and asked, "Why?"

She said t it had to be this way and started crying. We sat there holding each other for several minutes, before she, repeating I should try and not worry. That if anyone could survive this, it would be my father.

She wouldn't say this to me if there weren't some truth to it. But at the same time, in spite of all their planning, anything could happen, and something go wrong. But she would try her best to cause me not to worry myself sick over it all. She was aware I knew an awful lot about what had been planned, probably not everything I knew, but way too much for a twelve-year-old boy. I'm sure she never agreed with them using me the way they did. At the same time, she would never say no to my father either.

I told her I was going for a walk. If she needed me, I would be back in a short while. We were beginning to say goodbye to each other, as though it might be a long time before we would see each other again. That was just the state of mind we were in, one without any certainty about anything.

There were some woods not far away I had recently been frequenting to get away from everything, something I wanted now. They were quite wild for being on the edge of a big city like Fort Worth. It was a good walk, in spite of what had happened today. What my mother had said about my father being alright, had soaked in and made sense. After about an hour it was getting late and about to get dark, so I returned home.

Everyone was still in place in front of the TV. Now the announcer was saying a man named Jack Lawrence had been arrested on suspicion of involvement in the assassination and was being questioned by the FBI. Apparently, the night before the assassination, he had borrowed a car from the Lincoln dealership where he worked. Some co-employees state he was late returning to work the next morning, muddied, out of breath and sick to his stomach., all of which he blamed on being stranded in traffic. "Coincidentally" having to leave the car behind the Dealey plaza grassy knoll picket fence. Thankfully it was Jack Lawrence, not Tom. I wasn't overly concerned about the arrest because I had met Jack and was sure he had played no major role in the assassination. But was this whole scenario some part of the plan? (He would be released shortly.)

I kept waiting for the phone to ring, hoping it would be my father. I knew of no plans for him to call today, but I still thought he might at least do so to let us know he was alright and safe. But then he must be way too busy to call right now, dealing with any problems, anticipated or not.

My mother was just finishing preparing dinner and my siblings were already at the table, so I sat down with them. It was clearly a solemn occasion with everyone unusually quiet. We ate dinner without the give and take about daily events we talkative kids normally had. She kept trying to cheer everyone up by talking about things which had nothing to do with today's events, but it didn't work.

After dinner, she announced we were going to leave the television off tonight, everyone was going to go to bed early. This brought a loud objection from my older sisters, but she prevailed as usual. Shortly after dinner and the ritual cleaning of the kitchen and related chores by my sisters, the younger children were put to bed.

I decided to go outside again to have a look around the house now that it was dark, making sure there was no one in the yard or close by. My father had been very concerned that someone could find out about the assassination and told me to keep a look out for anyone snooping around, especially at night. It was a calm evening and after a good look, I sat on the front porch with the outside light off, so no one could see me. And of course, I continued to obsess about the whole situation.

I was outside for nearly an hour, before going back in. It was still very quiet out there; being somewhat paranoid, too quiet. But my mother, also paranoid, took me aside so as not to alarm my sisters, asking if everything was alright outside. When I responded that it was very quiet, she seemed to relax.

Stephanie spoke up, we should turn the television back on to get the latest and my mother agreed now that the three youngest children had gone to bed. On every station were reporters; excitedly talking about the assassination. It seemed John Connally was still alive and expected to live. The bullet found on the gurney had supposedly fallen out of his leg. That was ridiculous. Bullets don't just fall out of people who have been shot. Had they actually attempted to kill him? Probably not, I never heard them talking about killing him.

One station kept showing pictures of Jackie Kennedy in her bloodied pink dress and focusing on her and her family. She seemed so destroyed, so broken hearted. These pictures were something I didn't want to see, making me think once again, did the assassins do what was right by killing her husband. So, we changed the channel to one more focused on the events in Dallas and showing a film of Oswald being moved around the jail and being questioned about the murder by reporters.

We sat there quietly watching for about an hour. It was getting late, and we were all tired. It had been a day we would rather have never lived through and hoped would never have to experience anything like this again. So, my sisters and I went to bed. Before I fell asleep, I thought about tomorrow and what it might bring. Nothing good because it couldn't be over yet, what with Lee in jail, a man named Lawrence being questioned, and Tippit, dead.

I got up after only sleeping a few hours, knowing my mother must still be up, watching television. I walked down the hall. I was right. She was there, calmly listening to the announcer reviewing the whole day's events. I went to sit down next to her on the couch. Looking at me, she said, "Bruce, I have to be honest with you. This is even worse than I expected. I knew this day was going to be terrible, but not this difficult. You know some of what this is all about and I'm certain this is just as hard for you as it is for me. I haven't heard anything from your father yet, but I'm expecting to hear something tomorrow."

We sat there together not saying a word, just listening. There were no new dramatic events, so after about twenty minutes we turned off the television and went to bed. I laid there in thought about what my mother had said about it being even worse than she had expected. She was right. It was much worse for both of us. Knowing what we knew made it so much worse than for anyone who knew nothing prior to today. To have my father and all the men I personally knew directly involved, made it worse than words could describe. And I had to accept I was a direct part of it too, maybe not a fully willing participant, but nonetheless, I had played a role in it. I was finally able to go to sleep after lying there obsessing about it all for some thirty minutes. Somehow, I slept soundly through the night, probably because I was just so exhausted.

20

THE DAYS AFTER

November 23

The next morning, I woke up earlier than usual, my immediate thought the television. I had to get up quickly to find out if anything had happened during the night involving my father. He probably had had no sleep, but was with his people, dealing with yesterday's events, deciding how to correct anything that hadn't gone according to plan. I was certain of that.

It was already on and in front of it sat all my brothers and sisters. They had gotten up, without me hearing them, something amazing in itself. I stood behind a couch and listened for anything new. They were again showing the police holding up Oswald's Mannlicher-Carcano rifle; saying they had uncovered his palm print on an area under the gun's stock. And ballistics people were saying the bullet found on the hospital gurney, matched the rifle. Fortunately, following Orris' plan, they seemed to be naming Lee as the only assassin, not aware of the three actual shooters or the real motivation.

There were new film clips of his being dragged around the jail, the main Dallas Police headquarters, not actually a long-term facility although it had a few cells in which to keep suspects while interrogating them. They were packed with news-people, like sardines in a can. Lee looked nearly hysterical in one of the clips, as the media continued their completely unmerciful and frenzied effort to get his attention.

It was reported that Marina had visited Lee last night for about twenty minutes and they showed a film of her and Ruth Paine entering, Marina carrying her recently born baby. They were asking her all types of questions about Lee, even though she could barely speak English. I felt sorry for her and had never reached a conclusion as to how much she actually knew about the assassination and her husband's role.

She had to suspect something, but I had never heard my father discuss anything about it in front of her. But Marina was no dummy. She had to have put some of it together on her own from just knowing about Lee's activities and these very strange men with whom he was constantly involved, like my father. Besides, I think Lee was prone to telling her more than he was supposed to, so she might have known a lot more about the assassination than anyone imagined. Hearing Ruth and Marina's names now, I would probably hear about them before this thing was over.

There was now a lot of newly planted damning information about Lee. The false setup was beginning to kick into high gear, and I knew enough about it to see how well the machine was working. One person had reported to the FBI he had seen Lee at different shooting ranges, and Lee had actually shot at their target; when he approached to tell him not to do this, Lee responded, "Oh, I was thinking about that son of a bitch, Kennedy."

The information had surfaced about his trip to Mexico City and his going to the Cuban and U.S.S.R. embassies to try to obtain a visa. This indicated his plans for escape from the U.S. after the assassination. This planted evidence was working well and made him look guilty without question. What other explanation could there be?

They had already pieced together other corroborating evidence. Lee obtaining the job at the School Book Depository to give him that excellent vantage point. His purchasing the rifle, a surplus military Mannlicher-Carcano through a Chicago catalog order company using a false name, Alek Hidell. And found in his possessions at Ruth's house, the newspaper clip about the attempted assassination of ultra-conservative General Edwin Walker, along with that picture of him holding his weapons.

All this made it look as if he had been sent back to the United States for the main purpose of assassinating an American president. They were referring to him as a loner, a Communist 'nut', who hated America so much he quit the Marines to defect to the U.S.S.R. And the American people fell for it hook, line, and sinker.

On TV, they kept showing hordes of people crying all over the county. It was like the end of the world had come or was about to. People were saying Kennedy was a 'Great Man' and the country had lost a 'Great Hero.' I guess all you had to do was die, for the public and press to conclude you had been a great man and say only good things about you.

At this point, I really didn't know whether President Kennedy had been a great man or not; I was quickly shifting my opinion though.

All these people mourning his loss couldn't be wrong, not all of them; there were way too many shedding real tears over this man's death.

At breakfast together, we all seemed calmer and more confident that at least our father was still unharmed. It had been less than twenty-four hours, but it seemed like a week had passed. We had not heard from him, but at the same time, we had not heard his name on the damned television either.

Being Saturday with no school, I decided to go to the Meadowbrook Golf Course to take a long walk as another attempt to forget about everything. In reality, there was nothing I could do to influence anything anyway, so why fret so much about something I had no control over. On the way, there was still only one car out in the fifteen minutes it took me.

When I got there, probably close to ten o'clock, the only person there was the security guard whose car I recognized in the parking lot. He was in the clubhouse, and we waved to each other. The gate was closed. So I had to carry my bike over it.

Normally, there would be a number of golfers on the course by now, most of them already done playing the front nine. But not today. There weren't even any dogs on the course, and no one to throw rocks at them to chase them off. I had trouble believing it, but even the animals seemed to be affected by the humans' reaction to the catastrophe.

I tried not to think about anything, other than what a beautiful day it was and how lucky I was to have this big, quiet golf course all to myself. And the girls I met in Meadowbrook last summer, what they would be doing now and how the Kennedy assassination might be affecting them. Maybe, I should go visit one of them to help me forget what was going on. That had always worked for me this past summer, but no, probably not today.

I spent about two hours completely alone. Everyone seemed to be huddled together in their houses with their families, afraid to leave home for fear of the unknown. They didn't know what to do now they had lost their leader so suddenly and unexpectedly, so they did nothing, not even realizing why they were doing nothing. Finally, I did come across a 'walk-on' playing the back nine, obviously staying away from the security man up front.

I decided to take the long way home and cycle over to a lake a couple of miles to the north. I just wasn't ready to go back home. I knew they would still be glued to the television. As I thought more about it, I reassured myself there wasn't that much need to worry about my father, he had control of this. He had gone to meticulous detail to cover everything, with multiple backup plans for each possible situation. I had personally watched them put it together and it was nearly infallible. Besides, they had the CIA, FBI, Dallas Police, as well as Vice President Lyndon Johnson, all in their corner, working for them.

The lake was beautiful and hidden in a little high valley, right across the turnpike from Meadowbrook. I often wondered how it never had been developed, being in the middle of this metropolitan area. It was on a farm and the owner allowed me to fish there, as long as I didn't bring more than one person with me. So, I had fished it a number of times the past summer. He was a good man and I had always enjoyed seeing him. Maybe, he would be out to see his cows and I could get his 'take' on the Kennedy assassination.

When I got there, it was completely quiet as usual, with a large flock of ducks on the north end, mostly Mallards. I would have to come back later this winter to see if I could shoot a few of these beautifully colored ducks. I loved to eat wild duck, delicious. I would only stay here until I saw one of the large bass jump and take a bug on the surface, and then head back home. It was only about five minutes before one sailed high in the air and landed with a big splash. But my brain wasn't ready for me to head home just yet.

Instead, I fell asleep in the tall grass. I hadn't realized how exhausted I was until the seclusion of the lake hit me so I fully relaxed, the warm sun got to me, and I just passed out. I slept like a baby and woke up about two hours later. It was nearly two o'clock. I better get home. My mother might need me for something and maybe, my father had finally called.

Two Geese

When I got back to the house, I thought it best to sit down in the front yard for a few minutes to try regain my composure before going inside. I no more than sat down when for some reason I looked down the street to the far corner, and an extremely strange feeling rushed over me. A terrible, evil feeling, like a premonition, emanating from that corner. Then I realized a vehicle was about to turn onto our street; this feeling had something to do with the vehicle I couldn't even see yet. Was this something that Orris had been worried about?

Then an old, faded green Chevrolet pick-up did come around the corner; a truck I recognized, having seen it a number of times at different places over the last year, even at U.S. Sonics. It was unmistakable with its high, unpainted wood sides. But it was not the pick-up that caused me to feel this way, but rather the driver and what he represented. Something very strange and foreboding. Evil, as if the devil himself were riding its jump board.

I couldn't take my eyes off it as it came down our street to cross over and park facing, right in front of me. Jack Ruby's right-hand man, George Senator got out, the last person I expected to see. But just as surprising was that feeling I had been experiencing; I had always liked this man who had always been very polite and considerate of me.

I stood up and took a few steps to meet him as he started for the back of the truck. He gave me a serious smile, allowing me to relax a little. As he was unfastening the tailgate, calmly as though today were like any ordinary day, he said, "Hello, Bruce. I have something for your mother that's very important. Is she home?"

"Yes, she is," I replied.

"Good, I want you to go right in as soon as I leave and tell her, 'The geese are here, and there are two.'"

As he was saying this, he opened the tailgate and pulled out a heavy, wire cage with two live wild Canadian Geese. Certainly, the last thing on earth I ever expected. Geese from Ruby, a man who owned a strip club, not a farm. I knew that he wasn't just being a nice guy. There had to be something more to this.

After I nodded understanding, I accompanied him as he carried the cage into the carport. After we walked back to his truck, he said goodbye, got back in and disappeared around the corner, just as fast as he had arrived. I stood there a moment to watch him drive away, wondering what the hell this was all about; it had to have something to do with the assassination.

I turned and walked over to inspect this unexpected 'gift.' The geese were beautiful and obviously very frightened. When I approached, they moved as far as possible to get away. And when I picked the heavy cage up to move it a little further into the carport, they became frantic.

What in the name of God was this about. The devil himself, Ruby, has sent Canadian Geese to our house, and I'm supposed to immediately tell my mother that Mr. Senator has brought them and there are two of them. These geese must have some secret meaning. Just one more extremely strange thing, in one more very strange day.

I went inside and found my mother in the living room with the other kids still watching the television and listening to every word about the assassination and all the related events. I motioned for her to come over to me, not wanting to mention the geese in front of the others. I didn't know what they meant, if it were something only she should know about.

In the kitchen, I told her about Senator delivering these two Canadian Geese. She seemed instantly taken by this information and quickly asked, "Are there just two geese and are they Canadian Geese? Are they white or brown, like Canadian Geese?"

When I told her they were definitely Canadian Geese, not white, two of them together in one cage, I could see an obvious reaction on her face. She seemed to relax, sighed in relief, and told me, "Thank you, Bruce. I think everything will be alright now with your father and we will all be alright, too."

I didn't want to question her about it. She wouldn't tell me anyway. They had been delivered in such a covert manner, it was obviously intended to keep the meaning of some secret message just that, very secret. At the same time, it was clear these geese had some reassuring meaning to her. Whatever they meant, it was definitely a good sign. Making me feel a lot better.

Following up, she said, "Let's go have a look at these geese." So, we walked out to the carport where she looked at them as though they had been sent from heaven. She sighed as if for the first time in months, a large boulder had been lifted from her body. She said, mostly to herself, "Yes, we will be alright now," turned without another word, and walked to the back door. She paused and looked back at me saying, "Bruce, turn those geese loose in the backyard, please." Then, she went inside with a new step in her walk, looking like my mother from a year ago.

Obviously, this whole process was a message from my father, a very good message. It must have signified something specific by the number and type of geese. I didn't know at the time, geese represented happiness and success in Egyptian lore, and the 'two' probably represented two men; two men are safe and successful. Concerned that our house was being watched by some government organization, the whole scenario would look like two geese at Thanksgiving time being delivered by a farmer.

I carried the cage out to the backyard as my mother had asked, got them some oatmeal to eat and a dish of water. I wasn't sure they should be let out of the cage as she had asked, because they might fly away. But they did look very cramped and unhappy in the cage, so I opened its door and turned them loose. "*The backyard has a canopy of Oak tree limbs and leaves, above the high wood fence that should keep them in.* If they fly away, they fly away." But they just ran all over the yard, looking for someplace to escape, honking continuously at each other. They, finally, seemed to settle for one corner, putting their backs to it and staring at me, as though they would like to bite me, if they could or if I tried to get too close. They were definitely wild. And out of the cage, I could see they were huge.

The rest of the day was uneventful, but my mother seemed much better than she had been. Much more relaxed, no longer emanating that hidden tenseness she had been trying so hard to disguise. We had a much more relaxed dinner that night, my sisters' attitude toward me not so harsh, nor the staring that went with it.

After dinner, we all sat down and watched the ever-continuing coverage of the assassination. Not much had changed today, other than the rolling out of more of the preplanned evidence to convict Lee. One reporter asked him what had happened to his eye, to which he responded, "A police officer hit me." Another reporter asked him again if he had killed Tippit and Kennedy. And again, he responded he didn't kill anyone, he was just 'a patsy.'

The night went on with non-stop commentary from Dallas and Washington, but no more names of people I knew were involved. I had already heard too many. At about ten, we had heard enough after a long, extremely difficult day, one that we were eager to see the end of. The one thing we all wanted so much to happen, my father coming home or at least, call to say he was alright and safe, hadn't. So, we all went to bed early again and I slept through the entire night, after lying awake for quite a while, trying to really understand the meaning of the geese and why these two Canadian Geese had caused such a relaxing effect over my mother.

November 24th

The next day, Sunday, we all got up and had an early breakfast, just like the day before. Our maid called, saying she wanted to come back to work today, if that were okay with my mother. She had been given the last few days off with no real explanation. My mother agreed and she arrived about an hour later.

The day started out calmly enough, but changed rapidly. I was watching the Dallas news live, when the news people announced the police had decided to move Lee Oswald to another location, where he would be more secure. From the downtown station to the County Sheriff's Jail, located just west of downtown Dallas. This move was to take place around one o'clock and the police were making every effort to make certain that he would be safe during the move. Preparation was under way and throughout the rest of the morning, it was the main focus of the news media.

I needed someone to talk to, other than my family. Although much of the stress had lifted, they were still in shock and weren't really talking with each other at all. I needed to try to get someone else's perspective on the assassination. So about ten o'clock, after calling Danielle, a girlfriend, I went to see her. She lived about a half a mile away, so I rode my bike.

Her mother was home, but soon left to see her ex-husband. Danielle had a sister named Jan, so that left the three of us to talk about the assassination. They both thought that the reaction of the American public seemed normal. After all, it was the President of the United States. I didn't argue with my girlfriends, concerning their opinion, as to why the American public was reacting the way it was. They simply didn't know the truth and it wasn't my place to educate them. It must have been only my father and his associates who hated the dead president and knew what he was really about. But, surely, there had to be more people in this world, who knew the truth about him.

The two girls made lunch for me and as we sat down to eat, trying to go on with life as normally as possible. Just to be with these two good friends made me feel so much better, despite what was going on with the rest of the world. Time went by pretty quickly and it was getting close to the time they were going to move Lee to the other jail, so we turned on the television. The news media was making a very big thing out of the move and seemed to be going on forever about nothing, when they finally brought Lee out into the basement of the facility.

Lee A Dead Patsy

The planners of the assassination were appropriately concerned about the post- assassination investigation that would obviously occur. So, they created algorithms, a set of rules or processes to be followed in any possible situation they could foresee. This mandated first, the choice of the actual on-site participants must be made very carefully. And second, there'd be no chance of Lee Oswald being apprehended by unsympathetic members of the Dallas Police, Secret Service, FBI, or any other law enforcement agency. That could lead to his talking about the other assassination players, the end for everyone involved directly or indirectly.

So, the first and most important job following the assassination was to kill Lee Oswald. He was a willing fall guy, but he wasn't willing to give his life for this effort. Assassinate the false assassin was the name of the game.

The algorithm to accomplish Oswald's end consisted of several layers. First, was to kill him in the Dallas School Book Depository seconds after he had fired. If he did get away from the Depository without being killed, police officers J.D. Tippit. and Roscoe White were s to locate him along the walking route to the Theatre. Tippit was to kill him with his police service revolver and say he approached this suspicious acting man, who then pulled a gun on him. Leaving him no choice but to pull his own weapon and shoot.

If Oswald made it past White and Tippit, the larger force of like-minded Dallas police placed behind the Theatre were to apprehend and kill him before any other agency could get hands on him. (It has always seemed very strange and unusual to me that in all the literature on the Texas Theatre, no one has ever reached the conclusion that Oswald was, in fact, going there for a pre-conceived reason, such as to be picked up or meet someone. It hadn't been a spontaneous act.)

Failure of this plan would prompt a fourth one and intentionally placed suspicion on the Mafia. Infamous drug dealer and pimp, Jack Ruby, at the downtown Dallas jail. This would be a foolproof effort because he, with his deep relationship with the Dallas police, had no problem accessing the police station.

Unfortunately, as each attempt to kill Lee failed, the more complicated the investigation would become and the greater potential for exposure of the real and true assassins.

Jack Ruby Shoots Oswald

I wanted to tell my girlfriends what I knew about the assassination, and I personally knew Lee, but I obviously couldn't. The news media had continued all morning about Lee Oswald's move. Why such emphasis on something that would usually be seen as trivial? But that's exactly what they were doing, making one more, huge spectacle.

All of a sudden, the television flashed to the Police Station basement, dark and jammed full of news-people and cameramen waiting for Oswald. The scene looked chaotic, and Oswald was not in sight yet. The news-people seemed to be pushing each other, jockeying for a better position to view and film him when he would appear, which was promised to be very soon.

Finally, he entered from a door on the far right. Handcuffed and closely shouldered on either side by two policemen. At first sight, he looked confused and exhausted, as he was being quickly pushed forward by the supporting officers. The scene was tight, media men shoving in even closer to get a better look at him. I was scanning for someone I recognized, thinking they might try to free Lee in an escape attempt.

Suddenly from out of nowhere, a man jumped out in front of Lee and shot him in the stomach. I couldn't see who this man was as he had his back to the camera. I couldn't believe it. Lee Oswald was now shot and probably would die. Although my mother had implied they wanted him dead, I was completely shocked.

Very quickly, police officers grabbed the shooter, wrestling his gun away. It looked as though he was trying to get another shot. The scene became even more chaotic with cameramen moving about like cattle soon to be slaughtered, and people yelling and screaming.

Then an unconscious Oswald was seen on a gurney, being slid into an ambulance. He was being taken to the same Parkland Hospital as President Kennedy had been only two days earlier. Only this time, it was the fake assassin.

I was sitting there in sheer surprise. Impulsively, I started toward the door; I had to get home as fast as possible. I yelled goodbye to my girlfriends, as I picked up my bike. They were yelling at me, "What's wrong? Don't go." This had scared them too, and they didn't want to be deserted just now.

I pedaled as fast as I could all the way home, saying to myself, "*I can't believe that Lee is dead, I can't believe that Lee is dead. I should have stayed home. I should have stayed home.*"

It didn't take but about five minutes to get there and I burst through the front door to my family, once again huddled around the television looking completely frightened all over again. I stood behind the couch looking at the replay of the man who had shot Lee being wrestled to the floor. All of a sudden, I heard Jack Ruby's name. And when they flashed a live film shot of his face, there was no doubt it was him who shot Lee Oswald.

What the hell was going on in Dallas? They were shooting each other. I looked over at my mother and she looked right back at me with the same frightened expression I had seen on her face the first day it all started. That seemed like a week ago now and it had only been three days.

I had known both Oswald and Ruby for just about a year. It had been my understanding they were involved in the assassination together, on the same side. I had even once seen them together drinking at Ruby's club, just blocks from the scene where he had just assassinated Oswald.

The only way I could make any sense of this was, if Ruby had killed Oswald to silence him, it was to make sure he could never talk. But what was going to keep Jack Ruby from talking now he was in jail? Would they now have to kill Ruby in the Dallas jail too? When would it ever end? And was this the reason he had been making all those phone calls right before the assassination.

All of a sudden, the wind was out of my sails again. This was definitely getting too crazy. I was almost expecting to see my father appear any minute in his police uniform and shoot Ruby right there in front of us, live on television. This was getting way out of hand.

This started worrying about my father again, as I looked down at the three younger children Carolyn, Stuart, and Stephen and realized they still didn't have the foggiest idea what was actually going on, how could they. But they were definitely picking up on the vibes from the rest of us who knew our father was somewhere in Dallas, in the middle of it all and that he too could die at any minute. What with all these other people we knew being shot right and left. Obviously, this was very dangerous.

It was time to stop these little ones from watching television, before they saw something they would never forget. Nothing could be worse than seeing your father being shot and killed on live television, right in front of you. When I spoke to my mother about this, she agreed and asked them to go feed our Bassett Hound and our newfound feathered friends, the geese. They did what she asked, understanding that even though the animals did not need to be fed now, they kids needed to leave the room. It was clear Stephanie and Debbie weren't about to turn the TV off and leave the room.

My mother and I went into the dining room and sat down at the table. She knew I wanted to know if the plan were falling apart or if it was supposed to happen like this. She told me again not to worry so much, this was pretty much the way it was supposed to happen. We talked together for about ten minutes and went back in the living room to see if anything else had happened.

The news-people were saying Lee Oswald was pronounced dead at Parkland Hospital, the same one President Kennedy had been taken to just the day before yesterday. This hit me hard. I had liked Lee Oswald. Now he was dead, and I would never see him again. And his wife and children would be without him for the rest of their lives.

Then it hit me like a bale of hay on the side of the head. What was the difference between Lee Oswald's wife and children and President Kennedy's wife and children? Nothing. When it came to their father's death, it was the same. This started the pendulum swinging again. Had the assassination been right or wrong.? Could this have been done in a different way? Did they really have to kill President Kennedy?

Orris Goes into Hiding

About forty-five minutes after Jack Ruby killed Oswald, our phone rang. I was watching my mother when she answered it, as though she knew exactly who it would be. Finally, it was my father. Alive. Obviously, she knew he had to stay in Dallas as long as Oswald was alive, but once Oswald had been killed in one scenario or another, he would be free to leave. And had to. And she knew that. He had completed his responsibilities in the Kennedy assassination and should not be visible in Dallas for a while.

He was calling from a hotel on the Dallas/Fort-Worth Turnpike, halfway between the two cities. He and Jeff Miller were in Jeff's brown Cadillac-Eldorado convertible. She was to meet him beside the west end of the Turnpike, bringing me along with a suitcase of clothes and toiletries. We were to hurry and meet him in twenty minutes, just a little west of the last Fort Worth exit, on the right side of the road.

As my mother headed for their bedroom, I asked my sisters if there were anything they wanted me to say to him. "Just tell him that we love him and to be careful."

I went to see if I could help her, but she already had a packed suitcase on the bed and was putting in my father's shaving kit. Obviously, she had been expecting this phone call, just wasn't supposed to tell us about it. I carried the suitcase out to the car and put it in the trunk. She followed closely behind after saying goodbye to the other kids and giving them brief instructions in case something happened, and she didn't return within two hours. Stephanie was to call our aunt Martha to come and get all of them.

It was a cold, very windy day, completely overcast with dark snow clouds. A complete contrast to the day of the assassination just a few days earlier, when it had been warm, clear, and sunny. The Turnpike terminal was only about ten minutes away, so we arrived very quickly. Perhaps we might beat them to the rendezvous point. But why didn't our father just come home to get his suitcase, so he could say goodbye to everyone?

Then it struck me. He was concerned someone might be waiting for him there, so the FBI could arrest him or worse. A few of the key local FBI agents in the Dallas/Fort Worth area were working with him and his people, but not all of them. And, of course, J. Edgar Hoover was on the inside with the conspirators. But still an unknowing FBI agent could create serious problems.

When we arrived close to the rendezvous spot, we were on the wrong side of the Turnpike. I could see Jeff's Cadillac parked on the other side of the divided highway, about a hundred yards beyond the end of the Turnpike and the tollbooths. It was a great relief to see it sitting there, to see my father actually alive and somewhat safe. But we had no choice than to get onto the Turnpike going east toward Dallas, get off at the first exit, then cross over to get back on, going west.

We finally reached Jeff's convertible and parked behind it. But his car. It seemed rather dangerous to use it for their getaway vehicle. It was practically one-of-a-kind and very conspicuous. He had to order it from the dealership in this unusual dark brown color and had been driving it for the past year, during the entire time of the assassination planning. He seemed attached to it, now apparently wanting it with him wherever they were going. But I had to assume they knew what they were doing, since they had made it this far with their endeavor. Maybe, they really did have this much control over the situation and weren't as 'hot' as I thought they would be at this point.

We pulled up behind Jeff's car and parked. My mother and I were both very excited to be this close to my father after what we had been through the past three days. I couldn't wait to see him to make sure he was okay.

But when I looked around, I reached a quick conclusion. Under the circumstances, the situation looked dangerous. Here we were parked behind this very obvious, flashy Cadillac convertible, registered to Jeff, beside this very busy exit of the Turnpike. With two men who had just been involved in the assassination of the President of the United States. One, a main planner and shooter and the other, a major conspirator.

To add to my concern, my mother and I were in my father's yellow Ford Galaxy 50 that had been spotted in the attempted assassination of General Walker six months earlier, and which my father had driven for the entire past year. He had even gone to New Orleans to see Oswald, Marcelo, and Clay Shaw, several times, during the summer in it.

So, I all seemed very dangerous and questionable. I kept looking over my shoulder for the Texas State Police, which I knew patrolled the Turnpike on a regular basis. In my mind, I could just see a police car pulling up behind us and a shootout taking place right here. They obviously did not have full control over things as yet; they couldn't with so little time having passed since the assassination. They were winging it now or we wouldn't be here beside a highway like this. It was clearly the result of exhaustion and extensive stress, not one of clear rational thought. But maybe there is something to be said about hiding out in the open. I hoped so.

My mother and I got out of our car and started up to the passenger side of the Cadillac. My father opened the door, got out, and reached down to embrace his wife. They held each other for a long time and kissed, before pulling their heads back a little, so they could look each other in the eye. Seeing the expression on their faces and I understood what both must be thinking. They were both still alive, in love, and very happy that the worst part of it was now over, or at least they felt it was.

They let go and my father stepped to the side, so she could slide into the middle of the front seat beside Jeff, sitting in the driver's seat. Orris then turned to me and bent down a little to take me in his arms. His suit coat fell open just enough for me to see a shoulder holster containing a handgun. As he hugged me tightly, I felt it push hard against my chest. I had never seen him wear a shoulder gun before; it bothered and worried me, bringing the danger involved to full reality once again.

After a long hard hug, he leaned into the two-door car to tilt the front seat forward so I could get in the back. A blanket was covering the seat, a heavy, rough wool Mexican blanket, the kind that is sometimes used as a saddle blanket or a serape in the wintertime. And when I sat on it, something hard was underneath. I had an idea what it was, I had felt this same type of hard object before under my bottom. I didn't want to be so obvious, but I wanted to be sure I was feeling what I knew I was. I could see the long, narrow bulge underneath the blanket and even though I felt instinctively I knew what it was, I still had to pull the blanket back to see for sure. Exactly what I had thought, the barrel of a rifle. I covered it back up quickly and scooted forward a bit, so I wouldn't be sitting on it.

They were quiet up front at first, and I had a long, good look at my father and Jeff. They both looked dead tired, and I was certain any sleep in the past three days had been very little. I couldn't remember ever seeing my father look as exhausted. Jeff looked back at me, attempting a half smile that didn't quite come out right. I couldn't help but feel sorry for them. They had surely gone through literal hell in what must have seemed like weeks.

The silence didn't last but a few seconds before my father asked my mother how we children were dealing with things so far. After she responded somewhat noncommittally they were alright, they went on talking about this for a few minutes.

This was a strange meeting, a very strange meeting. I loved my father, but this wasn't the way I wanted to remember him. This was so dangerous, I might never see him again. Anything could go wrong, even though they thought they would be able to control everything. And no one knew what was going to happen with the investigation into the assassination, an investigation certain to come. Where were they going and for how long? And where were the rest of them?

Orris must have known we were waiting for some kind of explanation, and he couldn't sugarcoat it. Because, looking straight ahead out the window, he finally said, "It was difficult, very difficult." He then turned to my mother and asked, "How are you?" looking directly in her eyes and kissing her on the cheek.

Then he and Jeff, talking alternatively, stated it clearly had not gone as smoothly as they had wished. The facts that Tippit had been killed and they had to revert to bringing in Ruby to kill Oswald had been a tremendous problem. It lengthened their stay in Dallas and added so much stress to an already nearly unbearable situation.

Then he turned to pragmatic issues. My mother was to contact Searcy Dobkins if she needed help for anything. Dobkins was to take care of everything, financial and otherwise. This surprised me because

I had no idea of Dobkins' involvement. But then it shouldn't have because when the two men had conversed around me, there had been great secrecy, as if Dobkins didn't want me to hear; sort of like with Born, but unlike most of the other conspirators. I had just assumed their discussions were about other business dealings, he being so successful business-wise. I should have guessed because Orris visited him, and they talked on the phone. a number of times in the days just prior to the assassination.

Then he and started telling her what to do as far as his business affairs went. To refer everything to Ed Nesbitt, his attorney who would be running the day-to-day affairs at U.S. Sonics and would also contact her periodically to make certain all was going well at home or for any other business affairs that she might needed help with. And he might need her for something that came up pertaining to U.S. Sonics, because she was on the board of the company.

Orris also included my uncle, Luther Knox, and Charlie Lyon, as people who had agreed to help. Apparently because Lyon had never been involved with U.S. Sonics and his leaving town would have looked suspicious, he would continue his regular life and routine.

Then he turned to me, "Bruce, you're not going back to school again this year. I want you to stay at home with your mother to protect her and help her with anything she needs. Also, I want you to watch out for your brothers and sisters, while I'm gone. Keep your eyes open for anyone who might be watching our house, following your mother when she is driving, or who looks unusual or suspicious on our street or anyplace else. Anyone or anything that looks strange, I want you to tell her about it immediately.

"Keep my handgun in your bedroom at night and be ready to use it. During the day, keep it close. If anyone threatens you or your mother or your brothers and sisters, don't hesitate to shoot them; you might not get another chance, if you don't shoot first. Do you understand what I'm saying to you?"

As he was giving me this litany of instructions, I was leaning forward just a few inches from his face, trying to understand just what he meant by it all, and absorb it as quickly as I could. I looked him in the eyes, and obviously had no choice but to reply, "Yes, sir," as soon as I realized just what he meant. "Yes, I understand what you are telling me, and I'll do exactly what you are asking." Then I was able to ask that burning question, "But Daddy, where are you going and how long will you be gone?"

He answered, "Jeff and I are going to Los Angeles. Lundquist will be taking care of us. I don't know how long I'll be gone yet. It could be a long time, at least six months. We won't be able to have any contact with you. No phone calls, they could be tapped."

Jeff leaned around to ask, "Bruce, why don't you come back to your car with me and help me get your father's suitcase." He didn't really need any help, but wanted to leave my parents alone for a while to say goodbye. We got out and started back to the Ford Galaxy, which we got in to get out of the cold wind for a few minutes.

I wasn't really close to Jeff, even though he was my Godfather. But I looked over at him and asked, "Really, how was it?"

He hesitated, staring off into the distance, then took in a deep breath, trying to relax a little, probably for the first time in the last few days. Attempting to bring his thoughts together, he looked back at me and replied, "It was hard, Bruce, very hard. It was especially hard for your father. All of it was hard on him. He had to make a number of very difficult decisions, the worst being to have J.D. Tippit killed by

Roscoe White, which was completely unexpected. And then to have Lee killed by Jack Ruby in the Dallas jail. Although that was needed, it was still very hard for him."

Jeff was my father's best friend in Dallas and they saw eye-to-eye, so I trusted what he was saying. That thing about Tippit and White I had no way of knowing, but had wondered about.

In my own way trying to comfort him, I said, "I'm sorry, Jeff. I'm sorry it was so bad for the both of you."

He just repeated, "It was hard, Bruce. I t was very hard. It was the most difficult thing I've ever done in my life."

I looked closely at his face. He was someone I had known very well and for many years, even though we had never gotten close. Not just very tired, the expression on his face and in his eyes meant that all he was saying was the complete truth. Evident that this was something from which these men would never completely recover.

We intentionally stayed back in our car for about ten minutes so my parents could have their time. I sat there, looking at the car in front of us, trying to imagine what my parents were saying; it was a very sad time. Looking up over the top of the Cadillac, I could see the skyline of downtown Fort Worth perfectly. There was a gray sky behind it and, for some reason, the big square clock that rotated on top of the tallest building in the city was so distinct. I will never forget. It said three o'clock.

Jeff and I retrieved the suitcase and then walked back up to Jeff's trunk to store it away. The trunk was pretty full already, but the suitcase fit in well.

Then I instinctively turned when I caught out of the corner of my eye what looked like a police car. It was a State Police car and the officer was giving us a hard look. I immediately thought it might be all over for all of us. Normally, he would stop to see if there was anything wrong, but he was several lanes over, so it would have been hard for him to maneuver to where we were. So thankfully, he kept on going with one final look at us over his shoulder.

We then got back in Jeff's car, me near the barrel of the rifle again. This time, I sat forward to avoid sitting on it. But I couldn't help but pull the blanket back to have a closer look; it was an M1 Garand. I pulled the blanket back over it, tucking in the edge so it wouldn't show so easily.

It was obvious they needed to get going. It was dangerous out in the open like this on the Turnpike for Orris and Jeff. After all, they had assassinated the President of the United States just two days earlier and only twenty miles from here. The State Police car had just driven by and all the cops in the Dallas/Fort Worth area would be real edgy right now.

So, my mother and I first said goodbye to Jeff. Then my father, mother, and I got out and I stood next to the car holding the door open in the wind, while they kissed goodbye for maybe the final time in their lives.

My father then turned to me and bent down to hug me, again revealing the holstered gun. He hugged me hard for a long time and then gave me that kiss on both cheeks. The feel of the gun hard against my chest made me even more frightened for him. He said goodbye to me and once more made it clear he was depending on me to take care of everyone.

Glancing over at my mother I could see tears in her eyes. I know she was trying to be brave and not cry for my father, but it was hard to control herself. It was all very sad, all of it. Killing the President is a very sad thing, even if you do hate him as my father and Jeff did.

My father got back in the car and Jeff pulled away, starting their long drive to L.A. My mother and I went back home quietly. There really wasn't anything to say; we both knew how long and hard it would be till we would see Orris again. Today had been a terrible event, verging on horrendous, mirrored by the weather; a bone chilling cloudy day with gusting winds, and no sun. Winter, in so many ways, was finally here.

In retrospect, this meeting on the Turnpike was rather foolish and could so easily have gone wrong. It was only by chance that a State Policeman didn't pull-in to determine what was happening on the roadside.

Ruby in Jail

After Ruby killed Oswald, the planners now had to deal with him in jail, probably as much a risk as Oswald himself. Chief Justice Warren and several other Warren Commission members came to Dallas to question him about any involvement in the assassination or knowledge of anyone else's. Ruby told Warren he knew the truth about who actually killed Kennedy, the conspiracy was far-reaching and astounding, it went all the way to the top.

But he couldn't talk about what he knew while in the Dallas jail, because he would certainly be killed, asking to be taken to Washington. However, Warren had no such authority and no way to protect him there.

At this point, Ruby began telling Warren about a meeting he attended at the Dallas Love Field Airport, doing so without naming David McCord and the Fox brothers, mysterious Mafia figures expelled from Cuba. Giving the names would make him a dead man in the Dallas jail. However, Warren cut him off at this point, feeling Ruby was just rambling, when in fact he was beginning to cave in. Warren and his entourage left without procuring any of the details that Ruby had which was a hell of a lot; not everything, but damn near everything concerning the Dallas side of the assassination. As to be expected all this was denied by Warren.

And this left Ruby to certain death. Knowing personally how frightened he had been before the assassination, I'm sure he was even more frightened now, trapped in the Dallas jail. In March 1964, he was convicted of murdering Oswald, and sentenced to death. That conviction was overturned by the Texas Court of Appeals finding that his confession while in police custody was inadmissible, ordering a retrial in a different venue.

Foolishly, Ruby stated that in the new trial. he would tell the truth about the assassination. However, he would never have this chance. In January 1967, he died quickly and mysteriously of an embolus to the brain, after being hospitalized for pneumonia and where he was diagnosed with cancer in the liver, lungs, and brain. Technically unconvicted.

I'm convinced the people in Dallas, still in control of the cover-up, simply gave him a heavy dose of radiation in some form that gave him this cancer, probably in his food.

If Oswald had just gone to the sixth floor and adhered to the plan, the deaths of two others would have been avoided. Tippit and Ruby.

My Life After the Assassination

At this time, we had a maid come to the house six days a week to help our mother with everything. She was black and sometimes her twenty-year-old daughter would substitute. I suspected Orris had been sexually involved with the daughter because he would always make it a point to take her home. I could tell by the way he would look at her. After all, I knew my father pretty well by then and had been around enough women with him to know when there was involvement.

He had been gone only a few days, when at about nine on Thanksgiving morning, the 28th of November, I came home from a bike ride to find the maid in the backyard, sitting on a wooden stool with goose feathers all around her. She had caught one of the geese, killed it, and was now plucking it to prepare for Thanksgiving dinner. She hadn't asked anyone about this, and didn't know about the bought turkey already in the fridge. She just naturally thought these recently arrived geese were for Thanksgiving dinner.

When I went in and told my mother the maid had killed the goose, she looked at me as though she couldn't believe this and sighed very hard; we both felt the same way. So, not saying a word to her that the geese were intended to be pets and not to be eaten, we gave it to the maid for her own dinner.

The other goose flew away about a month later when I was out in the backyard. As I watched it clear the eight-foot fence with ease and continue to gain altitude until out of sight, I couldn't help but wonder why it had stayed at all in the first place.

School was to resume on the second of December, the first Monday after Thanksgiving and ten days after the assassination. My siblings felt secure by now our father was okay. They were ready to go back to school. I was excited for them. Following the assassination, Stuart, Stephen, and Carolyn had been put into a private school for their own protection. The school was instructed not to allow anyone from outside to make contact with them; if this were attempted, to contact our mother immediately.

Stephanie and Debbie refused to leave their public school where their friends were. They were actually acting sort of snobbishly about the whole thing. It turned out they happened to have liked President Kennedy, as well as Jacqueline. They still didn't have any right to act this way and take it out on our mother. It wasn't she who killed President Kennedy, it was their father. Our parents must have felt the two of them were old enough to have their own opinions and could be trusted to take care of themselves and the rest of us, by not talking about our father's involvement in the assassination.

As ordained, I would not be going back to school myself. Perhaps because of my missing school and my visibility with Orris over the last many months, they saw me as a more potential object of any investigation. Or as a child, I might begin to talk about it to people on my own, now it had taken place and I had experienced the true immensity of the murder.

But also, as my father had instructed, I was to stay home with my mother while our father was hiding in Southern California. They considered kidnapping a possibility, or worse. So, that was the way it was. I stayed home, pretty bored. I missed being in school academically and socially and frequently imagined what my schoolmates might be doing.

What they really should have been concerned about was something they had no knowledge of, my excited reaction in school to the announcement of the assassination. And, in fact, my teacher called home on the 6th of December, four days after school had restarted, to ask where I was, if I were alright, and if I were alright, why I wasn't in school. Mother told her I was going to start school at the same private school as my siblings.

The teacher apparently didn't accept this story and contacted the private school to inquire about me. When she found out I wasn't enrolled there, she contacted my mother again to ask her why she had been lied to. And expressed a strong concern about me, explaining she had gotten very close to me while staying after school with her. Blows to my mother, the "closeness" and my staying after school. Unfortunately, the teacher also discussed my reaction to the Kennedy assassination.

So, now there was a serious problem with my teacher, who knew something was wrong and suspected it had something to do with the Kennedy assassination. I'm sure she could not even imagine what or how I could have been involved. It had to be a gut feeling on her part. She became so persistent in her continued enquiries, she ended up first going to the school board about my not being in school, and in February, actually to the Fort Worth FBI.

My mother had to go to extreme measures to silence her. With the help of several influential and powerful people from the Fort Worth/Dallas area, she was able to contact the superintendent of the Fort Worth school system, who happened to be my Aunt Ethel, and have her threaten my teacher with dismissal if she didn't cease and desist. She finally stopped in frustration.

Christmas came and went and not one word came from our father. I constantly worried about what was happening with him in Los Angeles. But, during this time, I was able to see all of my relatives from my father's side; they all knew about his involvement in the assassination and were very supportive. And, on the weekends, we would sometimes go to the Lyons' for dinner.

Before the assassination, I had been a very social person. And despite my father not wanting me to interact with other children for fear it would lead to questions as to why I was missing so much school, I still did so, especially during the summer. Now, not going to school at all, things changed, and I would only occasionally run into one of my friends. And, of course, this friend would ask the inevitable question as to why I wasn't attending, which I would have to answer with a lie. That always bothered me. And I realized I was depressed, spending much more time alone. I was missing school and everything that went with it, especially the girls.

One of my friends contacted me, wanting to sell a 410-gauge shotgun. I didn't have a shotgun and wanted one to go duck hunting down at the lake where I had seen the mallards a few months earlier. So, I bought it, without even asking my mother; I didn't really want to discuss with her that I was still seeing some of my friends. If I were old enough to stay home to protect her, I was old enough to buy a shotgun on my own. Even though this might have been a sign of my own rebellion, like my sisters', when I brought it home, my mother didn't object.

A few days later it snowed, and I decided to try my new shotgun on the ducks. When I arrived, they were all huddled up against the dam on the north end of the lake, trying to stay out of the cold wind. It was cold, very cold. I went down to that end of the big lake, snuck up over the dam, and there they were, right in front of me. About twenty of them, way too close for this old single-shot gun. I had no choice, but to fire into the middle of them and hope for the best. Even though they scattered fast, I was lucky and got a nice mallard.

The remaining ducks finally settled on the middle of the lake and wouldn't come back near the shore, as long as I was there. They appeared to be keeping a close eye on me. It was getting late, so I started home with my one duck, feeling fairly successful, given the conditions. At least, I wasn't empty-handed. After I cleaned it, my mother cooked it that night. It was delicious and satisfied my hunting efforts.

Was there a psychological relationship between my need to kill something and the Kennedy assassination? I'm not sure, perhaps there was. If anything, I think it was more aimed at my father and his associates for exposing me to the terror of the assassination. I had to take out this frustration in some manner and hunting with a gun was one way to satisfy this urge to retaliate on them. Not that I wanted to kill them, just maim them a little, as they had done psychologically to me.

21

ORRIS' RETURN

Winter and Spring, 1964

After the assassination, June Lawrence was working at a television station close to our house. She would come by nearly every day at lunch or after work to visit. Husband Norris, was still working at U.S. Sonics, but most of the other key people in the assassination were in hiding. Ed Nesbitt stayed behind to keep the doors open and work with a number of people to help keep the truth under the table. My mother would call him once or twice a week to keep in touch on any new information, as well as several others.

Charles Lyon had bought his farm outside of Waxahachie with the money from his part in the assassination. He had planted about ten acres in some sixty sapling Pecan trees, something he had wanted to do for many years. But because there was an unusually severe drought that spring, he came to get my help watering his thirsty trees before they died. He had borrowed an old four-thousand-gallon water truck that he drove, while I muscled a four-inch hose as best I could at the base and between each tree, holding it higher than the water level in the tank in between. It was a hot, dusty, grueling job, but we got it done that afternoon and saved his trees.

It had been nearly five months, and still no word from Orris; I had nearly given up expecting anything. But then toward the end of April, there was a surprise. It was about two o'clock in the afternoon and I was relaxed, walking home from a long walk in a wooded area. I had become accustomed no school and my private life, alone with my mother at home. My brothers and sisters weren't due home from school for another two hours and when I approached our house, doing my "scout" routine, no sign of unusual activity.

No one knew how worried I was the FBI was going to invade our house any minute during these long months. It wouldn't be the local Fort Worth police or Texas State police, but rather the FBI who I knew were investigating the assassination. I worried they might uncover U.S. Sonics' involvement. Our father had deserted us without adequate protection or explanation, leaving everything to me; and that angered me.

Every night I would go outside several times and walk all the way around the house in the dark. Usually stopping to hide behind the bushes and just look and listen. Nightmare was when they might come to find Orris or anything that could lead to him. This was real, not a little boy stumbling around, looking for the bogey man. My father and his men had just killed the President of the United States, and this house was where the ringleaders lived.

When I opened the front door, voices were coming from the living room. No one should be here, or I would have been told by my mother. She kept nothing from me now. It wasn't just my father who could be punished or prosecuted for Kennedy's assassination, but my mother as well, and I was very aware of that. I felt responsible to help her, in every way possible, to keep her as well as my brothers and sisters, safe.

If someone were coming to visit, I knew about it. If one of my brothers or sisters were going to a birthday party after school, I knew about it, everything. I made the decisions about what was too dangerous and not dangerous, what we could accommodate and what we couldn't. If one of my sisters wanted to spend the night at a girlfriend's house and I thought we couldn't get to her fast enough if we needed to leave suddenly, I said no, she couldn't do it.

So today when I heard the voices in the living room, I was instantly very concerned, nearly shocked. But then, I thought I heard my sister Carolyn's voice and cautiously approached the door to the living room. Then, I heard my father's voice and my heart stopped beating. He was home.

But I didn't know whether I wanted to see him or not. He might be angry about my not being home, but away on my own. Or that I had seen some of my friends. Definitely about what had happened with my teacher. But beside all that, I had changed and matured over the past five months, with time to think about the assassination and my having been used by my father and his people.

When I looked through the doorway, there sat Carolyn in his lap, the other kids scattered around him. Our mother on the *divan*. I looked directly at my father and our eyes held, staring for what seemed a long time. It felt as if a million words passed between us, a million thoughts in that few seconds. His eyes were piercing, and his expression became one of hate. I was shocked because this was not the same man I had known as my father five months earlier. It would have been frightening and startling then, but now I stood my ground and continued the stare.

Why? Why is he so different? This man is not my father -- I actually believed for a moment that maybe, he wasn't. And why was he so angry with me, hate me? What did I do? I had done what he requested of me and done a good job. I had protected my brothers and sisters and mother. And before that, we had always been close, especially during the assassination planning when I had become his confidant, someone to talk to in the way he did to me, to help him get through it. Understanding the tremendous stress he was experiencing. Someone who cared and I had cared.

Now, we hated each other equally, but for very different reasons; we had become polar opposites. The Kennedy assassination had changed us both. It was over, there was no bond between us now and there never would be again.

I approached him from across the room and leaned down to kiss him on the cheek, as I always did. He was cold and didn't even stand to hug and kiss me. He didn't even offer his hand to shake, the only words, "Hello, Bruce." My siblings continued huddled around him, expressing their obvious love and that they had missed him so terribly. To them. he responded with obvious love.

After about an hour he stood up, he would have to go now. He asked me to come out into the hall with him, so he could talk with me privately. Coldly told me he would be back in about a month to stay, but he now had to return to California. I asked him when he had arrived in Fort Worth and he replied, "This morning." And that was that.

He didn't hug or even say goodbye to me, but went back into the living room where he hugged and kissed everyone else. So, I was never really alone with him that day and no verbal information about anything could be exchanged. But there was that clear, very unusual, nonverbal exchange of information between us. It is amazing how much can be said between two people with their eyes in just a few seconds, when they know each other as well as we two knew each other then.

In thinking about this later, I know it couldn't have been because of the issues that had taken place with my teacher and the few things I had done he might disagree with. Rather, I concluded it was my being home alone with my mother for the past six months that had made us much closer, something he could feel. An Oedipus situation on his part, severe jealousy. He was a very jealous man when it came to her, despite his own transgressions. And as he had actually wanted six months earlier, I had to a large degree, taken his place as the dominant male in the family.

Orris' Return in Late May; The Story

In the second week of May, the family, minus Orris, moved into a new house between Dallas and Fort Worth and north of Arlington. The purchase had been arranged by Searcy Dobkins. I don't think my mother even saw it before it was bought. The move was because the CIA felt my father should change everything in his life he could easily; residence, phone, job, car, as well as put the children, including me, in new schools. And to stay away from U.S. Sonics as much as possible, and any other thing or pattern that had been distinctive to his life before, including the travel he so enjoyed. Not so much to hide from the FBI or any other investigative agency, but rather to sidetrack any individuals who might have learned something by mistake or through snooping.

At this time, Bedford was still somewhat rural, but developing quickly. Along with Hurst and Euless, it was the home of Bell Helicopter's primary assembly plant. The area is fairly large, very conservative; middle and upper-middle class, with several wealthy neighborhoods and a number of estates in the surrounding country. And with my developing liberalism, I thoroughly disliked it.

My father returned from hiding on about May 22nd. He was different now from when he had visited a month earlier, when he had been very serious and worried. Now he seemed happy and even, somewhat carefree and even smiling a lot, as though the Kennedy assassination had never taken place. And what was most important to me, his attitude towards me had softened and become cordial again, he was polite and even friendly as though nothing had taken place between us a month earlier.

When he returned, he did resume one old pattern, my accompanying him on his different errands and visits. The first trip, on the second day he was home, was to downtown Fort Worth. On the way, we talked about where he had been in Southern California and basically what he had done. He had been living comfortably in a Beverly Hills house with Jeff, and had access to a second house on the beach further north. The two of them had gone out on Lundquist's yacht a number of times, several times ending up in San Francisco for a few weeks.

We didn't talk about the Kennedy assassination at all that day. He didn't seem to want to even bring it up, so I didn't. We went to an office building where I waited in the receptionist area while he went to see some men in their offices. I don't know who they were and I didn't ask. And because the CIA wanted him to 'lose' his so obvious yellow Ford Galaxy, we then stopped at Frank Kent Cadillac, where he looked at several cars.

The next day he, Steven, and I returned to the dealership where he purchased a new Cadillac, a green Sedan Deville with white leather interior and all the custom features, contingent on my mother's approval. It turned out she liked the color, so he kept it. I thought it was extravagant, flashy, and inappropriate for a man just returning from hiding after killing the President, so close to that very location. Besides, this custom color green Cadillac was too unusual and expensive, it would attract unnecessary and unwanted attention. In the long run, I was right. (Actually, for the rest of his life, he would only have Cadillacs, the symbol of the best of America, and the car used at the time by Air Force generals. A symbol, too, of achievement and something he deserved.)

The next day, he asked me to go with him to U.S. Sonics for what would be the first of six separate meetings with his main co-conspirators between late May and June 12th. On the way, we talked about what had gone right the day of the assassination.

I Hear the Story

He talked about Charlie Lyon's shot and his own with the fulminate of mercury bullet. About he, Lyon, and Tom Lawrence knowing without question, on seeing the President's head literally explode, their efforts were successful. He seemed to speak about Kennedy with respect and referring to him as 'The President'; something had changed, even the tone in his voice was different. There was no sarcasm.

He talked as though he were separate from these events, with little or no emotion, as though he were reading from a text. He seemed pleased and content with the results, but not overly excited. He might as well have been talking about a successful business trip and the signing of a profitable contract while gone, for all I could tell. I was surprised because I had been anticipating this conversation for over six months, imagining he would be more emotional. He had certainly expressed much more emotion, during the planning.

Next, he couldn't say enough about Jeff's complete and unselfish assistance, he didn't believe the assassination would have been as successful without it. Jeff had been by his side and his personal *protégé* since the very beginning. He was referring to all of it, not just the assassination, but also to the cover-up, the necessary Mafia involvement, the use of Jeff's wife as an envoy with Lyndon Johnson, and his aid with the Dallas police.

He was especially impressed by how Jeff held it all together with the planting of the fake 'magic bullet' at Parkland Hospital; there was a lot more to that effort than met the eye, and it had gone even better than they could have anticipated. Without the bullet fired previously from the Mannlicher-Carcano with the ballistics to match, the public would not have been as easily convinced by the cover-up scenario.

Next, he talked about everything that had gone wrong that day, beginning with Oswald not coming to the sixth floor at all. Thankfully, they had the backup plan with Roscoe White to shoot in Oswald's place, but at the same time, that was unfortunate because Oswald knew Roscoe would substitute for him, so he had been able to leave before Roscoe could shoot him. We would never know whether this had been planned on his part or if he had just chickened out at the last minute. Of course, he knew he would still be blamed for the assassination.

Orris explained that the first shot had to come from the sixth-floor window of the Depository, so that all the people in Dealey Plaza would hear and look up at it, distracting them from the actual shooters and, eventually, helping to place the blame on Oswald.

He described Roscoe White's late firing from the sixth floor and how that complicated everything. The three actual shooters couldn't just empty their clips at the president, because that would defeat their scenario of one shooter and four shots. Although the clips in their three rifles each held five rounds, with one additional round in the chamber, they obviously couldn't fire a collective group of eighteen shots.

Tom was a disappointment, never hitting the president, getting Connally instead. Kennedy's back wound was an exit one from the throat shot fired by Lyon, not from Lawrence, whose shot was supposed to be the first after the decoy one. After his first missed shot, he fired twice more as he was supposed to, but still missing.

Orris went on to tell me about the several plans to kill Oswald and how he had managed to avoid them until Ruby finally succeeded. My father must have known that by now, I had already realized that it had been a setup for Oswald, that he had to be killed to make their plans work. Still, I think he must have felt it was best to be honest with me about it all, that I would understand their rationale. It had been relatively easy for me to figure it out, when I knew the players as I did. He also knew I had liked and found Oswald very interesting, so this subject was a touchy one for me and himself.

For some reason, my father didn't go into the J.D. Tippit killing and how and why it had to happen.

By now, nearly to U.S. Sonics, we stopped our discussion. This would be the first time there, for him since the assassination. When we arrived, Ed Nesbitt was waiting, as was Norris Lawrence. Apparently, they had gotten a new contract of some kind from the Air Force and were back in the business of cleaning rocket or aircraft parts because the place looked busy.

Nesbitt had taken my father's place as president of the company, which he would continue, until its closure in the future. I was surprised, always assuming they would end U.S. Sonics and close the doors for good right after the assassination, to get rid of the location where the assassination planning took place; gone and forgotten was my theory. But here it was, up and running, they would come to regret this in the not-so-distant future.

What was occurring with Sonics now didn't make a lot of sense to, actually worried me. Many people had come and gone during the planning, making Sonics so active at times. It seemed inevitable someone would talk to the wrong person. Not any of the men I was now with or any of the tight insiders, but someone's wife talking to the wrong friend, would divulge the secret. Or someone, at Jaggars-Stovall-Chiles, who had seen my father coming and going with Oswald and knew my father was president of Sonics.

Jeff Miller showed up about thirty minutes later and greeted Nesbitt and Lawrence, as though this were the first he had seen them in the six months, as I'm certain it was. He even gave me a hug and kiss on the cheek. After more pats on the back, lots of smiles, and joyous greetings, we all went back to my father's office, which Nesbitt had taken over. This was something of a reunion, a private meeting of the four men who were key to the assassination. Probably this was why my father had invited me along; he wanted me to be a part of it.

Nesbitt and Lawrence asked Orris about his six months in California and how Lundquist was doing, telling me my father and Lundquist had had no contact with Nesbitt, Lawrence, or U.S. Sonics, since the assassination. During this twenty-minute conversation, I learned the most about my father's stay there. No one seemed to want to bring up the serious side of the assassination and turn this happy occasion into a depressing discussion, even though it was inevitable the topic would come up before the day had passed.

After our initial hellos and meeting, it was time for lunch. We went to the same German restaurant we had frequented so many times during the planning, fitting for the occasion. The same attitude prevailed, no one even mentioning the assassination, but instead, what they were now going to do with U.S. Sonics. It was nearly as though it had never happened. They were relaxed in a way I had never seen them before.

After lunch, we returned to U.S. Sonics and went back to my father's office, always the center of activity. There they finally began to talk about the assassination. First, Tippit's death and how they had never believed, if it came to the point where he would need to kill Oswald, he would lose it, threatening the plan. As bizarre as it might seem after the death of so many people who knew too much about the assassination and who were deemed expendable, they spoke of Tippit's death as something of an unfortunate tragedy. They were fond of him as a completely trusted insider, the only person who had met his death in the operation, who really mattered to them.

They weren't bothered by Oswald's death at all, but I still wanted to believe that at least my father was. Since he hadn't yet told me about what was supposed to happen with Tippit and Oswald, nor what had actually happened, I was feeling very confused. Just like when I first heard that Tippit had been killed.

They then turned to how they had been concerned that Oswald might not end up at his Texas Theatre pick-up point, what should have taken place there and what actually occurred. It became clear now, they had never intended to 'pick up' Lee Oswald at the Theater. They seemed to blame the situation there, not on Roscoe White or Tippit, but on the allied Dallas police who didn't shoot and kill him, as they were supposed to.

With Oswald still having a gun, the public wouldn't have seriously questioned 'deadly force' being used. And, certainly, there would have been no problem once the Mannlicher-Carcano rifle left at the Depository was tied directly to him. All of the problems that had arisen from his being in the police station with the resultant exposure to the media, and then the complications of Ruby's involvement, could have been avoided.

Then they talked about the potential problems of Ruby alive in a Dallas jail. Someone would eventually get to him, and he would talk. Something had to be done about this too dangerous of a situation; they would eventually have to kill him now.

We didn't stay late that day, but left about two thirty. On the way home, I asked my father to explain more about Oswald's role, the burning question. And for obvious reasons, not an easy subject for my father to discuss with me. One easy thing, why such an emphasis on his going to the sixth floor, if the end result would have been the same, whether he or White fired the decoy shot. They had obviously been able to convince the public anyway that Oswald had killed the President.

More importantly, why did he have to be killed in the first place? He explained they had meant for White to kill Oswald because that would make it much easier to convince the public he was the assassin. They had no choice; in order for their plan to work, they had to have a single person on whom to blame the assassination and this person had been Oswald from the very beginning. They couldn't leave him alive, he would eventually talk. I asked if Oswald agreed to this plan. No, they had to lie to him that they were going to get him safely out of the country and make sure he was safe.

Visiting Charlie Lyon

Shortly after this, Orris asked if I wanted to visit Lyon with him. Of course, I did. We met for lunch at a restaurant in Arlington, the first time they had met face-to-face since the assassination. He appeared happy, contented, and relaxed. As with the earlier meeting at U.S. Sonics with the other assassin players, Lyon seemed to be confident all was well and under control, and he and his family were safe.

They were hesitant to speak openly about the assassination in public, only mentioning it in passive terms. After lunch, we went to his house in Arlington which he still owned, even though he had already purchased his farm in Waxahachie. He and his wife were still working, she in Arlington and he close by for Chance Vaught.

Once comfortably seated in his living room, they began to talk about the assassination. It was the first time they had the opportunity to get together to compare notes, feelings, and emotions about what took place. These two men were such good friends and knew each other so well, there was no reason for bullshit or bravado between them. They were hunting partners, only the game had been the President in November 1963, instead of deer in Colorado.

First about the actual shooting. They literally talked about their individual shots and how simple it had been to shoot the President from the distance they had. As I sat there listening, I thought about the many times I had heard these men talk the same way about shots they had made shooting a deer; there was little difference. It was over and the stress gone, it was just another hunting trip now.

Then they talked about the greatest problem, waiting for the shot from the sixth-floor window, which was markedly late; even though only a few seconds, it seemed like forever, causing them to worry it might not come at all., and throwing the firing sequence off. Creating a serious problem, leaving them with literally only a few seconds to make their own shots.

So Lyon had had to fire before Lawrence. A screw-up, despite all the planning.

They discussed the protocol of the Secret Service driver, a key accomplice. His job had been to slow the limo down to a point where they could accomplish their shots. Because that first shot was late, he had to slow down the limo even more. Apparently, such a late shot had been taken into consideration and in the extreme, the driver was supposed to literally stop at a designated spot on Elm St. to allow my father to make his head shot. As it was, the driver nearly did stop the limo at this location.

(There has been a lot of speculation about why the driver slowed, turned around to watch Kennedy very closely until he saw the President's head explode, and then began to accelerate the limo. All seen in the Zapruder film.)

Apparently, if my father would have missed with his headshot, both he and Lyon would have fired second shots.

In the course of their discussion, it was obvious the two men were unhappy with both Roscoe White and Tom Lawrence. Unhappy with Roscoe, because he fired late and threw the entire firing sequence off. With Lawrence, for a number of reasons; he missed Kennedy, fired a little late himself, forcing Lyon to fire before him, and then shot Governor Connally. They now questioned choosing Lawrence to be the third shooter, as a decision made in haste.

Then the 'second team' was brought up. How complex and difficult it was to deal with them being arrested and in custody, all while Oswald was being arrested and in custody. Thankfully, Nesbitt had solved that problem.

After they discussed all this, I heard something that actually surprised me. Lyon asked my father what it was like for him to have to go into the downtown Dallas Police station to talk with Oswald the first night they had him there. My father said that even though he was wearing a regular Dallas Police uniform, they still had to smuggle him in. He wasn't with Lee very long, but long enough to deliver the message he needed to. They were working on getting him moved to a more secure location where a Dallas attorney would come see him and control the situation.

Lee was quiet and listened, but appeared to be a little bit in shock at all that had taken place. Orris could tell Lee knew he had been deceived and set up, and didn't think Lee believed him entirely. But Lee had agreed to keep his mouth shut because he knew if he started talking and naming names, he would be killed immediately; he had no other choice.

But even though Lee agreed to all of this, Orris was very worried that Lee could fall apart and say something to the wrong person that could be catastrophic. So, he knew they had to move as quickly as possible to kill him. before he had a chance to talk.

Hearing all this, I couldn't imagine my father having to go down to the police station on the same day he shot the President, to talk with Oswald about keeping his mouth shut. But who else would Lee respond to, who else could away with it. Lee was a loner, and they had wanted him to be a loner close to, or trusting no one other than my father.

To my surprise, Orris stated it was hard for him to set Lee up to be killed, very hard, and that he considered him a national hero for giving his life for this to be successful, even if it wasn't consensual. Perhaps, the only hero. In fact, he had anonymously made arrangements for Oswald to be buried at Rose Hill Cemetery, the same cemetery where Orris' father and mother were to be buried.

My father could be open in this way with Charlie, and I didn't find it at all unusual for them to have this conversation. After discussing the assassination, they changed course. Orris asked Lyon about the new farm he had bought. Lyon described the terrible drought that was plaguing North Texas and not knowing if he could save the crop or the trees. He credited me for having helped him do the watering that had been necessary. Orris had to come out to see his new farm and rural life in Waxahachie.

Lyon's wife came home about this time with her two children; a boy about five and their daughter, about ten months, a baby. Charlie's wife was a very pretty blonde, tall at bout five foot elven, who, with Lyon, made an attractive couple. Lyon at six foot two or so, and in excellent condition was a strong, large-framed man, handsome with very dark brown hair.

Even though she knew all about their involvement in the assassination, Orris and Lyon were hesitant to continue further conversation about it in front of her. It wasn't they didn't trust her, they trusted her emphatically; they just didn't want her troubled with these details. It was already very difficult for her and all the other supporting spouses.

At this time, at age thirteen, I was still uncertain about whether these men had done the right thing in assassinating the President. Still open to hearing all sides of the issue and very eager for all the factual information I could get. At least, I was open to the possibility that what they had done had been a mistake. However, that was a long way from where I had been on November 22nd, when I cheered their obvious success in front of my seventh grade teacher and the entire classroom.

Visiting General Born

Charles Born had not been present when Orris and I met with Jeff and the others at U.S. Sonics. He, like my father, limited his presence and involvement there after the assassination, although I did see him there a few times until they closed the doors for the last time. He continued lobbying for Texas Instruments, providing them Air Force contracts.

Three days after our visit with Charles Lyon, my father asked me again to go to Dallas with him. Was this the beginning of a repeat of the previous year, accompanying him to Dallas two or three times a week? But I did want to learn as much as I could about what had actually happened in the assassination.

When we arrived at U.S. Sonics about one o'clock, my father informed me we were here to see General Born. I wasn't particularly looking forward to seeing Born, but it probably meant there would be more about the assassination. This would be the first time I had seen Born since November, and I realized as we walked through the doors, I had changed. None of that apprehension I had always felt before about seeing him because of his attitude toward children. I didn't feel like a child any longer, and I was actually interested in seeing him and hearing what he would have to say.

And Born surprised me He seemed to be relaxed and in a good mood, whereas he had always been a tense, serious man. Today he was overly friendly and cordial with me at first. He actually smiled at me and seemed sincere when he asked how I had been for the past several months.

We weren't there for more than ten minutes and had just started talking, before deciding to go for lunch first. So, we headed out together in my father's new Cadillac, which he wanted to show Born. On the drive over, he made reference to meeting Orris and Lundquist in California, so they wouldn't be talking about the assassination the same way as in the meetings my father and I had with the other participants. The two had obviously discussed and moved past all that.

What Born did want to know though, was how Lyon, Nesbitt, Norris, Lawrence, and any of the other insiders Orris had see since his return, had responded in their meetings with him. He wanted to know if any of them had acted unusual or suspicious when they talked about the assassination. My father assured him, no, they all seemed to be themselves and rather relaxed about the whole situation.

We had lunch at a very good, formal restaurant in north central Dallas. It was well past the usual lunchtime, but surprisingly, it still seemed quite busy. We were seated alone off to the side in a quiet area, as my father requested, so we could talk openly, not concerned about being overheard.

Shortly after being seated, General Born asked me about my mother and how she had fared the previous seven months. under the pressure following the assassination. I responded that right after the assassination she seemed preoccupied with it, watching everything possible on TV. But she seemed to relax after January, busying herself with the household and we children.

He then asked if anyone had asked me anything unusual about the assassination; "No." Had I seen anyone or any suspicious activity on our street, in our neighborhood; cars, men walking, or anything at all unusual. "No, I didn't. Everything seemed quiet and normal.". Did any of my brothers or sisters tell me anything about anyone approaching them or talking with them in any way unusual. Again, I reassured him, "No, they hadn't."

Then out of the blue, he asked me to explain what happened the day of the assassination at school, concerning my teacher. How could he even know about this? Both he and my father listened closely as I explained in detail why I reacted the way I did. Had I had any direct contact with her since. "No.."Did I know what had taken place between the teacher and my mother since. "Yes, most of it, if not all."

What led up to her being suspicious about anything, in the first place? At this time, I hadn't told my mother or father I had been the teacher's chosen student to stay after school and help her. I knew they would never give their permission. But my mother had later learned this from the teacher herself. Now I explained she had asked me to stay after school because she felt sorry for me, since my parents didn't let me play football and she personally liked me. At the time, I hadn't seen any harm in it; I certainly couldn't foresee the future and her concern about my not coming to school when I went with my father, my reaction to Kennedy's death, or the fact I didn't return to school after the assassination.

I didn't explain that despite knowing my father's desire, I needed another person in my life separate from the assassination. Nor share my fantasy that when I didn't return to school, she couldn't accept that she may never see me again. That was the reason she had gone to the extreme measure to find out why I hadn't returned to school.

But it was time now to come clean about how it was easy to hide all this from my parents. I walked home from school every day, so it was easy to make it seem as though I had just taken my time. And if my mother ever asked why I were late, she knew I had a girlfriend named Suzie who lived in a house I passed on my way home, so I would just say, "I stopped by to see Suzie." Which I did sometimes.

As I told my father and Born about all this, they both looked at me in shock, hanging on every word. They had thought they knew everything about my life during the planning. The thought of my being able to spend these many hours alone with another adult and their not knowing anything about it, took them by complete surprise.

They wanted to know everything we talked about that could have any association to Kennedy or politics. Anything that could have given her any indication that I, or my father, was prejudiced against him in any way. I told them I had no memory of ever discussing Kennedy with her. Although I knew she was a strong Kennedy supporter, I didn't say anything to give her any reason to think I, or my father, hated him in any way or for any reason.

Anything that might give her reason to believe my father could have been involved in the assassination. "Anything?" "Yes, anything." I had told my father back in early October about her asking me why I had missed so much school, when she knew I wasn't really sick; where had I been, what was I doing. Even though my mother wrote an excuse note, it was the same one over and over again. Now, I brought that back up again. The teacher knew my mother and I were lying to her, how could she not; it was obvious I had never once been sick.

But what was on my mind was really something else, which I decided I had to bring up. I turned to my father and asked, "Daddy, do you remember that gun-rack that I made for you at school and gave you at home?" Born looked surprised as hell, leaned forward, and in a loud whisper asked, "What gun-rack is Bruce talking about, Orris?" My father explained I had surprised him with a gun-rack I had made for him in a shop class. He had known nothing about my making it until a week before the assassination, when I surprised him with it.

Born asked, "What about this gun-rack and your teacher, Bruce?" I explained that my shop class was in the morning. So, since I was going to bring the rack home that afternoon, I had taken it back to my homeroom after shop class and set it against the wall behind her desk. When she asked me why I had chosen a gun rack to make, I had explained it was a surprise for my father who was a deer hunter, and he didn't have a rack for his rifles. At that time, what was the harm?

How could she ever relate this to the assassination; after all, this was Texas and many fathers were deer hunters and didn't have gun racks.

The two sat there with mouths nearly agape, thinking about how I could have had this discussion with my teacher a week before my father was due to shoot the President with a deer rifle and they had known nothing about it. Now, I recalled my father's expression when I handed him the rack that day, the shock, bewilderment, confusion, and that I had thought he didn't like it.

After I explained the gunrack, General Born asked if anything else had transpired between me and this teacher that could lead her to be suspicious about my father's involvement in the assassination. "No, I don't think so."

Eventually seeming to be satisfied I wasn't keeping anything from him, the conversation changed to Michael and Ruth Paine. Had Orris talked with either of them? My father answered he had met with both, and they seemed to be doing well and holding up, considering the pressure they had been dealing with. He went on to praised Ruth; she was an amazing woman to be able to pull everything off as well as she had. Including at the Warren Commission, where she convinced them she was telling the truth about the assassination. She had just been a 'good' Quaker, giving Marina aid during difficult financial and marital times. And, of course, she had no way of knowing anything about Oswald's intentions, how could she have!

Born seemed to accept this report as well, and asked my father to stay in touch with them as often as he felt necessary to keep them comfortable. They both needed to know they would always get all the support they needed, to just keep Orris informed. It was obvious they both nevertheless felt the Paines were potentially the weakest point in the cover story and would require all the support possible to keep them confident they would remain safe, as long as they did what they were supposed to. I think he suspected that she would probably be called to testify again, which she would.

Then the conversation turned to the possibilities concerning the aerospace industry under Lyndon Johnson's administration. I knew Johnson was solidly in the conspiracy with them. It was obvious he had agreed to give Born and his defense industry *protégés* the continuation of the Vietnam War. And whatever else they wanted as far as a military budget was concerned, in exchange for his Presidency and a lifelong dream of supreme power, albeit a puppet's dream. Even though he would be able to continue and expand Kennedy's liberal social agenda, probably in part to satisfy his own self- image, he would always be under the control of the 'Military Industrial Complex' Eisenhower had prognosticated.

The Celebratory Trip Around the World

At this time, Lundquist owned the largest yacht in L.A., which he moored at Marina Del Rey and used for both pleasure and business. On June twelve, Orris told me the co-conspirators were going to take an around-the-world cruise on it, to celebrate the successful coup, the Kennedy assassination, and promote the ringing in of the 'New World Order.' It would be both a diplomatic mission and a continuous party, first class in every way. The yacht would dock at ports to entertain businessmen and political dignitaries. Certain individuals from these foreign countries would be invited to join on the next leg of the voyage.

I was one of two children invited. The other, the daughter of a wealthy Los Angeles businessman, who had strong connections with the Mafia and Richard Nixon. I had known this girl since I was six years old and these men actually planned for us to marry in the future.

Orris naturally believed I would want to go, so he first made it sound like more of a matter-of-fact situation than an invitation. It would last a year and I would have to stay on for the duration. Three men would be in charge of the voyage alternately, Lundquist, Orris, and Miller. They would change positions after each individual leg of the voyage. The first leg was to be from Los Angeles to Hawaii, where they would stay for about two weeks before going on to Japan, the second leg of the trip.

I only had one week to make up my mind, because they were planning on leaving on the 22nd. He stressed he wanted me to participate and everyone else was expecting and wanting me to come. The girl would be very disappointed, if I didn't go. When he saw the hesitation on my face, he almost became an ultimatum, emphasizing the importance to him. He didn't actually demand I go, "But come along or you will regret it in the future, if you don't."

I was conflicted. I wanted to go because it was going to be a luxurious trip seeing the world in a way I had always wanted. And loved the ocean. But over the next four or five days I decided not to go. There were many reasons. At this point, I had reached the conclusion there wasn't anything to celebrate. They had probably done the wrong thing by killing the President.

And after witnessing their proclivity for killing those who they thought might be security risks, I didn't trust some of the men who would on this trip. If they would kill the President, if they would kill Oswald, if they would see the death of Tippit as 'collateral damage', if they could kill all the people who they felt might know too much and were expendable, such as strippers from Ruby's club as they had, then they would surely kill a mere kid like me to protect themselves.

And especially General Born who thought I knew way too much about the assassination. He might take advantage of the isolation on the trip to kill me. I actually had visions of him throwing me overboard in the middle of the Pacific one night.

On the other hand, I really didn't believe this would happen because of my father. After all he had done for the 'cause', they wouldn't do this to him.

But importantly, I should decline in order to continue the six months I had just spent as the dominant male in the house, taking care of my brothers, sisters, and mother. They now depended on me. And obviously if Orris were on the trip, their need would continue.

But even more importantly, I wasn't looking forward to the time my father and I would be together. He had changed the past six months. I didn't like what I was seeing. Although our recent togetherness had lessened the extreme coldness between us during his April visit, he was still colder toward me and actually, to all of us. The Kennedy assassination had obviously left its mark.

Orris continued his attempts to persuade me. Five days after he initially invited me, I told him I didn't want to go. That night, I got a call from Lundquist asking me to change my mind. I told him I would think about it and call him back tomorrow to let him know. And before I could, the next morning there was a call from the girl; please come, it wouldn't be any fun without me. I would miss a great time. I knew she really liked me and knew why they had asked her to come along in the first place. But I didn't change my mind, another step of rebellion against the future they had planned for me.

They were gone for nearly a month before Orris flew back from Hawaii. When I saw him, after his return, he again urged me to come along, I was missing a very good time and the chance to experience something at my age that was life changing.

The trip apparently was very successful and progressing well until March of 1965, after they had been in the Mediterranean for a while. I don't know when their 'enemies' found out about the voyage, but there was no way to keep such an outlandish trip and its purpose quiet for long. They were meeting openly with businessmen and political leaders from around the world, obviously an 'in your face' kind of venture meant to internationally state that these men now felt confidently in control in America.

They had been in the European area for about two months, already having visited Italy, France, Spain, and England, when these 'enemies', certain powerful Democrats, created a major problem by stigmatizing the voyage and the men on it. Although the Warren Commission Report had been released, there were a lot of lingering rumors, suspicions of conspiracies. Most people didn't know what was really true. And many Europeans were not sure how the final Kennedy assassination investigation was going to eventually play out, so didn't want to associate themselves with what might, in the end, be the wrong group.

So, as this situation was simply getting too 'hot' politically, the voyagers realized that pushing the issue too far and confronting the Democrats would make the political fight and their own audacity public, something they couldn't risk. Although they had reasonable control over the U.S. media, they might not be able to control the situation and media in Europe.

On his part of the voyage, Lundquist was to captain the yacht from Europe to Brazil, Colombia, through the Panama Canal, and on to Acapulco, the final stop before returning to Marina Del Rey. This was all scrapped. Orris and Lundquist immediately flew back from Europe, leaving Miller in charge of the return as quickly as possible.

Of course, this was a strong blow to the new power structure and an embarrassment to all of them, especially Lundquist, whose yacht they were on. So, returning to the U.S., they would lick their wounds and get ready for battle with the Democrats. If it was war they wanted, then it would be war they would get. But fought behind the public scene, because both sides knew if it came out publicly, it could become a full-blown civil war. Neither the Joint Chiefs nor the CIA would go down, without a fight. And because there were both Democrats and Republicans in the military, a strong division there could also lead to anarchy.

The Democrats also realized that at this point, the Cold War could blow up at any time. The Russians could take advantage of a fractured America, and attack. And complicating things, Curtis LeMay still had his finger on the nuclear trigger. So, there was no advantage in the Democrats going public with what some knew about the assassination if it led to total destruction.

22

POST VOYAGE

My Life, Age Fourteen

As ordained by Orris, I would not go back to school for nine months and completely bypassed the seventh grade all together. In September of 1964, I returned to another school, in another district, in another town, and in the eighth grade. I never fully recovered from this academically or socially. How could I? I didn't like the new Junior High School. I didn't like the other children at all, and during the following years my isolation worsened; I became introverted. The Kennedy assassination had spelled its toll on me; John Kennedy wasn't the only casualty of his assassination.

At the age of fourteen, I started going to the ranch at Palo Pinto, alone. At fifteen, I went to Mexico alone, and Padre Island in South Texas, alone. However, during these years I always had at least one close girlfriend. But we would spend our time alone too, rarely with others. Going out where there were others, I would feel comfortable if I were with one of these girls. These relationships were deeper, more involved, and complex than those of my peers. I chose girls more sophisticated and intelligent.

And we would do things that adults did. Expensive restaurants, museums, plays, and movies that appealed to older people. Shopping at better stores and listening to classical music, along with rock and roll. I grew further and further away from my father and even my mother; they never should have put their son in the position they did at the age of eleven/twelve, it was just plain wrong.

Of course, I never told any of my girlfriends about my or my father's involvement in the President's assassination. I didn't want to discuss this with anyone during these years. Besides, I knew that discussing it with them would change our relationship in a negative way. They just wouldn't understand. How could anyone understand an enigmatic thing such as this?

One of the things I did alone in the fall, as one of my escapes from the aftermaths of the assassination, was use the shotgun I had bought after the assassination to continue duck hunting; and was quite successful. Often, I would go to the Palo Pinto ranch that had been used by the assassins for practice, as a place to reflect on the assassination when it was bothering me, which was often. But, I also hunted there for many years with Charlie Lyon.

Orris was away nearly all the time. Since he had come out of hiding, his life had taken on a new and different meaning. Beside the time on the around the world trip, when he wasn't home, he was usually in some foreign country or Washington or L.A. He had developed new contacts while hiding in L.A. and was spending time there. We had all gotten used to him being gone by now.

But that fall, Orris and Lyon twice took me and brother Stephen hunting at the San Saba, Texas ranch. Hunting with the two assassins was now a different experience. They had not been together that often since the assassination, and these were times they could discuss it in a relaxed environment. They were 'the real thing', having intelligence, guts, and nerves of steel. And comfortable with each other, with none of the competing bravado that sometimes comes out in men who are insecure with one another.

The first time they discussed the assassination in front of us while we were hunting, it was again in an open manner. Of course, they were aware I knew a lot more it after the meeting we had had at Lyon's house. But there were still some things I couldn't put together. My father had never ignored any questions I had asked him before. He still trusted me thoroughly, as I had never talked outside of the group about my knowledge. (This 'filling me in' about the assassination would continue for the next eight years, as I got older and my questions became more complex.)

At first, they were fairly serious about their recall. But after a while, they lightened up and even began to laugh about some of the more colorful, unexpected events of the assassination. I sat there with Stephen while the campfire burned in front of us and thought, "*These guys are crazy, sitting here, less than a year, since they killed the President and they can find humor in it…*" I don't believe Stephen had the foggiest idea of what they were talking about because he knew nothing about our father's life away from home.

The four of us continued hunting at either San Saba or Palo Pinto every year, until 1968, when I joined the military. I also hunted at the Palo Pinto ranch with Orris and some very radical right-wing friends from the aerospace industry. They would fire fully automatic weapons between hunting forays just for the fun of it, shooting at targets with faces of liberal Democrat politicians. Too much for me, and I told my father not to bring me hunting with people like this again. Orris agreed they were crazy.

Later, in December, Orris, Lyon, and my grandfather, Emmett Delmon Bell, went deer hunting in Durango, Colorado with a group of about eight CIA men who participated in the assassination. A professional photographer shot a group photo at the hunting lodge where they were staying. It depicted my Grandfather sitting in a Kennedy style rocking chair, holding the rifle my father used in the assassination in his lap. My father and Lyon, stood on either side of the chair, hands on its pedestals, the CIA in a line behind them. (When I saw the photograph in 1998 for the first time, I recognized all the CIA men.)

At the Bedford house we moved to in late May 1964, a few blocks away was an undeveloped wild area of about four hundred acres. Until 1968, I would go by myself to this heavily wooded area to be alone and hunt. The first year it was rabbits, squirrels, quail, and dove. But after that first year, I stopped hunting there and just went to the woods to escape and be with nature. I continued to bring a rifle and would target practice, but enjoyed just observing the various flora and fauna as the seasons changed. I must have fired several thousand rounds of ammunition over this four-year period target practicing.

Orris' Personal Compensation

Apparently, Orris was well rewarded for his role in the assassination. It wasn't just the obvious monetary compensation which provided for an even more upscale lifestyle. He could have always afforded a Cadillac if this had been a priority to him, but he had changed. Now, he saw himself a man of privilege; after all, not everyone could have done what he had done. And in fact, his success elevated him to a superior level in the eyes of everyone who knew what he had accomplished.

He continued his activities prior to the assassination, representing aerospace defense companies and other areas of the defense industry and continuing to provide female 'companionship' to his clients. When he traveled, he lived a life of wealth and stayed at the best hotels, ate at the best restaurants, drank at the best bars, went to the best clubs, always flew first class, and usually took one or two 'business associates' with him that he paid all the expenses for.

In addition to cold cash, which had to be limited due to a possible IRS investigation, he received non-monetary compensation. For instance, he now had even more extraordinary access to primary Air Force aerospace, Navy submarine, NASA, and other military contracts. His for the asking and which he provided to companies he represented at a considerable profit.

But just as importantly, an Air Force contract provided him and Miller the salvage rights to all Air Force Atlas and Titan 1 Missile Silos now or in the near future, abandoned due to Kennedy's prior cancellation of the Atlas ICBM program. These silos were flush with gold, silver, and platinum wiring, and ballast copper on the rocket doors.

In the late spring of 1965, I accompanied the two men to Altus, Oklahoma, where they were to inspect a group of these silos. Because it was a classified site, I was not actually able to enter; I was to spend the day driving around. But in the hotel room that night, there was a suitcase strategically placed in the middle of the floor. Jeff asked me, nonchalantly, to bring it over to him. I went over to it, thinking nothing unusual, and reached down to pick it up with my right hand. To my amazement, it didn't come up off the floor. I was a pretty strong, young man and wasn't about to give up. It took both hands, and when I glanced over at the two men, they were grinning at me like two jackasses eating cactus and enjoying it.

I set it down and asked what was inside. Jeff composed himself and said, "Gold. That's about one-fourth of the gold from one of these silos. They use twenty-four karat gold in all the electrical wiring in the missile launch sequence."

Sure enough, when I opened the suitcase, it was full of gold wire, stripped of its plastic coating, folded into various size packages. There was also a large copper plate from the silo ballast door. This would mean that every Atlas missile silo would have at least two hundred and forty pounds of solid gold and tons of pure copper, along with other precious and semi-precious metals.

The suitcase contents were basically samples they were taking back to Dallas. They would return later with a work crew to complete the salvage. It was ironic that Kennedy had been responsible for the cancellation of the Atlas ICBM program which had hurt U.S. Sonics' business, but would now yield compensation to his assassins.

One day in 1966, I was with him when he received and opened his tax returns from his accountant and declared to himself, "My expense account ran over one million dollars last year."

"Daddy, how do you possibly spend a million dollars traveling in one year?" (In today's dollars, that would be like spending somewhere between $15,000 and $20,000 per day.) How can anyone spend this much money?

Much of this I was privy to. When I became old enough to drive in Texas at the age of thirteen, he made a deal with me. If I took him to the airport and picked him up on his return, he would let me use his

Cadillac while he was gone. So, I took him to and from the airport, until I left home in November of 1968. I was the only person in my family who chauffeured him during this time. Of course, my older sisters had upon rare occasion taken him, but they soon left for university. And Orris always preferred I do the airport trips, because he could talk with me openly about where he was going and what he was actually going to do. On his return, we would usually have dinner together, giving us more time to discuss his business.

Orris' Move to Chicago

At the same time, there were now two problems for Orris. He always drank heavily, as did most of his business associates in the aerospace defense industry and Air Force. This was a way of life in the industry, and Air Force pilots were known as hard drinking daredevils. But I had never seen him drink this much before. Never during the day when working, but late in the afternoon and at night, too much.

And his efforts to lay low in Dallas didn't work as anticipated. The CIA's advice to change his social life in Dallas wasn't enough. He continued to frequent restaurants and bars he had patronized prior to the assassination. But the planning had just been too complex and wide in scope, with too many people involved. And a few people in upper Dallas circles leaked the truth about his and U.S. Sonics' involvement, potentially a catastrophic situation.

The main source of this gossip turned out to be Clarence Bentley, the man formerly on the U.S. Sonics board and originally the designated third shooter. And unfortunately, his active socialite wife was also spreading the rumors as fast as she could. Most people didn't actually know whether this was true or not, but the word was it was true. So, Orris could no longer go to these places without people pointing at him and talking openly about his involvement. Once when I was with him at a Dallas restaurant, three people actually yelled out, "Orris, we hear you look really good in a Dallas Police uniform."

In mid-1965, when the Bentleys were discovered as the actual source of these vicious, but honest rumors, they were finally silenced. Killing them under these conditions wasn't really an option, even though that had been the fate for many others who had too much knowledge of the assassination, especially during and around the time of the Warren Commission investigation. Killing would have created greater problems than already existed. There were too many people able to point the damning finger at Orris Bell and U.S. Sonics.

The Bentleys were finally threatened in a way meaning that in no uncertain terms it would not be tolerated any longer. They clearly got the message. However, the gossiping continued, and though Orris tried his best to ignore it in public, it just got worse and worse. The pressure on him became intolerable, and to control the rumors, impossible.

The situation was now a danger to everyone directly involved in the assassination. The problem was compounded because he was such a recognizable man, standing out with his black hair, dark complexion, and the fact he was very handsome. And, of course, he was so well-known in these Dallas upper class circles associated with the aerospace industry.

So, his close friends and the CIA initially suggested for his own safety and sanity, as well as for that of everyone concerned, he should stop going to public places altogether for a while to let things cool off. And once they fully assessed the problem, they went further, and suggested they shutter U.S. Sonics, because it had become too well known as associated with the assassination. And Orris should leave the Dallas/Fort Worth area until they could get a grip on this dangerous situation. Orris agreed.

They did formally shut U.S. Sonics down, a personal disappointment for him, and not just because that cost him a small fortune. I could read his feelings about this when we were there about a week before they closed the doors for the last time. And shortly after we left and said goodbye to Nesbitt and Norris Lawrence, he told me he was going to go live in Chicago until he could return without the problems he had been experiencing lately.

He settled in Chicago in January 1966 at the invitation of the Chicago Mafia. They gave him a suite at the Chicago Playboy Club, the Mansion, at no cost. Hugh Hefner lived there at the time and the two became good friends. Orris fell into a decadent lifestyle, not drinking as much, but involved with a number of the Bunnies and becoming closer to the Mafia.

He went to work with Kropp Forge Inc., located in Cicero, right outside Chicago. He became close friends with a man he referred to as Jerry Lachardi, a major figure in the firm.. The two would travel to Italy, several times a year to visit Lachardi's family and friends. Kropp was very active in the aerospace defense industry having the largest forge available. That gave them a major advantage because a number of contracts required a forge this size. Orris negotiated these and other very profitable contracts.

Orris worked with Kropp, until he died in 1987. It opened a subsidiary in Fort Worth in the 1970s and elected Orris as its president, Fort Worth Forge and Manufacturing Inc. Under his control, it became very successful.in conjunction with another company he set up in Fort Worth, MAKOR Inc., to exclusively negotiate aerospace defense contracts. Almost immediately, it was operating at capacity.

Orris would return to Texas on a regular basis while living in Chicago, at least every two weeks and usually more often, between two and six days. When in Bedford, he limited his time to visiting friends and the local aerospace companies, staying away from the restaurants and clubs he used to frequent, at the behest of the CIA. Things quieted down rather quickly, with no Orris physically around to harass.

He continued his extensive travel in the U.S. and abroad, primarily to Europe, most often Italy, but also to the Orient, Mexico, and South America. He was busy, very busy. He missed living in the Dallas area, but did his best to enjoy himself and concentrate on business, in which he became more successful than ever.

Orris And the CIA

From the beginning, there is no question Orris was a working for the CIA and U.S. Sonics was a front for them, like many other businesses. This collaboration essential to the assassination.

After, the relationship continued. During Orris' time in Chicago, he was still functioning as a CIA operative. To him, the CIA was like the 'Boy Scouts of America' are to 'normal' people. He agreed with most of what it was doing and what it stood for. And would openly discuss with me, when he was working for it, referring to it as the Government or the Company or just the CIA.

There would be two other assassinations he and they were involved in, those of Martin Luther King and Robert Kennedy. (I chronicle this in a sequel, "*My Descent Into Hell.*") But following those, Orris wasn't doing that anymore. I believe his work for them, at this time, was more business-like and diplomatic, such as arranging arms or aircraft for military groups the CIA wanted armed. When he would travel to Mexico, Japan, France, Italy, or South America, as he did at least once a month, I'm sure it was usually for the CIA.

(That he, Born, and Lundquist were significant operatives for the CIA was confirmed in 2002, when an ex-CIA agent, I knew in Albuquerque, discussed it with a CIA deputy director from the late 1960s, who stated that he knew them personally.)

23

CONCLUSION

Orris and Me, Afterwards

Looking back as an adult, I realize now how badly I had been impacted by those three years in my life: 1962, '63, '64. The intensity of it all, the burdens of expectations and responsibilities, the awareness of the immensity of what was being undertaken, and having to live in this secret world while trying to be a normal child. I was being traumatized by what amounted to severe abuse, exploited, manipulated, and taken advantage of in a cruel manner. Those men, including my father, knew what this would do to me in the long run, and they didn't care. They were too overtaken by their insane effort to assassinate the President, to stop and think about what this exposure would do to me, a young child.

I continued living at home, witnessing his involvement in the other two assassinations, until I could no longer deal with my father and his role in them; he had gone too far. I left in November 1968, joining the Army to escape.

It was only after Orris' death, because of the promise I had made to him and my mother in 1978, not to reveal this story, that I was able to do so here. I do so, despite Charles Lundquist's strong warning in 2002, "They will kill you, if you do."

Ramifications

During this time, I was aware a new United States was being formed; one very different from that under President Kennedy. Not only would the country return fully to its Cold War position with Russia, but it would also reach new heights in its aggression toward its Army. Everything Kennedy had done to move quickly toward *détente* with Khrushchev after the Cuban Missile Crisis, would be fully reversed. The public knew little or nothing of the secret meetings between the two adversaries. Given two more years and the Cold War would have been over forever and the Vietnam War ended, curtailing the loss of American young men.

Most obvious perhaps was the immediate loss of Kennedy's liberal philosophies, the plans and accomplishments to improve the human condition here and abroad. In order to please Eisenhower's Military Industrial Complex and the oil barons.

Although I have written this primarily to chronicle what I know about the assassination, perhaps what is most significant is what my story has to say about the depths that the agencies of our government, particularly those of the military and federal law enforcement, stooped to, and are possibly capable of in the future.

On the one hand, it is common knowledge now that Hoover was corrupt, spying, disseminating false stories, and in essence blackmailing individuals, much of which he did to Martin Luther King. We also know that Hoover and Robert Kennedy were alienated, particularly about how to deal with the Mafia. But for Hoover to have participated, even passively, in the assassination, is another level of corruption.

When it comes to the CIA, we acknowledge its clandestine activities, turning a blind eye to murders and torture. By law, they are supposed to be limited to outside the U.S, and certainly not to undermine our democracy. To operate to further its own agenda, rather than hat of the nation. And troubling is their willingness to work with the Mafia, whose operations profited by their participation, with significant inroad into our economy in so many ways.

But perhaps more significant was that the assassination marked the beginning of a long political war between Republicans and Democrats. One that the assassins and fellow Republicans won. Consolidated after the assassinations of Martin Luther King and Robert Kennedy, and then electing Richard Nixon. A major move from a democracy to something on a continuum to fascism. Prescient of recent events, with not only a disregard for constitutional norms, equality and compassion, but a seeming pride in that disregard.

And so, I am hoping this book will spur further investigation to not only corroborate my story, but to promote serious consideration of the ramifications of it. How the effects of the political coup continue to prevail with a profound conservative shift, socially and politically, the pre-eminence of the military-industrial complex, and the present-day power of the Republican Party. With continuing racial bias and the power of the 'elite' and privileged, one is reminded of the adage that 'power corrupts, and absolute power corrupts absolutely'.

Validation

As I stated at the beginning of this book, I am aware that my story will face close scrutiny and rebuttal. Because, of course, proof is hard to come by, as planned by the assassins. Their layering of the cover-up continues to be effective. But also because nearly all the major participants have died. But there are a number of specifics and a number of 'coincidences' corroborated by an investigative consultant, that support my story:

- Orris Bell's name appears to have been scrubbed from an on-line search; even his children's biographies do not yield his name. But I am submitting a photograph of his gravesite and documents, validating his U.S. Sonics involvement.
- General Charles Born's involvement with U.S. Sonics as a corporate officer is documented, something 'unusual.'
- Charles Lyon's farm in Waxahachie is reality.
- Oswald's burial site is in the same, very small Fort Worth Cemetery, Shannon Rose Hill, as Orris' father and mother, Emmett Delmon Bell and Mabel Estelle Bell.
- In subsequent years, I had a 'protector' arranged by my father, an influential U.S. Senator, Pete Domenici, who acted on my behalf on several legal issues and about whom there are substantial rumors of his own Mafia ties.
- The use of the fulminated mercury bullet is not generally known, but that possibility has been independently professed because of the autopsy results.
- The motivations for the assassination that I have written, are fully acknowledged by historians.
- The acknowledgement by many that there had to have been several shooters because of the bullet trajectories and what several witnesses heard.

- The 'coincidental' out-of-country location of LeMay at the time of the assassination, but later 'supervision' of the autopsy at the Bethesda Naval Hospital.
- Dulles' 'surreptitious' location at the CIA's 'alternate' operation site; the 'Farm' for the entire weekend, where he could 'monitor' the event, despite his 'retirement.'
- "Irish Central", the leading North American Irish digital company, revealed that in tape recorded interviews by Arthur Schlesinger Jr., Jackie Kennedy revealed her belief that a "cabal of Texas Tycoons" and Johnson orchestrated the assassination. This statement was repeated by the U.K.'s "Daily Mail," adding that Oswald was merely "part pf a much larger conspiracy."
- Dr. David Crenshaw, one of the Emergency Room physicians, described a small wound to JFK's throat and a significant wound o the back of the head, neither of which could have realistically come from behind and behind. He considered the throat wound to be an entry wound. Along with many colleagues, he believed that JFK was hit twice from the front.
- Several people in the motorcade smelled gun powder coming from the picket fence on top of the gray knoll. And an official photographer in a following vehicle stated he heard shots come from that area.
- An analysis by William Orchard indicates eight shots from four different locations.
- And Robert Groden's endorsement.

I assume this notation will not be included, but the actual photos listed will be included:

Orris Gravesite
Oswald Gravesite

Emmett Gravesite
Emmett Gravesite
U.S. Sonics Incorporation papers
U.S. Sonics bankruptcy notification
Parade Route